THE  CAR HANDBOOK

by Robert Ireson

PENGUIN BOOKS

Penguin Books Ltd, Harmondsworth, Middlesex, England
Penguin Books Inc., 3300 Clipper Mill Road, Baltimore, Md 21211, U.S.A.
Penguin Books Australia Ltd, Ringwood, Victoria, Australia

—

First published 1960
Reprinted with revision 1961
Reprinted 1964
Reprinted with revisions 1967

—

Copyright © Robert Ireson, 1960, 1967

—

Made and printed in Great Britain
by Hazell Watson & Viney Ltd
Aylesbury, Bucks
Set in Monotype Times

CONTENTS

ACKNOWLEDGEMENTS

THE author wishes to acknowledge with thanks the assistance given by the following organizations in freely providing information and illustrations for incorporation in this book:

The Automobile Association, AC-Delco Division of General Motors Ltd, The Austin Motor Co., Ltd, Automotive Products Co., Ltd, The Avon Rubber Co., Ltd, Messrs Belling & Lee Ltd, Messrs Borg-Warner Ltd, Britax (London) Ltd, Citroen Cars Ltd, Clear Hooters Ltd, Cleveland Petroleum Co., Ltd, Connolly Bros (Curriers) Ltd, Cords Piston Ring Co., Ltd, Crypton Equipment Ltd, The Daimler Co., Ltd, DAF Concessionaires Ltd, The David Brown Companies, Messrs Docker Bros, Messrs Alexander Duckham & Co., Ltd, Dunlop Rim & Wheel Co., Ltd, Dunlop Rubber Co., Ltd, Esso Petroleum Co., Ltd, Ferodo Ltd, Fibreglass Ltd, Ford Motor Co., Ltd, The Free Piston Engine Co., Ltd, Girling Ltd, The Glacier Metal Co., Ltd, Goodyear Tyre & Rubber Co. (Gt Britain), Ltd, Hardy Spicer Ltd, The Holset Engineering Co., Ltd, Imperial Chemical Industries (Hyde) Ltd, Jaguar Cars Ltd, Kenlowe Accessories & Co., Ltd, K.L.G. Sparking Plugs Ltd, Laycock Engineering Ltd, Lectra Merchandising Ltd, Joseph Lucas Ltd, Metalastik Ltd, Michelin Tyre Co., Ltd, Morgan Motor Co., Ltd, NSU (Great Britain) Ltd, The Nuffield Organization, Messrs Oldham & Son Ltd, Distributors Peugeot, Philips Electrical Ltd, The Pyrene Co., Ltd, The Royal Automobile Club, Renault Ltd, Rolls-Royce Ltd, Rootes Motors Ltd, The Rover Co., Ltd, Salisbury Transmission Ltd, A. Schrader's Son, Division of Scovill Manufacturing Co., Serck Radiators Ltd, Servais Silencers Ltd, Shorrock Superchargers Ltd, Smiths Industries Ltd, Solex Ltd, The S.U. Carburetter Co., Ltd, Triplex Safety Glass Co., Ltd, Triumph Motor Co. (1945) Ltd, Tyresoles Ltd, Vanden Plas (England) 1923 Ltd, Van Doorne's Automobielfabriek N.V., Vauxhall Motors Ltd, Volkswagenwerk G.m.b.H., Walter A. Wood (Sales) Co., Ltd, Weathershields Ltd, Wellworthy Ltd, Westinghouse Brake and Signal Co., Ltd, Wipac Group Sales Ltd, Messrs Wilmot Breeden Ltd, Messrs Woodhead-Monroe Ltd, The Zenith Carburetter Co., Ltd.

Thanks are also due to Mr P. G. House for assistance in preparing the section on Insurance, to Associated Iliffe Press Ltd for permission to make use of material and illustrations appearing in the journals *The Autocar* and *Automobile Engineer*, and to Mr Charles Sully for his valuable help in reading the proofs.

PREFACE

THE trend in automobile design is such that the driver is becoming more and more 'insulated' from the machinery, as an increasing proportion of the effort of driving is taken over by automatic and power-operated controls. This is commendable in that it enables the driver to give full attention to the highly responsible matter of piloting the car, and brings the car nearer to its ultimate state as an utterly reliable means of getting from place to place. However, for many of us there is more to motoring than merely travelling, and there is no doubt that a fuller knowledge of the mechanics of the car adds to the appreciation not only of its potentialities but also of its shortcomings.

The object of this Handbook is to present a broad picture of automobile practice, without involving the reader in too deep a morass of technicalities. Inevitably, the description of mechanical devices necessitates the use of a minimum of technical terms; some of these are given more elaborate treatment at the end of the book.

As the motor car develops, the functions of its various components become more and more closely interlinked. An outstanding example of this is the introduction of 'unit' construction, in which the body of the car, instead of being merely a shelter set upon a chassis frame, is designed as a rigid box strong enough in itself to act as the foundation of the car so that the separate frame can be discarded. Again, we find that the car rides more satisfactorily if each front wheel is hinged separately instead of being set at the ends of an axlebeam. We therefore do away with the axle which immediately allows us to move the engine forward. As a result, all the seating can be shifted towards the front so that the rear passengers are no longer sitting directly over the back wheels. From these examples it is clear that alteration in principle, or even in point of detail, can have a profound influence on overall design. In these circumstances it is inevitable that there should be a certain amount of overlapping in the following chapters which are necessarily divided between the various main 'departments' of the car.

In addition to the purely descriptive chapters, the Handbook includes sections on the simpler aspects of maintenance and running the car, on the common types of breakdown, and on law and insurance in relation to motoring.

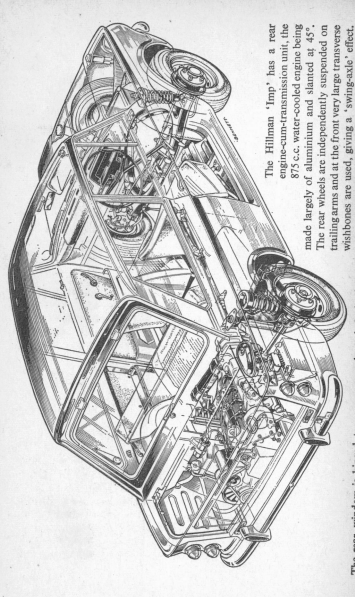

The Hillman 'Imp' has a rear engine-cum-transmission unit, the 875 c.c. water-cooled engine being made largely of aluminium and slanted at 45°. The rear wheels are independently suspended on trailing arms and at the front very large transverse wishbones are used, giving a 'swing-axle' effect. The back seat squab can be folded flat; air outlet vents are provided above the rear window to ventilate the interior of the car. (*By courtesy of Rootes Motors Ltd.*)

The rear window is hinged to open upwards and the back seat squab can be folded flat; air outlet vents are provided above the rear window to ventilate the interior of the car. (*By courtesy of Rootes Motors Ltd.*)

CHAPTER ONE

BASIC LAYOUT OF THE CAR

THE MAIN REQUIREMENTS

THE motor car is essentially an individual means of transport; for many users its principal appeal lies in the sense of independence which it affords. To achieve this independence a number of essential requirements must be met and although many years of evolution have produced a remarkable number of variations in general layout it is common knowledge that all cars share the following features:

(a) A carriage unit which, since it cannot be confined to rail tracks, must be steerable from within itself and must be able to travel in safety and comfort over roads of varying surface finish and flatness.

(b) An entirely self-contained power unit, that is, one which does not need to draw energy continuously from an outside source.

(c) Arrangements for making use of the power output to propel the vehicle, by rotating its road wheels.

(d) Means for stopping the vehicle.

This first chapter is mainly concerned with the choice of power unit and the various ways in which it may be positioned in the car.

CHOICE OF POWER UNIT

If the car is to be entirely independent it must utilize a *prime mover*. This is a general title for any device which can produce mechanical energy directly from a fuel, and by ' classical' methods this is done by extracting the fuel's heat energy and using this to bring gas to high temperature and pressure. The gas is then permitted to expand in a suitable mechanism and produce motion.

A simple form of prime mover is the rocket, in which the gas produced directly by combustion of a fuel expands through a nozzle and creates a propulsive force by jet reaction. Clearly, the rocket has no place in practical motoring.

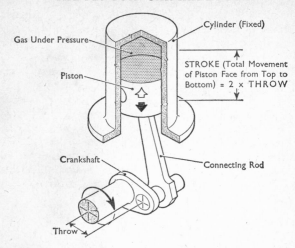

Fig. 1a. In the piston engine the up-and-down sliding (*reciprocating*) motion of the piston within the cylinder is converted into rotary motion by a crank mechanism. This is a *single-acting* engine – gas pressure acts on the top face of the piston only.

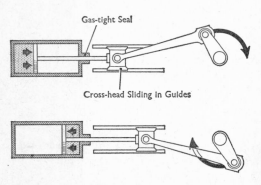

Fig. 1b. In the *double-acting* engine, gas pressure acts upon each side of the piston alternately. This system is not used in automobile engines.

Prime movers which depend on combustion of a fuel may be divided into two classes, namely those in which the gas is obtained by external combustion separately from the engine (for example, steam generated within a boiler), and those in which the high pressure gas is derived from the burning of fuel within the engine itself (internal combustion).

For practical purposes the classes may be further sub-divided between piston-type engines and turbines.

Briefly, in a piston engine (Fig. 1a) the gas is used to force a 'plug' along a smooth bored cylinder, the plug, or piston, being coupled mechanically (normally by a crank mechanism) so that its motion can be utilized as the rotation of a shaft. In a turbine (Fig. 2), the gases blow through a type of 'fan' which rotates at high speed.

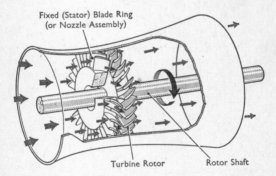

Fig. 2. In a turbine, gas is fed at high pressure into a casing containing a ring of fixed (or *stator*) blades, which direct the gas on to a further set of blades fixed around the rim of a *rotor*. The latter is thus made to rotate at very high speed. There may be more than one series of stator and rotor blades.

These sub-divisions present four basic types of power unit:

(1) External combustion piston engine, e.g. steam engine, complete with boiler

(2) External combustion turbine, e.g. steam turbine with boiler

(3) Internal combustion piston engine, e.g. petrol and diesel engines. These are essentially 'hot air' devices, i.e. the expanding

gas is air which is drawn into the engine and heated by the burning of fuel. An incidental function of the air is that it provides the oxygen essential for combustion. This applies also to: (4) The internal combustion or gas turbine.

It is well known that, despite its high degree of complication and essentially crude operating principle, the i.c. piston engine reigns supreme in automobile applications. In order to appreciate the shortcomings of this type of engine it is necessary to understand the manner in which power is produced by a rotating machine.

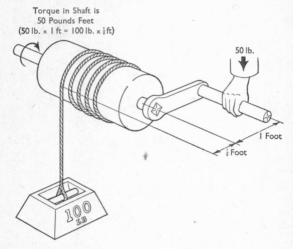

Fig. 3a. Torque is a measure of twisting effort.

The power transmitted by a spinning shaft is determined by two factors, firstly, the twisting effort or *torque* in the shaft, and secondly, the speed at which it is rotating. It is essential to distinguish between *torque* and *power*. For example, if a man pushes down with a force of fifty pounds on the handle of a winch and the arm of the winch is one foot long, then the torque in the winch shaft is fifty *pounds feet* (i.e. pounds × feet) (Fig. 3a). If the shaft has a drum six inches in radius this torque will support a load of one hundred pounds hanging on the rope (100 pounds × $\frac{1}{2}$ foot = 50 pounds feet). Clearly, torque is closely linked with leverage and is, in fact, quoted in the same units. If we wish to increase torque we can use the lever principle, but because we are dealing with rotary motion this has to be done by means of gearing (Fig. 3b). In the example a torque of 50 pounds feet is increased to 150 pounds feet, but this is achieved at the expense of a reduction in speed. It is characteristic of a torque conversion system that an increase in torque is accompanied by a reduction in speed, and vice versa.

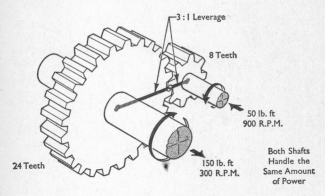

Fig. 3b. Torque increase by gearing.

Torque in a piston engine is obtained in the first instance by a straightforward lever principle. In the example (Fig. 4) gas pressure of 100 pounds per square inch acts on the top surface of a piston having an area of 3 square inches. The resulting total force of 300 pounds is transmitted, via the connecting rod, to a crank 1½ inches (⅛ foot) long and gives a torque of 37½ pounds feet (300 × ⅛) at this instant (i.e. crank at right angle to cylinder axis).

In the electric motor torque is produced by the interaction of magnetic fields and is less easily defined than the simple lever effect of the piston and crank arrangement. In the turbine, torque is due directly to the pressure of gas on the 'fan blades', but here again the leverage varies at different points along the length of the blade and the output torque is the measure of the total effect.

The effect of torque is to tend to 'break by twisting' and the

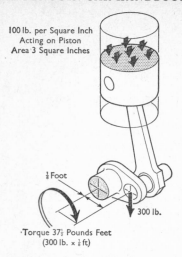

100 lb. per Square Inch
Acting on Piston
Area 3 Square Inches

⅛ Foot

300 lb.

·Torque 37½ Pounds Feet
(300 lb. × ⅛ ft)

Fig. 4. Torque developed in piston engine.

design of rotating parts, such as axle shafts, is decided fundamentally by the torque which they are intended to transmit.

In this short discussion on torque all reference to the term power
has been omitted, because it must be emphasized that torque is an
all-important factor in evaluating performance. It decides what
thrusting force is available 'at the road' to overcome the forces
resisting motion and to accelerate the mass of the car. It is not
until the matter of speed is introduced that power need be considered. That is to say, if it is known that a torque of 100 pounds
feet is required at the road wheel in order to start the car moving,
then this torque might equally well be produced by directly coupling
a large engine or by using suitable gearing to multiply the low output torque of a small engine. If, however, we now require the
torque to be maintained as the car accelerates to high speed, then
the small engine is no longer suitable because its *power* output is
insufficient. Power implies the ability to do work at a specified rate.
The term *horsepower* was derived directly from an experiment to
determine the rate at which a horse could work; the result was that
the horse was credited with being able to lift a weight of 33,000

pounds through a height of one foot in one minute, i.e., it worked at the rate of 33,000 foot pounds per minute (or 550 foot pounds per second). All everyday power measurements are based on this standard.

In the case of rotating shafts the calculation of horsepower is not quite so straightforward, but is found by suitably combining torque (the job to be done) and speed of rotation (the rate of doing the job). The expression is:

$$\text{Horsepower} = \frac{\text{Torque (pounds feet)} \times \text{Speed (r.p.m.)} \times 6 \cdot 283}{33,000}$$

For example, a typical touring car engine is stated to develop a torque of 46 pounds feet at 2,500 r.p.m. Its power output *at this speed* is, therefore:

$$\frac{46 \times 2,500 \times 6 \cdot 283}{33,000} = 21 \cdot 9 \text{ horsepower}$$

Since power output depends upon the combination of torque and speed, a given amount of power may be derived either from a big low speed engine exerting massive torque, or from a small engine generating comparatively low torque but at very high speed.

TORQUE AND POWER REQUIREMENTS

The force resisting the progress of a car increases rapidly as speed rises, and therefore the power required also increases disproportionately. For instance, the power required at 80 m.p.h. may be not four times, but sixteen times the power required at 20 m.p.h. Additional torque will be required to accelerate the car from any given fixed speed or if a gradient is to be climbed. Therefore, there should always be an excess of power in reserve to meet these requirements. Also, if hill-climbing is to be at all adequate, it is essential that a fall in speed does not result in a serious reduction in the torque available.

It is evident that the power unit should be able to supply heavy torque at low speed in order to accelerate the car away from standstill; relatively light torque is required to maintain a steady cruising speed on a level road.

CHARACTERISTICS OF SOME PRIME MOVERS

The torque characteristics of the steam piston engine, the steam turbine, the gas turbine, and the electric motor match the above requirements admirably. At the instant of starting the full pressure of steam or gas can be applied to the piston face or turbine blade so that the maximum torque is developed while the unit is stationary. As speed picks up, torque gradually falls away. Similarly, the full voltage applied to an electric motor causes maximum torque to be developed at standstill. Both steam and electric locomotives are able to exert tremendous starting efforts when accelerating heavy trains from standstill.

The internal combustion piston engine compares most unfavourably. Not only must it be revolving *before* the vehicle can start, thus necessitating a clutch which allows it to be disconnected from the driving wheels, but it does not develop its maximum torque until it is turning at fairly high speed. Its torque characteristic is, in fact, nothing like that actually required, so that it is necessary to provide some device such as a gearbox which will allow the engine to maintain high speeds throughout the whole range of road speeds. The falling off of torque as speed also falls is familiar to every motorist by the manner in which the car gradually becomes less and less able to maintain a satisfactory 'pull' on a hill which is being taken slowly in a high gear; hence the advantage in 'taking a run' at a rise. The ability to accelerate on a hill when a low gear is engaged is due to the combined effects of allowing the engine speed to rise to a value where satisfactory torque is developed, coupled with the torque multiplication provided by the gearing.

The torque characteristic of the piston type i.c. engine is determined initially by the designer, when considering the purpose to which the engine is to be put, and depends on such 'built in' factors as valve dimensions and timing. If the engine is destined for competition work, where speeds are high and the gears freely used, then the torque developed at low engine speeds will be limited by a design which enables a very high torque to be obtained in the upper speed range. In the touring engine the high maximum torque will be sacrificed in favour of 'flexibility', i.e. the development of

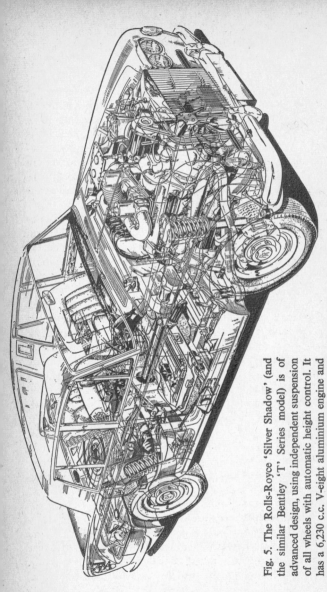

Fig. 5. The Rolls-Royce 'Silver Shadow' (and the similar Bentley 'T' Series model) is of advanced design, using independent suspension of all wheels with automatic height control. It has a 6,230 c.c. V-eight aluminium engine and fully automatic transmission. Disc brakes, with triple hydraulic systems, are fitted to all wheels and steering is power-assisted. The body is of stressed steel monocoque construction, with aluminium-alloy doors, bonnet top and boot lid. (*By courtesy of Rolls-Royce Ltd*)

useful torque at the lower engine speeds, thus making possible the use of top gear over the greater part of the road speed range. High torque output at low speed is a characteristic of large engines and particularly of diesel engines.

Since the i.c. piston engine is apparently so unsuitable for motor car application it is worth while considering the drawbacks of the alternative power sources.

Steam power has always been an attractive proposition, because it offers high starting torque and smooth, silent acceleration. The steam pressures used can be high, enabling the size of the unit to be kept to a minimum. At one time the high performance and silence of the steam engine made it a serious rival to the petrol engine in cars. However, the need for both fuel and water supplies was a disadvantage, and although early in motoring history the time taken to raise steam had been reduced to a matter of minutes (probably less than that taken to start the average petrol engine of that day), the advent of the electric self-starter on the petrol engine assisted in the demise of the steam car.

There is little doubt that, had the steam car enjoyed the vast amount of research subsequently devoted to the petrol-driven car, it would have become universally adopted. It is rumoured, from time to time, that leading manufacturers are interested in steam propulsion and it had been forecast that the application of atomic power to cars might take the form of a power unit fed with steam generated by heat derived from a reactor; however, it has been stated that radiation hazards make it unlikely that atomic power can ever be utilized directly in the private car.

The adoption of the gas turbine for the larger type of vehicle is a matter of time only, and a short section devoted to this power source is given at the end of Chapter Two. Briefly, the gas turbine possesses favourable power characteristics and is smooth and vibrationless in action, requiring no clutch and little or no gear changing. Furthermore, it can be run on a variety of fuels of the cheaper and safer kind.

Electric power is attractive from the point of view of starting torque, ease of operation, silence, and cleanliness. However, present methods of storing electricity are so bulky and heavy as to restrict the range of electric vehicles; performance is low owing to the need to limit the size of the propulsion motor in order that a reasonable distance can be travelled without re-charging the battery. However, battery/electric cars for town use are in fact already in production by at least two manufacturers in the U.S.A.; there have also been developments in the electronic control of battery/electric vehicles, replacing the jerky and wasteful method of control by mechanical switching of resistances, which will help to extend the range and scope of this type of propulsion. On the same theme, it has been forecast that one contribution to easement of the traffic problem in large cities, both in respect of space and pollution, could be in the provision at city outskirts of small battery/electric runabouts which could be rented from the municipal authority; motorists would be obliged to transfer to these cars for travel within the city, where internal-combustion vehicles would be forbidden.

It is foreseeable that, as the petroleum resources of the world dwindle, much research will be devoted to the problem of compact storage of electricity. It appears that, in our present state of knowledge, battery/electric traction offers the only method of applying atomic energy to road transport. Electricity generated in atomic power stations would be distributed as alternating current by the National Grid network. The recent development of very compact semi-conductor rectifiers for converting the mains supply to the direct current necessary for battery charging would make it possible for each vehicle to carry its own charging plant. This would be plugged into the mains overnight and would have the incidental but valuable advantage of helping to even out the day and night loads on the generating stations.

FUEL CELLS

A new source of power, which cannot be classified strictly as a prime mover in itself, is the *fuel cell*, the development of which is being pressed ahead with special impetus from spacecraft projects. The fuel cell might be visualized in a very crude sense as a car battery operating 'in reverse'; whereas in a battery from which electricity is being drawn there is a generation of hydrogen and oxygen gases, in a fuel cell these gases are brought together at specially constructed plates in such a way that the interaction of the gases produces a voltage between the plates. It is important to recognize that, whilst such a combination would normally be highly explosive, the bringing together of the gases in a fuel cell is done in such a way that there is no *combustion* or burning of fuel; thus, by supplying the cell with gases, there is a direct release of electrical power without the losses of energy inherent in systems dependent on the cyclic expansion of hot gases. The linking of a system of fuel cells with an electric motor results effectively in a prime mover, in the sense that mechanical energy and motive power can then be derived from a self-contained power-pack.

The theoretical efficiency of the fuel cell is very high, though 70 per cent is probably a realistic figure, and the overall efficiency of a fuel cell/motor power unit should be at least twice as high as that of conventional prime movers. Its fuel need not necessarily be supplied in the form of gases, the cell being capable of development to operate on various 'conventional' fuels, important amongst which are petroleum constituents not normally suitable for use in engines. The fuel cell is silent in operation and its exhaust products are innocuous; its possibilities appear boundless but it is at a relatively early state of development and its use commercially in motor vehicles must be regarded at present as one of its more distant fields of application.

SUITING THE ENGINE TO THE JOB

The inevitability of the internal combustion engine having been recognized, the history of the automobile has been largely concerned with adapting its unsuitable characteristics. Apart from the brutal, but practical, arrangement of providing variable gear ratios, other means of adjusting torque to suit conditions have been proposed. They include using the engine to drive an electrical generator the output of which is supplied, under suitable control, to traction motors, and similarly, using the engine to drive an oil pump feeding individual 'oil motors' mounted on each road wheel. The first system is widely used in diesel/electric locomotives where the weight involved is not especially disadvantageous.

However, such arrangements introduce additional weight and

complication and also power losses in the converting process, so that much research has been devoted to the direct utilization of engine power by easing the process of changing gear-ratios 'on the move' and, lately, in completely eliminating gear changing by the driver.

Finally, the choice of power units of the i.c. piston type rests between the diesel and petrol engines. Briefly the distinction between these is that in the petrol engine an electric spark is used to ignite the fuel/air mixture, whereas in the diesel engine no spark is required, the gas being ignited by the temperature generated when it is highly compressed within the cylinder. This high compression brings about large internal forces and necessitates a more robust construction than is used in the petrol engine. For this reason the diesel, or compression-ignition engine, is comparatively heavy, and this, combined with its tendency to rough slow running, has not favoured its application to private cars. However, the diesel engine makes use of a safe, relatively cheap fuel with a high heat value and consequently is an economical power unit. The capital cost of the diesel engine is higher than that of the petrol engine owing, at least in part, to the complex fuel injection pump which is made to an exceptional degree of precision. The remarkably long periods between overhaul make the diesel particularly suitable for commerical vehicle use and it is widely used in taxi-cabs. A few private cars are marketed with a choice of either petrol or diesel engines, and research which is proceeding to develop smoother running might foreseeably result in its more widespread adoption in cars.

EFFICIENCY

Efficiency is concerned with 'how well a job is done', and in the case of the engine it is a measure of the effectiveness of the engine in converting into mechanical energy the heat energy available in the fuel. This is quite simply determined by burning a sample of the fuel to measure the amount of heat produced, and then observing the rate at which fuel is consumed when the engine is working at a certain power output. The latter is measured by causing the engine to work against a *dynamometer*, which may take the form of a large brake or an electrical generator.

The petrol engine converts only about 25 per cent of the fuel energy into useful power output. This may seem low, but it compares favourably with the most efficient power installation, the electricity generating station. Here every effort is made to recover heat which might otherwise be lost in boiler and turbine exhausts and yet the greatest efficiency is only a little over 30 per cent. The diesel engine has the relatively high efficiency of 34 per cent.

POSITIONING OF THE POWER UNIT

The arrangement of front-mounted engine driving the rear wheels has remained basically unchanged for more than sixty years as the accepted standard to be found on the great majority of cars and it is still very widely used, particularly in cars of medium size or larger. The reasons for the popularity of this layout are easily understood. The weight of an engine of any considerable size tends to have adverse effects on the behaviour of the car if it is placed at the rear; moreover, forward positioning is obviously favourable from the point of view of cooling and also means that the controls directly associated with the engine and gearbox are well placed in relation to the driver, without the need for elaborate remote-control linkages. With the engine thus placed logically at the front it might seem that the obvious choice would be to take its power direct to the front wheels but this introduces a number of problems; for example, there is the need to design the drive mechanism such that the front wheels not only propel the car but can also be twisted through considerable angles for the purpose of steering. Although this difficulty was overcome successfully by Citroen in the 1930s it is only comparatively recently that front wheel drive has made a big impact, following the success of the British Motor Corporation 'mini' range.

There are other advantages in using rear wheel drive in a car of 'traditional' design. It has been virtually standard practice to place the rear wheels at the ends of a rigid axle casing, inside which are the actual driving shafts. The car structure is spring-mounted on the complete axle and there is therefore considerable up-and-down movement of the axle relative to the engine; this movement is easily accommodated by simple joints in the rotating shaft between the engine and the axle since, because of the length of the shaft, its angular movements are quite small. This long shaft can also provide a degree of cushioning in the power transmission.

Nevertheless, this straightforward arrangement has its disadvantages, particularly in respect of weight and the need to allocate space to the transmission shaft. Therefore, the problems of alternative engine and power transfer layouts have been faced and it is noteworthy that, as is often the case when compromises are sought in engineering, a number of widely differing designs have been produced, each of which is evidently satisfactory in its own right.

One advance is to dispense with the rigid rear axle and to suspend the rear wheels independently of each other by some form of linkage, each wheel having its own drive shaft arranged to take up the wheel movement. The chief merit of this is that the weight of the 'un-sprung' parts is reduced so that the wheels are more apt to follow road surface irregularities without passing these on to the main structure; an incidental virtue is that the absence of the massive axle casing bouncing up and down beneath the car allows the designer a little more freedom in arranging the layout of the rear seats, luggage space, and so on. The long transmission shaft is still needed but its 'tunnel' can be much reduced or eliminated altogether.

However, a more obvious step is to position the engine as close as possible to the driven wheels, either at front or rear. Rear engine mounting is to be found in a number of makes of small car, the engine usually being arranged in a single unit with the gearing which transmits the drive to the rear wheels. A notable British design is that used by the Rootes Group for their smallest cars (see the Hillman 'Imp' illustrated on page 12) in which the objection of engine weight at the rear is overcome by the extensive use of aluminium engine components to reduce the weight to only half that of the conventional cast-iron engine. Possibly the most revolutionary developments in car layout have been those by B.M.C. in not only adopting front wheel drive but also mounting the engine 'east-west' across the front of the car so as to leave the absolute maximum space free for passenger accommodation; this layout has proved capable of extension into the medium car range.

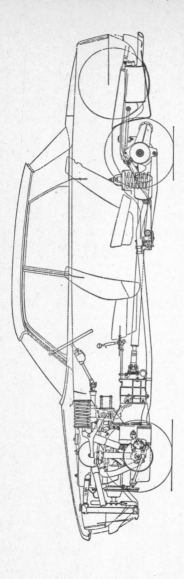

Fig. 6. This sectioned view of the Rover 2000 shows how the front suspension loads are taken by horizontal coil springs against the bulkhead. Other notable points are the universal joint in the short steering column, the remote selector lever for the gearbox, the three chambers in the exhaust silencing system, and the fore-and-aft links of the de Dion rear suspension. (*Courtesy of the Rover Co. Ltd and the Iliffe Marketing Co. Ltd*)

Whether it is placed at front or rear, the engine combined with the power transmission system and road wheels forms a convenient unit for pre-assembly; in some designs this combined unit can be detached from the main body of the car and rolled away on the wheels for servicing, and this includes, of course, the steering linkage in the case of a front wheel drive arrangement.

CHAPTER TWO

THE INTERNAL COMBUSTION ENGINE

BASIC CONSTRUCTION

IN order to explain more clearly the type of engine usually employed in cars it is proposed to describe a less complex 'motorcycle' type engine which is similar in basic construction and operation. Fig. 7 shows a simple engine of this kind. It will be seen that,

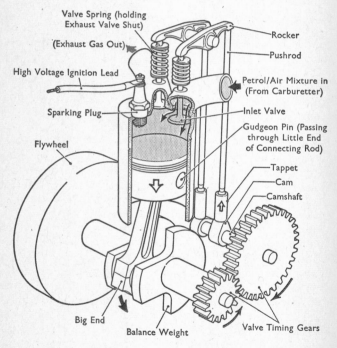

Fig. 7. Single cylinder overhead valve (o.h.v.) engine, shown on the induction stroke.

in common with all piston engines, it has a barrel or *cylinder*, closed at its upper end and having a truly cylindrical inner surface with a high degree of finish. Sliding within the cylinder is the *piston*; in order to provide a gas-tight seal between piston and cylinder, a number of grooves are cut around the piston and into the grooves are sprung *piston-rings*, which press outwards on to the cylinder wall.

The reciprocating motion of the piston is converted into rotary motion of the shaft by the familiar principle of the crank (Fig. 1*a*). The distance between the centre of the crankshaft and the centre of the crankpin is termed the *throw*; twice this distance is the *stroke* of the engine and is the distance moved by the piston in one sweep up or down. This crankpin is coupled to the piston by a connecting rod, the ends of which are termed, logically, the *big-end* and *little-end*. The little-end is hinged to the piston by a large pin known as the *gudgeon*, or *wrist-pin*.

The crankshaft itself revolves in *main bearings* (not shown), often called simply 'mains', the portions of the shaft which are in actual contact with the bearings being highly finished and known as *journals*.

This type of engine is termed *single-acting* because the gas pressure operates on the upper side of the piston only. Since this means that there is no necessity to seal the lower end of the cylinder the piston is designed with sufficient depth to maintain it 'square' to the cylinder and also to carry side-thrusts. (Compare this with the thin plate-type piston of the double-acting steam engine shown in Fig. 1*b* where a piston-rod and cross-head is provided.)

In its movement upwards from *bottom dead centre* (*b.d.c.*) the piston traverses a space which is known as the *swept volume*. This volume (multiplied by the number of cylinders in the case of a multi-cylinder engine) is termed the *capacity* of the engine, and is commonly measured in cubic centimetres (c.c.); it is usual nowadays to refer to the 'size' of an engine in c.c.s or litres (1 litre = 1,000 c.c.), rather than 'horsepower', since, as is explained later in this chapter, the latter term is used in two senses. As a very rough guide, one *taxable* horsepower usually corresponds to a swept capacity of about 100 c.c., so that a 'Ten' would have a capacity of the order of 1,000 c.c.

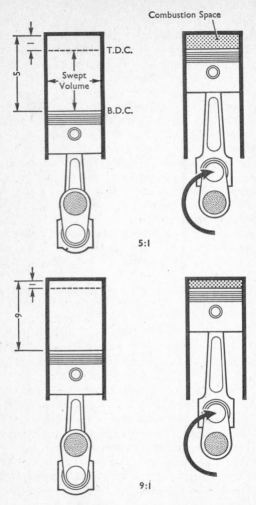

Fig. 8. Compression ratio indicates the degree to which the mixture is 'squeezed'.

The cylinder has dimensions such that with the piston at its topmost position or *top dead centre* (*t.d.c.*) there is a space remaining in which the combustion occurs. In comparing the volume of the space left above the piston at bottom and at top dead centres we use the term *compression ratio* (Fig. 8) which indicates the degree to which gas would be squeezed on the up-stroke.

Opening into the combustion space are two *ports* which can be closed by valves. In our example the valves are of the most usual type and are known as *poppet* valves. These are normally held closed by springs, but can be pushed open at predetermined instants by a mechanism such as that shown. This particular arrangement is that commonly used in modern touring car engines and is known as '*overhead valves* (*o.h.v.*) *operated by push-rods and rocker gear*'.

The movement of each push-rod is obtained by the use of an associated *cam*, which is simply a carefully shaped protrusion on a revolving shaft. The camshaft is driven at half the speed of the crankshaft and thus ensures that in two revolutions of the crankshaft each valve is pushed open once. This is an essential requirement of the *four-stroke* or *Otto* cycle of operation (Fig. 9), the sequence of which is as follows:

(1) The piston is at top dead centre and one valve, the *inlet*, is open. The piston begins to descend and creates a partial vacuum in the cylinder; a mixture of petrol droplets and air, which may be regarded as a gas, is 'drawn in', i.e., induced to flow through the open port. This downward movement is therefore known as the *induction* stroke.

(2) At the end of the first stroke, the piston now being at bottom dead centre, the inlet valve closes. The crankshaft, continuing to revolve, pushes the piston upwards, and by the time it has reached top dead centre all the gas contained in the cylinder has been squeezed up into the combustion space; thus, at the end of the *compression* stroke the gas is at a pressure which relates to the compression ratio of the engine, this being round about 8 to 1 in touring engines.

(3) The compressed gas is now ignited by an electric spark which jumps between the electrodes of a *sparking-plug*. The petrol vapour burns rapidly and heats up the air, which attempts to

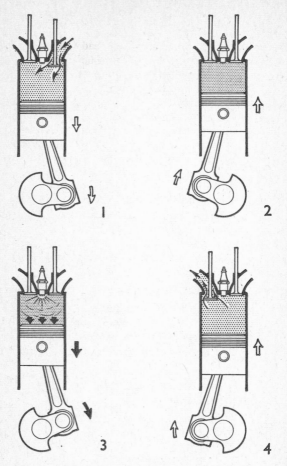

Fig. 9. Four-stroke (Otto) cycle.
1. Induction Stroke – Petrol/Air mixture drawn in. 2. Compression Stroke – Mixture compressed. 3. Power Stroke – Mixture ignited. 4. Exhaust Stroke – Exhaust gas ejected.

expand and creates high pressure on the top or *crown* of the piston. The resulting downward thrust of the piston is called the *power* or *firing* stroke.

(4) The piston having reached bottom dead centre, the *exhaust* valve is opened and during the following up-stroke the products of combustion are expelled through the exhaust port.

Clearly, in order to initiate this cycle of events it is necessary to rotate the engine by external means until at least one firing stroke has occurred, after which the energy stored up by a *flywheel* attached to the crankshaft keeps the engine turning between power strokes. The engine then becomes 'self-supporting' and the four-stroke cycle is repeated in rapid succession, perhaps as many as forty times per second in a touring engine.

PRACTICAL CONSIDERATIONS

In practice, the four-stroke cycle is not applied in the rigid manner described above, for considerable modifications are required, especially to suit high-speed running. Therefore, imagine that the engine has been started and the piston is descending on an induction stroke.

Basically, the power developed by the engine will depend on the extent to which the cylinder can be filled with the petrol/air mixture flowing through the inlet port. In general the aim is to obtain a high *volumetric efficiency*, which is a measure of the amount of mixture actually packed into the cylinder, compared with the space available. The longevity (and inefficiency) of some of the early engines was due to the fact that the design deliberately restricted volumetric efficiency and power output, by providing small valve ports.

Owing to the rapidity of events the column of gas in the pipe leading to the inlet port may be regarded as a continuously flowing stream, and because of its momentum the gas will continue to enter the cylinder even with the piston moving upwards and apparently tending to push it out. This means that the inlet valve can safely be left open until the piston has risen a short way, on the compression stroke. A further benefit to be gained from this is that, since it is impossible to open or close the valve in an instant, the retarded closing of the valve permits it to be kept fully open for the whole of the downward stroke.

The next point is that the burning of the gas is not instantaneous and takes some time to 'build up', so that at high speed the full pressure would not be developed until after the firing stroke had commenced. To counter this it is necessary to ignite the mixture some little time before the piston reaches top dead centre, i.e. the point of ignition is advanced relative to the crankshaft movement. Since the speed of combustion is always approximately the same, the faster the engine runs the more the ignition should be advanced, and, fortunately, the electric ignition system allows this to be done.

DETONATION

A further point, concerning combustion, involves mention of compression ratio. Generally speaking, the higher this ratio can be raised, the more efficient the engine becomes, but limitations are imposed by the phenomenon known as *detonation* or *knocking*. The rather obscure term is now taken to imply an abnormally rapid burning of the mixture, comparable to an explosion, and it gives rise to a tinkling sound or *pinking*. Instead of all the mixture burning smoothly and progressively away from the point of ignition, only a portion burns normally, and the remaining mixture then detonates violently. This occurs particularly when the flame initiated by the sparking has comparatively long distances to travel in order to ignite all the mixture, and also when the compression ratio of the engine is too high in relation to the anti-knock property of the fuel in use.

The desirable short flame path can be achieved by judicious placing of the sparking-plug (or by providing duplicate plugs), by eliminating awkward corners in the combustion space, and by encouraging the mixture to circulate or swirl around the sparking-plug.

The anti-detonating properties of fuels vary considerably and are denoted by *octane numbers*. This matter is treated more fully in Chapter 3, but, basically, the higher the octane number, the less prone the fuel is to knocking.

Detonation is to be avoided because it causes high pressures to be developed prematurely in the cycle, producing abnormally high temperatures and also reducing power output. Similar effects are produced if the ignition is too far advanced or if *pre-ignition* occurs; in the latter case the gas is fired prematurely by an incandescent particle of carbon or other prominence, before the ignition spark occurs.

VALVE OVERLAP

When the piston descends on the firing stroke the pressure within the cylinder is rapidly reduced; also, as the crank revolves past the 'sideways' position the leverage is reduced so that, beyond a certain point, little useful work is being done. Advantage is taken to increase efficiency by arranging for the exhaust valve to open before the piston reaches bottom dead centre, so that the remaining pressure assists in expelling the burnt gases from the cylinder. The latter process is known as *scavenging*. Finally, in order to encourage the rapid influx of fresh mixture, the inlet valve is opened before the end of the exhaust stroke so that the outgoing blast of burnt gas creates a 'follow through' effect. To complete the scavenging the exhaust valve is not closed until a little after top dead centre. It will be noted that for a short period both inlet and exhaust valves are open simultaneously, and this is known as valve *overlap*. The inlet and exhaust entries are shaped to reduce the tendency for the incoming gas to escape via the exhaust port.

The sequence in which valve operations occur is shown figuratively on a diagram such as Fig. 10. The points at which the various events occur are stated, in practice, either as a given number of degrees of crankshaft movement or as a given amount of piston movement, before or after top or bottom dead centre.

It must be emphasized that the timing of valve events is determined by the designer according to the use to which the engine is to be put, and once the engine is built the valve timing cannot be altered, being decided by the permanent disposition of the cams on the camshaft. Therefore, because any particular arrangement of valve timing only confers the greatest benefit at certain critical speeds, the original design must always be a compromise.

THE MULTI-CYLINDER ENGINE

It will be appreciated that the power output from the single-cylinder engine is produced as a succession of distinguishable

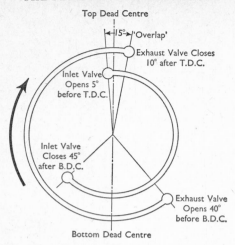

Top Dead Centre

15°

'Overlap'

Exhaust Valve Closes
10° after T.D.C.

Inlet Valve
Opens 5°
before T.D.C.

Inlet Valve
Closes 45°
after B.D.C.

Exhaust Valve
Opens 40°
before B.D.C.

Bottom Dead Centre

Fig. 10. Valve timing diagram for a touring engine.
(*By courtesy of the Austin Motor Co. Ltd*)

pulses, and whilst this may be acceptable in motor-cycles it cannot normally be tolerated in cars. Therefore, the car engine is multi-cylindered, commonly having four or six cylinders, though eight- and twelve-cylinder engines are used. Generally speaking, the larger the engine the more cylinders are used, because combustion troubles become more acute as the cylinder size increases, unless special provisions are made, such as duplicating the ignition arrangements. In the majority of British cars, four cylinders are used in engines of up to and including 2 litres, and six cylinders thereafter. The two-cylinder engine or 'twin' is widely employed in motor-cycles and in a few cars. The operation of the multi-cylinder engine is identical with that of the single-cylinder type described above. The cylinders are usually formed as *bores* in a single block and all the pistons and connecting-rods operate on a common crankshaft. The latter is so designed that the pistons and connecting-rods are moving in such a way that they balance each other; crankshafts for four- and six-cylinder engines are illustrated in Fig. 11. The disposition of the cranks or throws is such that, combined with a suitable valve timing, the cylinders fire in regular

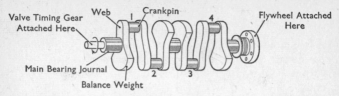

Fig. 11a. Crankshaft for Four-Cylinder Four Stroke engine. Cranks at 180° intervals, two power strokes per revolution, three main bearings.

Firing Order 1 – 3 – 4 – 2

With No. 1 piston at top of compression stroke (about to fire).
 No. 2 piston is at bottom of firing stroke.
 No. 3 piston is at bottom of induction stroke.
 No. 4 piston is at top of exhaust stroke.

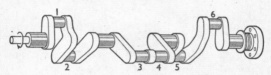

Fig. 11b. Crankshaft for Six-Cylinder Four Stroke engine. Cranks at 120° intervals, three power strokes per revolution, four main bearings.

Firing Order 1 – 5 – 3 – 6 – 2 – 4

With No. 1 piston at top of compression stroke (about to fire):
 No. 2 piston is on exhaust stroke.
 No. 3 piston is on induction stroke.
 No. 4 piston is on firing stroke.
 No. 5 piston is on compression stroke.
 No. 6 piston is at top of exhaust stroke.

succession, preferably so that no two neighbouring cylinders fire consecutively. With the cylinders arranged in line the latter condition is not obtainable with less than five cylinders.

FIRING ORDER

The cylinders are numbered from the front and the *firing order* for four- and six-cylinder engines respectively is:
 1 – 3 – 4 – 2 ... or 1 – 2 – 4 – 3 ...
 and 1 – 5 – 3 – 6 – 2 – 4 ... or 1 – 4 – 2 – 6 – 3 – 5 ...

ARRANGEMENT OF CYLINDERS

As already implied, the most common arrangement of cylinders used in automobile engines is that known as *vertical in line*. An alternative design is the *horizontally-opposed* engine, an example of which is the *flat-four* used by Volkswagen. In this case, four cylinders operate on a common crankshaft but are arranged in two diametrically opposed blocks of two cylinders (Fig. 12).

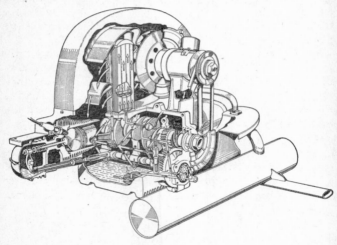

Fig. 12. This *Volkswagen* engine has two pairs of horizontally-opposed cylinders, air-cooled. The illustration shows the blower and air circulation, with oil-cooler placed in the air stream. Also shown is the oil circulation, with gear-type pump (right lower centre). Push-rod operated overhead valves are used. (*By courtesy of Volkswagenwerk G.m.b.H.*)

Crankshaft design plays an important part in determining cylinder arrangement, since it is essential for the shaft to have great strength in respect of both bending and twisting. If the shaft is long, one end of it may tend to twist very slightly with respect to the other end, so that, as the shaft revolves, it may also begin to 'wind-up and unwind' rhythmically, at a frequency depending upon its dimensions. At certain critical engine speeds this angular twisting motion, or *torsional oscillation*, tends to become more pronounced and results in rough and noisy operation of the engine or even, in extreme cases, actual failure of the crankshaft by breakage in shear. This phenomenon can be countered by fitting a *vibration damper* to one end of the crankshaft; a typical damper consists of a disc having a heavy rim bonded to a central hub by a ring of rubber compound carefully selected to give the required damping characteristics. Any tendency for the hub to oscillate is suppressed by an opposing oscillation of the elastically-mounted rim, the resonant frequency of the latter being calculated to match that of the crankshaft. In some engines the damper is conveniently incorporated as part of the fan pulley.

Support against bending loads is given by providing the crankshaft with a number of main bearings along its length so that only short sections of the shaft are left unsupported. At one time it was usual for a four-cylinder in-line engine to have three crankshaft bearings only, at each end and at the centre, so that there was a bearing on each side of each *pair* of cranks; on more recent *five-bearing* engines however, bearings are provided on both sides of every crank. Correspondingly, although many six-cylinder engines are made with four-bearing crankshafts, some are now provided with seven bearings. In short-stroke engines with large diameter shafts, additional stiffness results from the 'overlap' of crankpin and crankshaft journal.

When it is necessary to use more than six cylinders, to obtain a high power output, it is common practice to resort to the *Vee* arrangement so as to restrict the length of crankshaft and overall length of engine. In America, the V-8 engine is widely used in automobiles, and in this case the cylinders are arranged in two blocks of four at right angles on a common crankcase. A four-throw crankshaft is used, with connecting rods operating in pairs on each crankpin, the big-ends being arranged either side by side or 'forked' together. The crankshaft is thus only slightly longer than that of a four-cylinder in-line engine.

The compactness of the Vee arrangement has led Ford to produce engines of four and six cylinders in this configuration using a 60° angle. It enables the cylinder block to be made very short and extremely rigid, and of course, the crankshaft is so short that problems of torsional vibration do not arise. The V-4 engine, however, presents a special problem in that it is impossible to achieve dynamic balance simply by the addition of counter-weights to the crankshaft; this is overcome by providing an additional shaft geared to the crankshaft and revolving in the opposite direction, fitted with offset weights such that the out-of-balance forces are cancelled out. Balancing action is also provided by weights on the flywheel and fanbelt pulley.

INFLUENCE OF THE HORSEPOWER FORMULA

The true power output from an engine (i.e. the useful power actually available) can be measured by causing the engine to work against a dynamometer, and is called the *brake horsepower* (*b.h.p.*). The theoretical output at any particular speed can be calculated from the dimensions of the engine if the pressure of the gases within the cylinders is known. It is possible to measure this pressure using a device known as an *indicator*, and the average pressure found in this way is called the *indicated mean effective pressure* (*i.m.e.p.*). The theoretical power is calculated using this figure and is termed *indicated horsepower* (*i.h.p.*). Owing to losses inside the engine, brake horsepower is inevitably rather less than indicated horsepower; the ratio $\dfrac{\text{b.h.p.}}{\text{i.h.p.}}$ is the *mechanical efficiency* of the engine and is in some measure an indication of the care with which the engine has been assembled. The usual figure is around 85 per cent. Yet another term often heard is *brake mean effective pressure* (*b.m.e.p.*). This is an imaginary figure, and is obtained by calculating back from the measured brake horsepower to deduce what pressure would have produced this power output. The b.m.e.p. figure is obviously lower than the i.m.e.p. would be, since it makes allowance for mechanical efficiency; nevertheless, it provides a useful indication of engine performance within the cylinders.

When it was decided to tax motor vehicles according to their engine 'size', the Treasury adopted a formula which had been evolved by the Automobile Club of Great Britain and Ireland (later known as the Royal Automobile Club) in or around 1904. The formula gives what is known as the Treasury or R.A.C. rating, and merely requires knowledge of the number of cylinders and the bore diameter; it was arrived at by making certain assumptions which applied generally to all engines at that time and it did, in fact, give an approximate figure for brake horsepower. However, by the time the simple formula was adopted for taxation purposes there had been such great advances in engine performance that an engine with an R.A.C. rating of 10 h.p. might actually produce over twice as many brake horsepower. Despite the fact that the results given by the formula were no longer significant of power output, the formula was retained, since it gave a rough indication of the engine size, especially in view of the restrictions it placed upon engine design, as explained later in this chapter.

Some manufacturers used, at one time, to quote both Treasury rating and brake horsepower, e.g. 12/50. (This should not be confused with the practice of quoting the number of cylinders and brake horsepower, e.g. Wolseley 6/110.) Some Austin model names are prefixed with the power rating, e.g. A.60.

The derivation of the R.A.C. formula is given at the end of the chapter, and the formula itself is stated here.

$$\text{Horsepower} = \frac{D^2N}{2 \cdot 5}$$

N = No. of cylinders
D = Diameter of bore measured in inches

or

$$\text{Horsepower} = \frac{D^2N}{1613}$$

D = Diameter of bore measured in millimetres.

The important point to notice is that it appears that the *stroke* of the engine is not taken into account, but the assumptions made in evolving the formula did in fact allow for stroke, indirectly.

Now suppose that a manufacturer wishes to produce a four-cylinder engine of two litres capacity; this volume can be obtained by various combinations of stroke and bore, three examples being given below:

Bore	Stroke	Swept volume	R.A.C. rating
7·6 cm.	11·0 cm.	1997 c.c.	14·3 h.p.
8·4 cm.	9·0 cm.	1995 c.c.	17·5 h.p.
8·9 cm.	8·0 cm.	1992 c.c.	19·7 h.p.

From the sales point of view, the first example is the most attractive, since the taxable horsepower is only about three-quarters of that given by the last combination. For this reason the engines of pre-1947 touring cars were almost invariably of the 'long stroke' type, in which the stroke was large in comparison with the bore diameter. However, the use of long stroke and narrow bore has unfortunate effects on engine performance.

Firstly, a limiting factor in all reciprocating engines is the 'rubbing' speed between the piston and the cylinder wall. The piston speed at a given rate of rotation of the crankshaft depends on the distance through which the piston has to travel, and therefore the long stroke engine is restricted to lower rotational speeds than the short stroke design. Secondly, power output characteristics are dependent to a large extent upon piston area, particularly in respect of torque, and the wide bore engine is again at an advantage here. Thirdly, a narrow bore imposes a restriction upon the cylinder head design, and difficulty in accommodating the large valves necessary for high volumetric efficiency.

All these features limit the power output of a long stroke engine of given capacity.

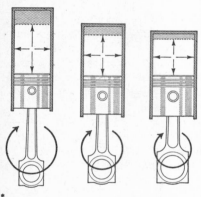

Fig. 13. This illustration shows the general trend towards reduction in length of stroke (and increase in diameter of cylinder bore), permitting higher rotational speeds without increase in piston rubbing speed. Also shown is the increase in compression ratio which has accompanied this change.

* 'over-square'			*
Stroke/Bore Ratio	1.45	1.07	0.90
Compression Ratio	5 to 1	6 to 1	7 to 1
Rotational Speed corresponding to mean piston speed of 2500 ft per min.	3460	4230	4760 r.p.m.
Piston area	45.4	55.5	62.3 sq. cm.
Brake horsepower at above speed assuming b.m.e.p. 100 lb. per sq. in.	53.3	65.0	73.0

However, with the abolition of the horsepower tax, in 1947, engine designers were no longer restricted in choice of *stroke/bore ratio* and the result of this has been a striking increase in the power obtained from touring engines. The modern tendency is towards what is popularly known as the 'square' engine; this term does not, of course, refer to the shape of the engine, but means that the stroke is equal to the bore diameter, or nearly so. In some cases the 'over-square' engine is used, with bore greater than stroke. Figure 13 illustrates engines having the dimensions given in the three examples above, showing the piston areas, and the maximum rotational speeds permissible assuming that piston speed is limited to 2500 feet per minute. Also given are the power outputs, assuming a b.m.e.p. of 100 pounds per square inch in each case (in practice, the short stroke engine would develop higher pressure than the long stroke engine, owing to its superior volumetric efficiency).

BRAKE HORSEPOWER (S.A.E.)

There has often been confusion in the past as to the exact meaning of the value of brake horsepower claimed by an engine manufacturer since the power output as measured on a test-bed under ideal conditions may be very different from that actually available at the driving wheels when the same engine is installed in a car, complete with all its auxiliaries, air cleaner, silencer, etc.

In order to present a common basis for comparison it is usual nowadays for power to be stated in *b.h.p. (S.A.E.)*, which means that the power output has been measured under conditions as specified by the Society of Automotive Engineers; basically, this requires the engine to be run without its air-cleaner, electrical generator or fan (except when the engine is directly air cooled) but using its standard fuel- and water-pumps and fitted with a laboratory exhaust system of specified back-pressure. The S.A.E. brake horsepower as measured has also to be corrected for standard conditions of atmospheric pressure, humidity and temperature. It will be understood that b.h.p. (S.A.E.) gives a higher figure than the nett power actually available for propulsion.

VALVE GEAR

Earlier it was stated that the poppet valve is almost invariably adopted for automobile engines. This is not to imply that the poppet valve is mechanically superior, since it shares in the outstanding drawback of the piston-type engine in that its action is reciprocating, i.e. the valve must be accelerated from a standstill, stopped, and reclosed. Other types of valve have been used in automobile engines, including the *rotary* and *sleeve* types. A well-known example of the former is the *Cross* rotary valve, which consists of a large hollow tube rotating in a housing mounted across the top of the cylinder head, with its ends communicating with the inlet and exhaust ducts. The valve has a diagonal dividing wall at the centre and on each side of this division are openings which, as the valve revolves, register in turn with a large port in the cylinder head. The valve thus opens the cylinder head to the inlet or exhaust system as required, and because the gas passages are virtually unrestricted in size a very high volumetric efficiency ('degree of filling') is obtained. Also, since the gas flow is exceptionally smooth and the combustion space near ideal in shape it is possible to use a high compression ratio, of the order of 12 to 1, and these factors combine to produce an overall efficiency giving high power output with low fuel consumption.

One version of the sleeve valve consists of a thin liner interposed between the cylinder wall and the piston and operated by a crank mechanism which causes the liner to slide up and down whilst rotating slightly. By these combined motions, openings in the liner are made to line up with inlet or exhaust ports in the cylinder wall. The sleeve valve has been used in the past in certain high-quality cars, notably by Daimler, and is also used in some aircraft engines, but it is expensive to produce. On the other hand, the rotary valve is probably on equal terms in cost with the poppet valve, but it is unlikely now that there will be any departure from the poppet valve before the eventual demise of the piston engine, especially in view of the vast capital which has been invested in its application. The virtues of the poppet valve are that it is simple, not prone to wear through abrasion, and does not require lubrication at the sealing face. The valve is in the shape of a mushroom and occasionally it is hollow or trumpet-shaped. It is located with respect to its port opening by a guide through which its stem passes. The close fit of the stem within the guide ensures gas tightness, and a synthetic rubber oil seal may be fitted to prevent seepage of lubricating oil. Both inlet and exhaust valves may be of the same diameter, though the exhaust valve is made of special heat-resisting steel. The exhaust valve is often made the smaller, the theory being that the exhaust gases discharge under considerable pressure whereas the fresh mixture enters at a pressure less than atmospheric.

The valve is held closed by a spring, which is normally of the helical type. A special design point here is that the natural frequency of oscillation of the spring and valve must be higher than the frequency of movement of the valve at the highest engine speed. If this is not so the valve may cease to follow the cam at high speed and tend to 'float' open, this being known as 'valve bounce' and being accompanied by the characteristic noise described as 'valve crash'. It can be disastrous if there is normally only a small clearance between valve and piston. The usual practice is to raise the frequency of the spring by using double coils, one placed inside the other, or a damping effect may be produced by winding the spring with its turns close together so that they become 'solid' under compression. In some racing engines, especially those used in motor-cycles, 'hairpin' springs have been used, resembling the springs used in clothes-pegs. Another solution to this problem, which avoids the use of springs altogether, is to employ separate cams to close the valves positively. The term 'desmodromic' is applied to this type of valve gear, which is rarely used.

DISPOSITION OF THE VALVES

The conventional motor-car engine uses one inlet and one exhaust valve per cylinder, though engines have been built using two inlet and two exhaust valves per cylinder. The disposition of the valves is largely a matter of economics, since the most desirable arrangement is not easy to achieve if cost is a primary consideration. It is generally agreed that the hemispherical combustion chamber is the most efficient, and this requires the valves to be arranged as shown in Fig. 14d. The operation of the valves then

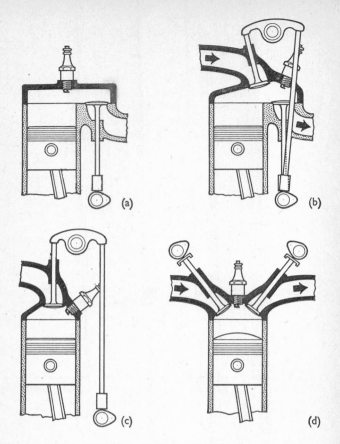

Fig. 14a. Side valves (s.v.) in 'L'-head. Inlet and exhaust valves side by side. (See Fig. 29.)

b. Inlet-over-exhaust (i.o.e.) in 'F'-head. (See Fig. 17.)

c. Vertical overhead valves (o.h.v.) operated by push-rods and rockers. Inlet and exhaust valves side by side. (See Figs. 7, 12, 33 and 68 and Pl. 1a.)

d. Inclined o.h.v. operated by twin overhead camshafts (o.h.c.). Hemispherical combustion space. (See Fig. 15.)

Four of the many ways of arranging valve gear. Fig. (c) is typical of the arrangement used in many contemporary touring engines.

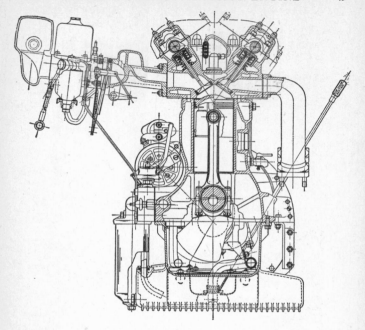

Fig. 15. The famous X K range of *Jaguar* engines use inclined overhead valves operated directly from twin overhead camshafts.

Note the inserted valve seats, the domed piston conforming to the hemispherical combustion space and the 'dry' cylinder liner. (*By courtesy of Jaguar Cars Ltd*)

requires either one (Fig. 16) or two overhead camshafts (Fig. 15) or a complicated system of pushrods and rockers.

The more common arrangement in touring engines is to place the valves side by side and operate them by a simple push-rod and rocker system (Figs. 12, 14c, 33 and Pl. 1a). The cylinder head then assumes an asymmetrical shape often referred to as 'bath tub'.

A cylinder head arrangement used in some refined engines (Figs. 14b and 17) is known as *inlet-over-exhaust* (*i.o.e.*) in which an over-

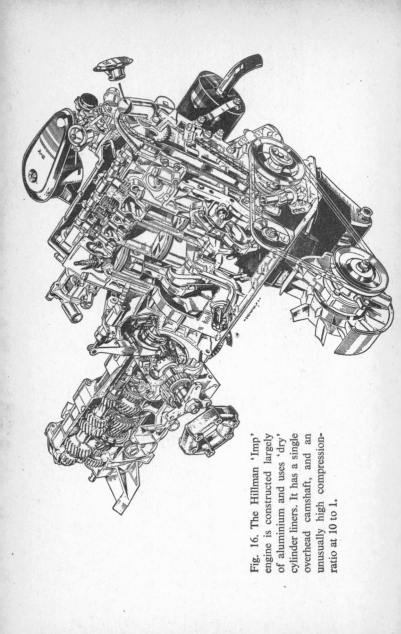

Fig. 16. The Hillman 'Imp' engine is constructed largely of aluminium and uses 'dry' cylinder liners. It has a single overhead camshaft, and an unusually high compression-ratio at 10 to 1.

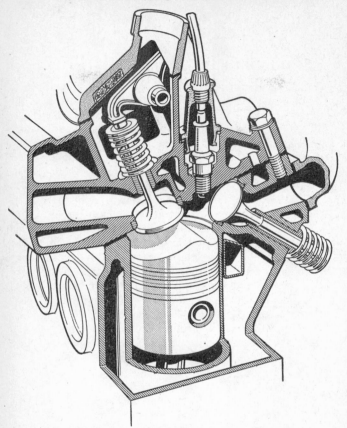

Fig. 17. In this *Rover* engine, overhead inlet and side exhaust valves are used, with an unusual piston designed to promote 'squish'. (*By courtesy of the Rover Co. Ltd*)

head inlet valve is used in conjunction with a side mounted exhaust valve.

The simplest valve arrangement, which is rarely found in modern engines, is that using side valves throughout (Fig. 14a). Side valve (s.v.) engines are generally less efficient than the overhead valve type because of the complicated shape of the combustion space which makes for stagnant pockets and uneven gas flow.

THE CAMSHAFT AND ITS OPERATION

The design of camshaft requires most careful consideration because its shape decides not only the *lift* of the valves (i.e. the distance through which they are moved in opening) but the relative points of opening and closing of the valves and the rate at which they are operated. The profile of the cam itself is carefully chosen so that the valve is smoothly accelerated and decelerated with a minimum of noise. In a sports engine, where noise is not so important a consideration, *quick lift* cams are used, being shaped so that the valves are fully open for the maximum period in the cycle.

The camshaft is required to run at half crankshaft speed and is therefore geared to it in a 1 : 2 ratio. A variety of methods of gearing have been used, all of them having the essential feature of positive (no-slip) drive so as to preserve accurate valve timing. By far the most common timing drive used currently is the *duplex* chain, which makes use of a double roller chain and twin sprockets (Fig. 18) and gives a quiet, positive, and highly efficient drive. In recent years there has also been introduced a camshaft drive system using a special type of steel-cored rubber belt which has teeth on the inside face to give positive engagement with the timing gears.

VALVE ADJUSTMENT

The valve stem or push-rod is not normally arranged to bear directly on its cam, but is operated by an intermediate sliding block, known as a *tappet*. The object of this is to relieve the valve stem or push-rod of the sideways thrust of the cam. The tappet rides slightly to one side upon the cam so that it is continually rotated and wear is evened out.

Because of the relative expansion of the various components it is necessary to adjust the valve gear so that there is a small clearance between adjacent parts, with the engine cold. If this were not done, the valves could not bed fully on to their seats with the engine hot. In the case of side valve engines screwed platforms are

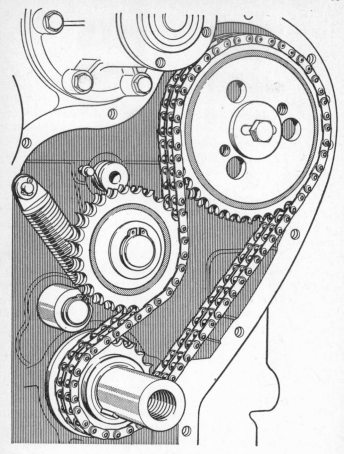

Fig. 18. Duplex chain drive between crankshaft and camshaft, with chain-tensioning sprocket (Rover). (*By courtesy of the Rover Co. Ltd*)

provided in the tops of the tappets and the adjustment of these to obtain the correct clearances is known as 'setting the tappets'. In overhead valve push-rod engines the adjustment is effected by a screw in the end of the rocker, which bears on the end of the push-rod; a similar effect may be achieved by providing adjustment of the pivot point of the rocker, this method minimizing the total weight of reciprocating components.

If the valves are operated directly from an overhead camshaft a 'thimble' is interposed between cam and valve stem. Adjustment of clearance is then a matter of removing or inserting shims (i.e. thin metal slips) under the thimble.

'Hydraulic tappets' are occasionally employed; in this arrangement, a cushion of oil is introduced under pressure into the clearance space and eliminates the tapping noise which normally occurs here when the engine is cold.

VALVE SEATS

The seatings for the valves may be formed directly in the surrounding metal, but often separate collars, made of very hard material, are recessed in, and this is clearly necessary if the main engine construction is in relatively soft aluminium alloy (Fig. 15).

ENGINE CONSTRUCTION

The 'carcase' of the engine consists structurally of three basic items; these are the cylinder block and crankcase, the cylinder head, and the sump.

The cylinder block is almost always made of high-grade cast iron and the cylinder bores are machined directly into it. The slightly porous nature of cast iron enables it to retain an oil film and it has excellent wearing properties. If the engine is water-cooled, the various water passages will be cast into it as 'jackets' surrounding the bores. If air cooling is used, the necessary finning will be cast integrally with the cylinders. The cylinder block is a complex casting and its manufacture requires the use of numerous 'cores' to form the internal cavities. A result of this is the appearance of circular openings, in the side of the block, closed by thin *core plugs*.

An incidental function of these plugs, which are only sprung into position, is that they may burst open and relieve internal pressure caused by freezing of the cooling water, though this is by no means to be relied upon.

A cast-iron cylinder wall must be of a certain minimum thickness, and to avoid the weight penalty and simplify production some manufacturers prefer to insert a separate cylinder liner or sleeve. This may be a simple 'dry' lining within the solid main cylinder block (Fig. 15) or it may be a 'wet liner', in which the cooling water is allowed to come into direct contact with the sleeve, sealing rings being used to retain the water. The practice of 'dry' sleeving is also used in the more conventional engine, when the cylinder is so worn that renewing the surface by re-boring is not practicable or when it is desired to restore an engine to its original bore diameter.

The use of liners makes it possible to cast the cylinder block in aluminium alloy and thus achieve a considerable saving in weight.

A process which shows promise for the future is that of chromium plating the walls of cylinders cast in aluminium alloy, thus obtaining a hard working surface combined with light weight.

Engines embodying the *Cross* system, in which an aluminium piston is used in conjunction with an aluminium alloy cylinder, have been run very successfully. The secret here is that alloy steel piston rings are used and so arranged that only the rings, and not the piston, are in contact with the cylinder wall. Such a combination shows very little wear, and this occurs on the piston rings rather than the cylinder, so that the need for reboring never arises, merely an infrequent replacement of the rings.

Unfortunately, despite the advantages which aluminium offers by way of easy machining and weight reduction, its high cost has ruled out its use in the quantity production of automobile engine cylinder blocks until very recently. Notable examples of aluminium engines at opposite extremes of the scale in size are those of the Hillman 'Imp' (Fig. 16) at 875 c.c., with four in-line cylinders, and the Rolls-Royce 6230 c.c. V-eight engine.

The bottom of the cylinder block is extended downwards to form a rigid skirt or crankcase, which also serves to house the upper halves of the crankshaft main bearings. At one time it was the practice to make the crankcase separate from the block, but the one-piece arrangement is invariably used nowadays.

To the bottom of the crankcase is secured the sump, which forms an oil reservoir. The sump may be a casting, sometimes ribbed to assist oil cooling, but very often it is a simple steel pressing.

The top of the cylinder block is closed by the *cylinder head* which is secured to it by studs. In a very few cases (racing engines) the head is cast in solid with the cylinder block (i.e. not detachable), to avoid a joint between the two parts. In quantity produced engines the detachable head is invariably used, and the joint, which must withstand the combustion pressure and also retain the cooling water which flows between block and head, is sealed by a *gasket*. This usually consists of thin copper sheets with asbestos sandwiched between them but thin steel gaskets of superior overall heat conductivity are being used increasingly.

The cylinder head is a casting in iron or aluminium alloy, and besides containing water passages it may also carry the supports for overhead valve gear. In addition it incorporates suitable screwed holes to take the sparking plugs, and may also include cavities which form the inlet and exhaust gas passages.

PISTON

Since the piston reciprocates at high speed it is necessary to keep its weight low and it is therefore made as a casting in aluminium alloy. The use of this material has additional virtues in that it rapidly conducts heat away from the piston crown and also that the piston is relatively soft compared with the cylinder wall so that wear is minimized. Although special low-expansion alloys are used, the thermal expansion of the piston is nevertheless greater than that of the cylinder and it is necessary to provide a slight clearance between the two when the engine is cold (in a worn engine the clearance may become sufficient to give rise to the characteristic noise known as 'piston slap', particularly when the engine is first started). The piston is not made perfectly circular but is given a slight ovality towards the bottom or *skirt*. Two bosses are provided to carry the gudgeon pin and the piston walls are often slotted to aid uniform expansion.

The gas tightness of the piston is maintained by cast-iron spring rings, which fit into grooves cut around the piston above the gudgeon pin bosses (Fig. 19). The number of rings varies between makes, but usually there are two or three plain compression rings in the upper grooves, whilst the bottom groove contains a special *scraper* or *oil control* ring. This is a channel section ring with slots which communicate with holes in the bottom of the piston groove. The ring scrapes excess oil from the cylinder wall and returns it to the sump via the interior of the piston.

The shape of the piston top or crown is influenced by the type of cylinder head arrangement, although in many engines it is quite flat. In a high compression engine with hemispherical combustion chamber, the piston is itself domed (Fig. 15). An interesting design is used in the Rover engine (Fig. 17), where the 'escarpment' shaped piston crown 'squishes' the incoming charge towards the sparking plug.

The use of higher compression ratios demands the accurate matching of combustion spaces and in many recent engines this is achieved by forming virtually the entire space as a hollow in the crown of the piston. This 'bowl-in-piston' technique enables the space to be accurately controlled whilst the cylinder head can be made quite flat and therefore easy to machine; it may also allow improved disposition of the valves and ports.

CONNECTING ROD

The connecting rod is usually a steel stamping with an I-girder cross-section, though tubular rods have been used. It is essential that the rod should be exceptionally stiff, but its complex motion, partly rotating and partly reciprocating, dictates that the weight shall be kept to a minimum to ease the problem of balance. The set of connecting rods destined for any particular engine are carefully matched in weight.

The circular ends or *eyes* of the connecting rod are called the *big-end* and *little-end* (or *small-end*), terms requiring no explanation. Two basic designs of little-end may be used. In one, the little-end is clamped to the gudgeon pin by a pinch-bolt (Fig. 19) and the pin is thus firmly located centrally within the piston while

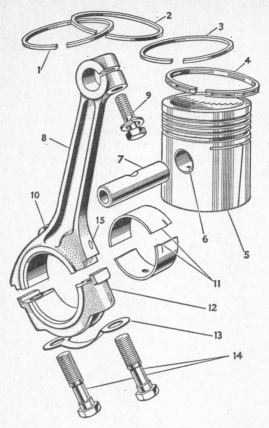

Fig. 19. Piston and connecting rod assembly (Austin)
1, 2, and 3 Compression rings. 4. Oil control ring (slotted). 5. Split skirt
piston. 6. Oil hole. 7. Gudgeon pin. 8. Connecting rod. 9. Pinch bolt.
10. Oil hole. 11. Bearing shells. 12. Bearing cap (note big-end split diagonally). 13. Locking plate. 14. Set screws. 15. Identification markings.
(*By courtesy of the Austin Motor Co. Ltd*)

swivelling in the piston bosses. In the other, the gudgeon pin is secured within its bosses by circlips at each end, or by making the pin an 'interference' fit in the bosses, and the little-end 'floats' on the pin. The little-end eye is then provided with a pressed-in bush, which may be a solid bronze tube, but is often of the *wrapped* type, i.e. made from a strip rolled to form a cylinder, the strip usually being of steel lined with lead/bronze anti-friction alloy.

The big-end eye is invariably split so that it can be assembled around the crankshaft. The eye itself is furnished with a special bearing liner, which is described in more detail later, and the two halves of the big-end are held together by accurately fitted high tensile steel bolts with positive lock devices (e.g. split pins, locking tab plate). In some cases the big-end is divided at an angle (Fig. 19) so that, with the bearing cap removed, the piston and connecting rod assembly can be withdrawn upwards through the cylinder bore.

CRANKSHAFT

The crankshaft is either a steel forging or a special form of iron casting, and the bearing journals are usually hardened. The shaft runs in split main bearings similar to the big-end bearings. The actual design of the crankshaft is dictated by the cylinder arrangement, but the *webs* which form the cranks are usually extended to form balance weights to counteract the effect of the whirling big-ends and connecting rods. However, it must be emphasized that in the normal vertical type engine it is only possible to obtain perfect balance over a narrow speed range. In a horizontally opposed engine the main reciprocating masses can be arranged to cancel out at all speeds.

The centre-line of the crankshaft may not lie directly beneath the centre of the cylinders but may be very slightly off-set (towards the left, if a clockwise-rotating engine is viewed from the front). The principal object of this arrangement, known as *désaxé*, is to achieve a more direct push on the crank during the period of maximum downwards thrust; at the same time, sideways thrust on the piston is reduced since there is less angular deflection of the connecting rod on the power stroke.

ENGINE MOUNTING

Because of the vibration inevitable in an imperfectly balanced engine, and also to cushion the tendency for the engine to rotate about its own crankshaft when being accelerated, it is necessary to insulate the engine from the car structure by means of absorbent mountings. The most common practice is the three-point mounting, in which rubber-bonded supports are provided at each side near the front of the engine and one under the gearbox tail. Since these mountings permit an appreciable amount of engine movement it is essential that such components as the throttle linkage, exhaust pipe, and clutch control should also be arranged in a flexible manner. The cable-operated throttle and hydraulic clutch control (Fig. 20) provide convenient solutions to this problem.

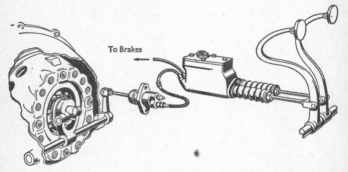

Fig. 20. Hydraulic control for the clutch. Master cylinders for the clutch and brakes are included in a single twin-bore unit (right) and the slave cylinder (left) operating the clutch is coupled to its master cylinder by a short flexible hose (Lockheed). (*By courtesy of Automotive Products Co. Ltd*)

In the original Hillman 'Imp' the problem of providing sensitive throttle control of the remotely positioned (rear-mounted) engine is solved by the use of a *pneumatic* coupling, in which the driver's foot movement deflects a diaphragm and so increases the air pressure in a pipe connected to a similar diaphragm which moves in sympathy to operate the throttle.

ENGINE BEARINGS

The connecting rod big-ends and the crankshaft main bearings carry the direct piston thrust and operate under particularly arduous conditions of loading and rotational speed.

With the modern trend towards very large crankshaft journal diameters, both at main bearings and crank-pins, coupled with higher rotational speeds, the surface speed at these bearings is ever increasing. Almost invariably, plain bearings are used at these positions, though ball- or roller-races have been used, especially for main bearings. However, plain bearings run more quietly and are cheaper to replace. For many years they were of the white-metal *thick-walled* type, i.e. the main and big-end bearings were thick shells lined with a substantial thickness of soft babbitt metal, comparable with tinman's solder, these linings being bored out and adjusted to mate with the crankshaft journals by a lengthy hand scraping process. In many cases the white-metal was not inserted as a separate liner, but was cast directly into the big-end eyes.

White-metal is particularly suitable as bearing material, because, being soft, it conforms readily to minor surface irregularities or inaccuracies and is reasonably tolerant of abrasive foreign matter in the lubricating oil. Furthermore, it can be operated in conjunction with a relatively soft shaft. However, it has low strength in itself, especially at the higher operating temperatures.

The modern technique is to use a bearing of the *thin-walled* type, which consists of an accurately made thin steel *shell* with a thin lining of white-metal or other anti-friction metal. A further development of the 'ready-made' bearing is the *micro* bearing, in which the lining to the shell is only about five thousandths of an inch thick; it has been established that the use of very thin lining results in an increased load-carrying capacity and is therefore suited to the high output of recently developed engines. The virtues of the thin-walled bearing are that it can be produced and installed at a fraction of the cost of the hand-fitted thick-walled bearing, no individual adjustment being required, and it can easily be replaced 'in the field' without the necessity for special skill. The thin-walled shell bearing demands a more accurately machined housing than the thick-walled type but it is considerably lighter and its use assists in reducing the weight of the reciprocating parts, very desirable in a high-speed engine.

The thin-walled bearing is made in two semi-circular halves (Fig. 19), with lugs to ensure correct assembly and lateral location within the split bearing housings.

In some particularly heavy duty bearings, such as those in diesel engines, the *overlay plated* bearing is used. This comprises a steel shell with a lining of anti-friction metal such as copper/lead, lead/ bronze or soft aluminium alloy. The lining is plated, to a thickness of approximately one thousandth of an inch, with lead/tin or lead/ indium alloy to reduce 'hot oil corrosion' of the bearing. With the development of more powerful engines producing high bearing loadings, yet stronger materials have had to be introduced. Aluminium alloys are being used increasingly, one of the most common of these being *reticular tin/aluminium* containing 20 per cent of tin (reticular meaning that the tin content is evenly distributed throughout the aluminium as a regular lattice structure). In recent years this material has superseded overlay plated copper/ lead or lead/bronze, the tin/aluminium having higher fatigue strength and little difference in production cost. These higher duty bearing materials necessitate the use of a harder crankshaft than would be required with white-metal bearings.

THE TWO-STROKE ENGINE

The two-stroke is mentioned only briefly here, its use in cars being comparatively rare. However, the two-stroke engine has undergone considerable development in the past few years and is, of course, widely used on motor-cycles. It has no valve gear, but uses the piston itself to act as a valve in uncovering inlet and exhaust ports in the cylinder wall. The name 'two-stroke' is applicable because all four stages in the cycle are completed in a single revolution of the crankshaft, i.e. two piston strokes. There is, therefore, one power stroke per revolution as against one per two revolutions in the four-stroke engine. This would seem to imply that twice the power output is available, but in practice the inefficiency of the two-stroke engine tends to offset this apparent virtue. The chief fault appears to be the poor scavenging, i.e., disposal of the exhaust gases, so that the cylinder is not fully charged with fresh mixture, giving low volumetric efficiency.

The advantages of the two-stroke engine lie in its inherent simplicity and smooth output (though it is prone to run unevenly at low speed). A special feature is that the lubricating oil is usually mixed in with the petrol ('petroil') so that lubrication is guaranteed, though it does, of course, involve continual consumption of oil. Provision is usually made for the automatic mixing of the oil with the petrol in the correct proportions during re-fuelling.

Three-cylinder two-stroke engines have been used very successfully by D.K.W. (Germany) and Saab (Sweden), but the latter have now adopted four-stroke engines, probably anticipating problems in complying with exhaust emission legislation.

THE WANKEL ROTARY-PISTON ENGINE

Many attempts have been made to develop a *rotary-piston* engine, that is, an engine working on a conventional combustion cycle but obtaining rotary motion direct without using reciprocating mechanisms. The outstandingly successful example is the ingenious design by Felix Wankel which has been developed on a commercial basis by the West German firm of N.S.U., its first application being in the N.S.U. Spider sports car. Engines operating on the Wankel system are being developed under licence by other organizations throughout the world, particularly in Japan.

In principle, the Wankel engine consists of a symmetrical lobed rotor which revolves eccentrically within a housing so profiled that the tips of the rotor lobes are always in contact with its inner wall. There are, mathematically, a number of possible combinations of rotor and housing profiles which have this curious *trochoidal* property of matching together in any position but that which has received most extensive development is the three-lobed rotor and figure-of-eight housing (see Fig. 21).

The engine operates on the normal induction-compression-combustion-exhaust sequence of the piston engine, but the combustion spaces are formed by the 'pockets' trapped between the rotor faces and the housing wall, which enlarge and contract as the

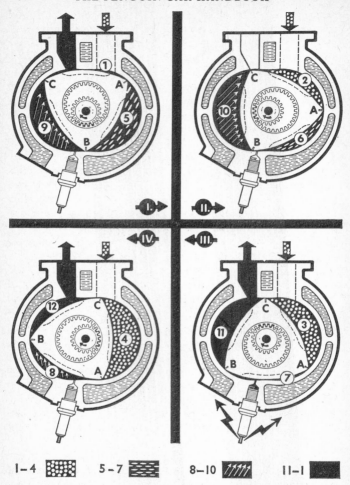

Fig. 21. The operating sequence in the Wankel rotary-piston engine (see text for detailed explanation). (*By courtesy of N S U (Great Britain), Ltd*)

rotor revolves. There are three such pockets and since each pocket completes a full cycle of operations for one revolution of the rotor the engine is equivalent in power-pulse output to a six-cylinder four-stroke piston engine. There has been some controversy regarding the capacity of the Wankel engine; in the N.S.U. Spider the maximum volume of one pocket or chamber is 500 c.c. but the overall effect and power output is about equivalent to that of a $1\frac{1}{2}$ litre conventional engine.

The Wankel engine has no valves, gas entry and exit being controlled by the rotor tips as they traverse ports in the housing wall. To follow the sequence of events as shown in Fig. 21 it is necessary to recognize that all three pockets are seen at different stages in the cycle; twelve diagrams are needed strictly if the phases in one pocket alone are to be traced but this is simplified in the illustration by considering events in all three pockets so that only four diagrams are used. Consider one pocket, that formed at rotor face CA, and note that the rotor revolves in the clockwise direction. In diagram I the induction phase 1 is commencing, with the pocket beginning to expand and drawing in mixture through the uncovered inlet port; this continues through diagrams II and III until at phase 4 in diagram IV the pocket is at maximum volume. We now have to consider this particular pocket 're-christened' as AB in diagram I; as rotation continues the pocket begins to contract, with the inlet port closed off by the rotor tip, until in diagram III maximum compression occurs and the mixture is fired by a conventional sparking plug. Phase 8 in diagram IV shows the beginning of the power 'stroke' as the pocket starts to expand. Returning to diagram I we again have to change letters, the pocket now being that marked BC; in diagram II at phase 10 the exhaust port is uncovered by the rotor tip and the burnt gas is ejected as the pocket diminishes through phases 11 and 12.

The centre of the rotor is formed as a ring gear so that power can be extracted by a central shaft geared to the rotor. Because of the perfect balance of the rotor and the complete absence of reciprocating parts the engine can theoretically run at very high speeds without vibration; in practice, however, the speed is kept down so as to minimize wear at the rotor tips and maximum power is produced at speeds comparable with those in an equivalent

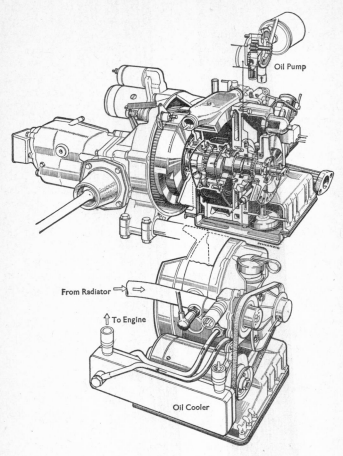

Oil Pump

From Radiator ⇒ ⇨

↑ To Engine

Oil Cooler

Fig. 22. The Wankel rotary-piston engine as installed in the NSU *Spider*; the engine is built in unit with a four-speed gearbox and differential and is installed underneath the rear boot of the car. (*By courtesy of NSU (Great Britain) Ltd*)

reciprocating engine. To preserve a gas-tight running fit at the rotor tips a flexible strip arrangement is used, analogous with conventional piston rings.

Apart from the absence of vibration, the striking feature of the Wankel engine is its remarkably small basic size (somewhat masked in Fig. 22 by the bulk of the usual auxiliaries such as generator and carburetter). It is possible to combine a number of rotor/housings on a common shaft to derive large power outputs without increasing overall diameter.

THE GAS TURBINE

A number of British car manufacturers are known to be experimenting with gas turbines. From the point of view of its application to cars the gas turbine may be considered as a scaled-down jet engine in which the exhaust stream, instead of propelling the vehicle by jet reaction, is used to rotate a turbine coupled to the road wheels. It is thus, to a certain extent, comparable to the type of aircraft engine known as the 'prop-jet' or propeller-turbine.

The turbine can be regarded as consisting basically of two sections, which are not mechanically coupled. The first section (i.e.

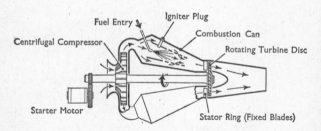

Fig. 23. The essentials of a 'straight-through' jet engine.

the jet engine, Fig. 23) has a single rotating part, namely a shaft carrying an *impeller* at one end and a turbine disc at the other. The impeller, as shown in the illustration, rotates within a closely fitting casing; air is admitted to the centre of the casing and is flung outwards by the impeller, which acts as a centrifugal compressor. The compressed air is led into one or more combustion chambers or 'cans' where part of it is used to burn fuel sprayed from a jet, while the remainder dilutes the hot gas stream so produced, and limits its temperature. (In an aircraft engine there are a number of combustion cans, disposed about the central shaft.) The gas then passes through stationary guide vanes and impinges on the turbine blades. The turbine disc is thus driven round, carrying the impeller with it. Only part of the total energy of the gas stream is required to drive the compressor, the remainder being expelled as the propulsive jet, if the engine is of the pure jet type.

It will be seen, therefore, that in effect the impeller supplies gas to the turbine, which in turn provides power for the impeller. The inevitable losses in this circulation of energy, and the useful energy output, are made up by the burning of the fuel, and the power output of the engine is controlled by the rate at which fuel is supplied.

Owing to the internal losses and the inefficiency of compressor and turbine at low speeds, the engine is not self-supporting below speeds of around 6,000 r.p.m. The rotor is spun initially (by an electric motor in the case of a motor car turbine) up to a speed of about 3,000 r.p.m., when fuel, usually paraffin (kerosene), is admitted and ignited by an electric plug of the surface-discharge type. The motor continues to drive the rotor up to its idling speed, the turbine then providing sufficient power to drive the compressor unassisted. A typical idling speed might be 10,000 r.p.m., and maximum rotor speed 50,000 r.p.m., although there have been hints of speeds as high as 90,000 r.p.m.

The second section of the turbine consists of a further turbine disc or discs, placed in the exhaust stream from the compressor turbine (Fig. 24). As stated previously, this *free power* turbine is not coupled mechanically to the compressor rotor, and, in fact, is usually arranged to rotate in the opposite direction, in order to minimize the gyroscopic effects arising from the very high rotational speeds. The power turbine shaft is normally geared to the final output shaft through reduction gearing, which is an integral part of the power unit.

The torque produced by the power turbine when the compressor is rotating at idling speed is very low, and the vehicle can easily be

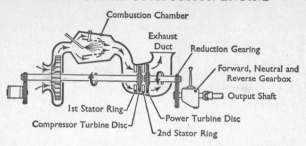

Fig. 24. Non-regenerative gas turbine. The compressor and power turbines are not coupled together mechanically.

held stationary by means of the handbrake. As the compressor speeds up, the power turbine torque increases until it is sufficient to move the vehicle with the brake released. If rapid acceleration is required the compressor can first be spun to its maximum speed and the brake then released. It is under these conditions that the torque of the power turbine is at its greatest, i.e. maximum torque is available with the car stationary. As the car accelerates, the power turbine (which is directly coupled to the road wheels) increases speed to a maximum about three-quarters of that of the compressor. As the speed increases the torque produced decreases. The very desirable torque characteristic of the turbine is partly offset by the fact that turbine efficiency decreases as speed drops; in order to minimize fuel consumption it may be necessary to provide a simple gearbox to enable the power turbine to operate within its most efficient speed range.

A simple gas turbine of the type outlined above is very inefficient, since the exhaust gases contain a great deal of heat energy which is lost to the atmosphere. Extensive research is being carried out to develop a *heat exchanger* which will enable the waste heat to be transferred to the incoming air (Fig. 25). This device, which resembles a normal car radiator in its operation, must possess a very large surface area and yet offer only low resistance to the passage of the exhaust gases. The problem of constructing a compact heat-exchanger is a major obstacle to the general adoption of the gas turbine in road vehicles; one type receiving attention com-

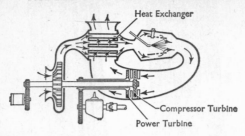

Fig. 25. Gas turbine with heat exchanger. The centrifugally compressed air is pre-heated by hot exhaust gases before entering the combustion chamber.

prises a slowly rotating bladed disc so arranged that its blades pass first through the hot exhaust gases to collect heat and then into the incoming cool air stream where the stored heat is given up.

Once the problems of heat exchanger construction and cheap manufacture of the turbine discs have been overcome, it is reasonable to assume that the piston engine will be displaced from medium-power and high-performance cars, though the inefficiency of the small turbine will probably preclude its use in the smallest cars. The gas turbine has numerous advantages, including the following: it can be run on almost any type of fuel; it is very easily started; it can be made almost noiseless and vibrationless; it requires no cooling system; it has a small number of moving parts and its ancillary equipment is of a simple nature (i.e. starter motor, fuel and oil pumps, elementary ignition system); it requires only a simple transmission system.

Although gas turbine powered cars have been raced successfully, production of passenger cars has been limited to small numbers for 'customer evaluation'. It seems certain that the first major application for road vehicles will be in large motorway transports of the articulated type for long-distance transit of goods at high speed. Distances as great as one million miles between major turbine overhauls have been forecast and this, together with the small amount of routine maintenance required with turbines would obviously be an important factor in the transport business.

COMPROMISE

A variation on the gas turbine theme which is reported to be under development for application to automobiles is the *free-piston gas generator engine*. The principle of this device, which is already in use in some Continental generating stations, is that a piston is allowed to reciprocate within a cylinder, as in the conventional piston engine, except that there is no connecting rod/crank gear; the cylinder is enclosed and the piston 'rebounds' off a cushion of trapped air at the end of the cylinder. The exhaust gases are led off through a power turbine as in the conventional gas turbine. The gas generator thus fulfils the functions of compressor, combustion chamber, and impeller turbine.

This arrangement is a 'flash-back' to the early history of the gas turbine, the development of which was largely based on experience gained with the exhaust turbo-supercharger. This device is widely used on certain large engines and is virtually a gas turbine 'in reverse'; the exhaust gases from the diesel engine are passed through a turbine which drives a centrifugal compressor feeding the air which the engine needs for combustion.

DERIVATION OF THE R.A.C. HORSEPOWER FORMULA

If the diameter of a single cylinder bore is taken as D inches, the area of the piston top is $\frac{\pi}{4}D^2$ square inches. Taking the average gas pressure on the piston during the firing stroke to be P pounds per square inch, the thrust on the piston is $P \times \frac{\pi}{4}D^2$ pounds.

Instead of taking account of speed of revolution, the piston speed, S feet per minute, is considered (this being determined jointly by length of stroke and rotational speed). Since work is calculated by multiplying together force and distance moved, the work done in one minute would be:

$$P \times \frac{\pi}{4}D^2 \times S \text{ foot.pounds}$$

But, in a four-stroke cycle, useful work is only done over one quarter of the total distance moved by the piston, so that the work actually done in one minute is:

$$\tfrac{1}{4} \times P \times \frac{\pi}{4}D^2 \times S \text{ foot.pounds}$$

Therefore, since 33,000 foot.pounds of work done in one minute is equivalent to an output of one horsepower:

$$\text{Horsepower} = \frac{\frac{1}{4} \times P \times \frac{\pi}{4}D^2 \times S}{33,000}$$

Not all this power actually appears at the crankshaft because some is lost within the engine, so the above result must be multiplied by a fraction E, representing mechanical efficiency:

$$\text{Horsepower} = \frac{E \times \frac{1}{4} \times P \times \frac{\pi}{4}D^2 \times S}{33,000}$$

At the time of the evolution of the formula it was assumed that the following would apply generally to all engines:

(1) The rated power would be delivered at a speed corresponding to a piston speed S of 1000 feet per minute.
(2) The average pressure P on the piston would be 90 pounds per square inch.
(3) The internal losses would be 25 per cent of the total power, giving a mechanical efficiency E of 75 per cent ($\frac{3}{4}$).

Substitution of these values in place of the corresponding symbols in the above formula gives:

Horsepower
(of a single-
cylinder engine)
$$= \frac{\frac{3}{4} \times \frac{1}{4} \times 90 \times \frac{\pi}{4}D^2 \times 1000}{33,000} = \frac{D^2}{2 \cdot 5} \text{ (approximately)}$$

For an engine with N cylinders:

$$\text{Horsepower} = \frac{D^2 N}{2 \cdot 5}.$$

CHAPTER THREE

FUEL, EXHAUST, LUBRICATION, AND COOLING SYSTEMS

Fuel Supply and Carburation

AT one time it was common practice to situate the fuel tank under the bonnet with a direct gravity feed to the carburetter. However, the risk of fire attendant upon this arrangement, and the requirements of space, caused the removal of the tank to a position remote from the engine. This also meant that the considerable weight of the tank could be positioned nearer the ground and thus assist in the lowering of the centre of gravity of the car.

The modern fuel tank is built up from steel pressings, usually with an internal anti-corrosion finish. The tank has internal baffles to limit surging of the fuel and it is necessary for the filler pipe to have a diameter large enough not only to accept the high rate of feed obtainable with filling station pumps, but also to permit the escape of the displaced air. Occasionally two interconnected tanks are used, each with its own filler.

The situation of the tank necessitates the use of a pump to raise the fuel to carburetter level, and the tank is connected to the pump by means of copper tubing. This pipe-line may enter the tank through the top as a leak here would be less serious and may incorporate helical coils where vibration is expected; the final connexion to the engine is made with an armoured flexible pipe to absorb the considerable sideways movement of the engine.

A feature found on some cars is the provision of a reserve fuel supply. This may be effected by ensuring that the main fuel-line terminates some way from the bottom of the tank, with a second branch finishing at a lower level. The second pipe is only brought into operation by the driver when the main pipe ceases to draw fuel and a facia lamp then indicates that the reserve supply is being used.

A means of indicating remotely the level of the fuel in the tank is almost invariably provided, and usually this is electrically operated.

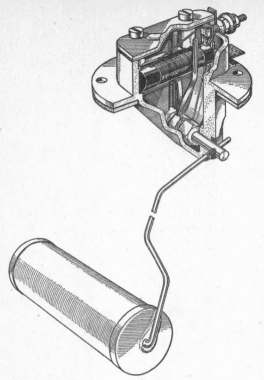

Fig. 26. In the tank unit of a fuel contents indicator the rise and fall of a float is made to adjust a resistance in the circuit supplying the indicating meter. (*By courtesy of Smith's Motor Accessories Ltd*)

A hinged float rises and falls with the fuel level and in so doing causes a contact arm to wipe over a resistance coil (Fig. 26). This varies the current flowing in a circuit which is connected to an ammeter mounted on the facia, this meter being calibrated in terms of the fuel remaining in the tank.

FUEL PUMP

The fuel pump, which feeds petrol from the tank to the carburetter, is almost invariably either the AC mechanical type or the

S.U. electric pump, the latter being used on all cars produced by the Nuffield Organization and on some other makes. Both pumps are similar in that pressure is applied to the fuel by means of a spring-loaded diaphragm. Also, both pumps have an inlet valve which allows fuel to enter from the tank, but not to return, and an outlet valve, which ensures that fuel cannot re-enter the pump from the carburetter.

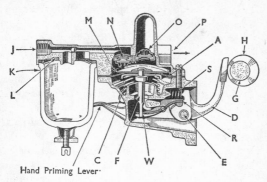

Hand Priming Lever·

Fig. 27. The AC fuel pump is operated mechanically from an eccentric H on the engine camshaft G. Other parts are:

A. Diaphragm.
C. Diaphragm spring.
D. Rocker arm.
E. Rocker arm pivot.
F. Pull rod.
J. Fuel intake.
K. Sediment chamber.
L. Filter gauze.

M. Pumping chamber.
N. Suction valve.
O. Delivery valve.
P. Fuel delivery.
R. Point of 'break' in two parts of pump lever.
S. Rocker arm spring.
W. Connecting link.

(*By courtesy of AC-Delco Division of General Motors Ltd*)

The AC Mechanical Pump (Fig. 27) is invariably mounted on the side of the engine, and has an arm which extends through the engine casing and is actuated by an eccentric on the camshaft. The action of the arm is to pull down the flexible pump diaphragm and the partial vacuum thus created allows atmospheric pressure, acting on the surface of the fuel in the tank, to push fuel along the pipe-line and fill up the pump.

The pump arm, or lever, is divided into two parts at its pivot and the joint is so arranged that the part operated by the engine only carries round the other part, attached to the diaphragm, when it is moving in the anti-clockwise direction. This means that, as the eccentric continues to revolve, the right-hand portion of the lever, being held against the eccentric by a spring, moves in the clockwise direction and 'leaves behind' the left-hand portion of the lever. The movement of the diaphragm thereafter is determined by whether or not the carburetter is full of petrol; if so, its needle-valve will prevent any more petrol from entering and the diaphragm will be compelled to remain at the bottom of its travel, whilst the right-hand part of the pump lever continues to oscillate without any effect. If the float chamber is not full, then the diaphragm will be pushed upwards by its spring and force petrol into the carburetter, so that the left-hand part of the lever 'catches up' with the right and is pushed down again on the next rotation of the eccentric in readiness for the next upward stroke.

Obviously, the AC pump can only function when the engine is rotating and therefore, where considered necessary, a manual priming lever is fitted, by means of which a dry carburetter can be filled without turning the engine. When the pump is in an inaccessible position the hand lever is fitted with an extension; it is operated by pushing the handle down and releasing it, several times, until the resistance is felt to disappear. A stationary pump is capable of retaining pressure up to about ten days.

The S.U. Electric Pump (Fig. 28) is usually mounted separately from the engine, often on the engine compartment bulkhead and sometimes at the rear of the car close to the fuel tank, where it is immune from the vapour-lock troubles which may be caused by engine heat. The diaphragm in this pump is operated electro-magnetically, i.e. an iron armature attached to the diaphragm is drawn towards an electro-magnet when the latter is energized. A spring tends to hold the diaphragm in the 'pump empty' position (towards the right in Fig. 28) but having reached this position an extension rod, attached to the armature, closes two contacts and allows an electric current to flow through the magnet coil. The armature is therefore pulled towards the magnet and the retraction of the diaphragm causes petrol to be sucked into the pump. When

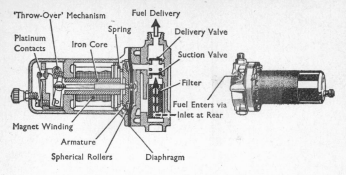

'Throw-Over' Mechanism   Fuel Delivery

Platinum
Contacts   Iron Core   Spring   Delivery Valve

Suction Valve

Filter

Fuel Enters via
Inlet at Rear

Magnet Winding

Armature

Spherical Rollers   Diaphragm

Fig. 28. S.U. Electric fuel pump.
(*By courtesy of the S.U. Carburetter Co. Ltd*)

the armature reaches the left-hand end of its travel the extension
rod operates a 'throw-over' mechanism, which separates the contacts so that the armature and diaphragm can return to the right,
under spring pressure, according to the rate at which the carburetter can accept the displaced fuel. No hand priming device is required on the S.U. pump since, provided the battery is not discharged, the pump will begin to operate as soon as the ignition
circuit is switched on, and continue until the float chamber is full.
This action is characterized by a rhythmic ticking sound. For some
of the larger engines, twin S.U. pumps are used side by side to
obtain greater fuel flow capacity.

Lucas Fuel Pump. A different type of electric fuel pump used on
some cars is the Lucas Model 2FP, which uses a rotary impeller
driven by a small electric motor. An interesting feature of this
pump is that the whole of the motor and impeller assembly is
enclosed within a single casing, and the bearings and motor brush
gear run totally immersed in fuel. This overcomes any problems of
sealing the spindle against leakage. The entire pump can be installed within the fuel tank below the surface, thus obviating the difficulties of vaporization of fuel on the suction side of the pump. The
pump is provided with a sealed armoured tube to carry the electricity supply to the motor. This type of pump runs continuously
when the ignition is switched on, re-circulating the fuel within itself;

a relief valve is provided to prevent excessive pressure causing flooding of the carburetters.

Motor Fuels

The bulk of motor fuel is obtained from natural petroleum, which consists of a mixture of chemical substances known as *hydrocarbons*. In the first stage of refining, the crude oil is separated into various *fractions* by a distillation process and the light fraction, known as gasoline, is suitable, after treatment, for use as motor fuel. Petrol obtained in this way is known as *straight-run*. The remaining heavier fractions appear eventually in such forms as kerosene, diesel oil, lubricating oil, and bitumen.

Only a very small proportion of the hydrocarbon fractions possess the characteristics essential in a fuel to be used in modern engines. Therefore, in order to meet the demand, it is necessary to treat certain of the other fractions to obtain additional gasolines for blending into motor fuel. For instance, the petroleum gases can be converted by a method known as *polymerization*, and the fraction called heavy gas-oil can be converted by the *catalytic cracking* process. This entails subjecting the oil to heat and pressure, in the presence of a chemical substance, in an apparatus known familiarly as the 'cat cracker'.

The straight-run gasoline and the gasolines obtained indirectly are then blended in suitable proportions as motor fuel. Very small amounts of special chemicals (*additives*) may also be included to produce certain desirable characteristics.

The main requirements of a petrol for use in motor cars are that:

(*a*) It must be chemically stable, i.e. it must not form substances which would block or corrode the fuel tank and pipe system. The natural tendency for petrol to form such substances is countered by the addition of *oxidation inhibitors*.

(*b*) It must not be excessively volatile (i.e., liable to evaporate) as apart from the tendency to vaporize and escape from the tank it might boil in the fuel pipe, especially in hot weather or at high altitude. The fuel pump would not then be able to deliver petrol, this condition being known as *vapour lock*.

(*c*) It must be sufficiently volatile to form the necessary petrol/air mixture for combustion. Gasoline contains a number of hydrocarbons with boiling points ranging from 30°C for the lightest to 200°C for the heaviest. The proportion of the lighter hydrocarbons must be high enough to ensure that the petrol will vaporize sufficiently to provide easy starting from cold, and to minimize the tendency for the heavier hydrocarbons to separate out in droplet form, which produces poor mixture distribution between cylinders and therefore rough running. The proportion of the heavier hydrocarbons is also limited by the possibility of their burning only partially and thus depositing carbon in the cylinder head. It is therefore desirable that the petrol should be highly volatile, but the problem of vapour lock forces a compromise here.

(*d*) It must possess adequate anti-knock properties. The influence of cylinder head design and compression ratio on the phenomenon of knocking or detonation has been mentioned previously. In particular it should be remembered that the high compression ratio required for high efficiency also demands a fuel of superior anti-knock rating. An important point is that so long as a given engine does not knock when run on a particular fuel, no advantage is gained by using a fuel of higher anti-knock value, i.e. if such a fuel is available its value in increased power output can only be appreciated by raising the compression ratio of the engine; some advantage may be gained by advancing the ignition, if the limit of advance has not already been reached.

The anti-knock property of a fuel is determined initially by the composition of the blend; it may be improved by the addition of a small quantity of *Tetra Ethyl Lead* (*T.E.L.*) or *Tetra Methyl Lead* (*T.M.L.*) but the amount is limited since an excessive concentration might cause deposits.

The anti-knock rating is usually indicated by quoting *Octane Number* (*O.N.*). A laboratory test engine is run on the fuel under specified conditions and the anti-knock property is matched against that of a mixture of *iso-octane* and *heptane*. The percentage of iso-octane in this mixture gives the Octane Number; a fuel with a rating equivalent to pure iso-octane would have an O.N. of 100. (In point of fact, certain fuels have an Octane rating superior to that of pure iso-octane and the Octane scale is arbitrarily extended to include them, special methods of testing being used.)

In order to obtain a general assessment of the performance of a fuel under all engine conditions it is customary to make tests in two stages, namely, at low speed and low temperature, and at high speed and high temperature. The latter condition gives what is known as Motor Method Octane Number and, until more recent times, this was the rating with which we were most familiar. The former condition gives what is known as the Research Octane Number, which, in general, is rather higher than that obtained by the Motor Method. The actual performance of fuel 'on the road' will fall somewhere between the levels determined by the two methods and will depend upon the type of car in which the fuel is used. Thus it will be seen that the estimation of Octane Numbers is only one guide to fuel quality.

To assist in clarifying the confusion caused by the wide variety of petrol brand names a British Standard has been prepared according to which petrols may be assigned *star ratings*; these ratings may be found marked on filling station pumps. The star ratings correspond approximately to the four main gradings already in use, the equivalent Research Octane Numbers being as given below:

British Standard	*'Grade'*	*Minimum Research Octane Number*
Five Star	Super	100
Four Star	Premium	97
Three Star	Mixture	94
Two Star	Regular	90

OTHER MOTOR FUELS

Besides gasoline obtained from natural petroleum, other fuels are used in limited quantities.

Benzole, which is a by-product of coal-gas manufacture, is sometimes blended with gasoline.

Alcohol has a remarkably high octane rating and is 'cool-running', but is only available in limited quantities in Britain and is relatively expensive. Its tendency to absorb moisture from the atmosphere, and low heat content, make it unsuitable as a neat commercial fuel. However, alcohol can be used to advantage in racing engines and is also blended into certain types of motor spirit to raise anti-knock value and improve slow-running.

MANIFOLD

The system or ducts which distributes petrol/air mixture to the cylinders is known as the *induction manifold*. In some engines the manifold is built as an integral part of the cylinder head, but in the majority of cases it consists of an aluminium alloy or iron casting bolted on to the side of the engine with its branches matching up to the induction openings. In order to simplify construction it is usual to 'pair up' the induction ports and thus reduce the number of manifold branches. The inlet and exhaust valves are not therefore arranged alternately but appear as in Fig. 29, and the induction ports are said to be 'siamesed'.

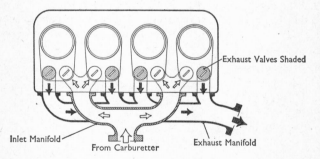

Fig. 29. Plan view of four-cylinder side-valve engine (head removed) showing inlet ducts paired (siamesed) within the cylinder block, to simplify external manifolding.

The shape of the manifold is also dictated by the type of carburetter (i.e., down-draught, side-draught, etc.) and quite elaborate branching systems are used to obtain even distribution of mixture between cylinders, especially when only one carburetter is used. When twin or triple carburetter installations are employed, an interconnecting balance pipe is provided to ensure equal depression on each instrument.

The *exhaust manifold* normally used on touring engines is an iron casting similar to the induction manifold, and the two manifolds are often clamped together to provide a hot-spot which encourages vaporization of the fuel when the engine is started from cold. The warming-up of the incoming mixture is not a desirable feature for normal running, and on certain engines a thermostatically controlled flap is used to deflect the exhaust gases so that they no longer play upon the hot-spot, once the engine is warmed up.

On sports engines, more elaborate high-efficiency exhaust systems are used with a view to minimizing backpressure and thus improving scavenging of the exhaust gases. Each exhaust port is provided with its own pipe, the individual pipes being united some way from the engine. On racing engines, where no silencer is used, the length and form of the exhaust pipes is often carefully determined since these features influence the resonance of the pipes to the exhaust pulsations, and this can materially affect engine performance. The system is, in fact, tuned to give an extractor effect in the high speed range.

The law requires that a car should make only a 'reasonable' amount of noise, so that a silencer or muffler is required to blanket the explosive effect of the exhaust pulsations. Commonly, the silencer consists of a chamber into which the exhaust gas can expand, with baffles to provide an extended path. Occasionally additional expansion chambers are provided between the engine and the silencer proper. A particular requirement of the exhaust system is that it shall not obstruct the passage of the gases and so create a back pressure, which would impede engine scavenging. The absence of back pressure is a feature of the straight-through absorption type silencer (Fig. 30). The Servais silencer illustrated contains no baffles, and consists of a diamond mesh metal tube surrounded by a blanket of glass silk, enclosed in a wire mesh spiral. The high pressure gas pulsations expand into the cellular structure of the packing and are then fed back into the central duct, at low pressure. A particular feature of the Servais silencer is that the continual working of the diamond mesh prevents the build-up of carbon in the silencer.

The silencer has to withstand severe conditions of corrosion and

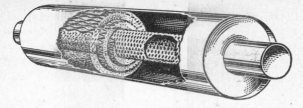

Fig. 30. 'Straight-through' absorption type silencer (Servais).
(*By courtesy of Servais Silencers Ltd*)

various methods have been used to combat attack by the hot exhaust gases and condensation products; these include the use of stainless steel for the silencer casing and the coating of the inside of the silencer with glass or ceramic materials.

In some parts of the world where the problem of atmospheric pollution by exhaust effluent is particularly acute, 'anti-smog' legislation is being introduced which requires vehicles to emit no more than specified amounts of hydrocarbons and carbon monoxide. These regulations have precipitated major research into the problems of accurate mixture control by carburetter and fuel-injection improvements, the development of devices which complete the combustion process after the exhaust gases have left the engine, and the elimination of emission of fumes from the crankcase; the exhaust fume problem is, of course, particularly severe with engines such as the two-stroke which burn lubricating oil in addition to petrol.

Lubrication System

It is common knowledge that if two rough surfaces are rubbed together there is a resistance to the motion and heat is generated. In an automobile engine surfaces which rub together are not rough by normal standards, yet if they are allowed to run in direct contact with one another the temperature may rise to so high a value that local melting will occur and the surfaces will stick or 'seize'. It has been shown that even if the surfaces are 'super finished', seizing will occur unless lubrication is provided.

In the internal combustion engine many rubbing surfaces

operate under extreme conditions of loading and/or speed, and in order to maintain a lubricating film between them it is necessary to supply oil continually under pressure. The oil is almost always contained in the sump, which is therefore known as a *wet sump*, although in some engines the oil reservoir is separate, the *dry sump* then acting merely as a pan from which the oil is continually drained.

The pressure of the oil is derived from a pump which may be either of the eccentric-vane type or the simple gear type (Fig. 31). The pump is submerged in the sump oil and a common driving

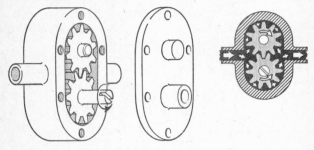

Fig. 31. Principle of gear-type oil pump.
Oil is carried round in the pockets formed between the gear teeth and the casing, but the barrier formed by the meshing teeth prevents the oil from returning to the inlet side.

arrangement is by means of an inclined shaft rotated by skew gears on the camshaft. Very often this shaft is extended upwards to provide a drive to the distributor.

The distribution of oil is by means of galleries and drillings within the engine components, rather than by vulnerable pipes. A typical lubrication system is shown in Fig. 33. The pump, seen low on the right of the end view, draws oil from the sump via a strainer and delivers it to a main oil gallery (on the left of the end view). Here some of the oil enters a by-pass filter whence it drains back into the crankcase. The remainder is led to the main crankshaft bearings and thence, via drillings in the crankshaft, to the big-end bearings. Some of the main bearing oil is ducted to the camshaft bearings and thence, via a vertical oilway, to the hollow overhead rocker shaft. It then escapes, through drillings in the shaft, to lubricate the rockers and also passes through drillings in the rockers to reach the push-rod ends. Oil which accumulates in the top of the engine drains back down the spaces surrounding the push-rods.

Oil feed is also provided for the tappets and for the camshaft chain drive.

A feature shown in Fig. 33 is the arrangement which prevents oil escaping from the rear main bearing and entering the flywheel housing. This consists of a *labyrinth* seal, i.e. a series of interlocking ridges and grooves, and a *thrower* ring, which is a more pronounced ridge which causes the oil to be thrown off the revolving shaft.

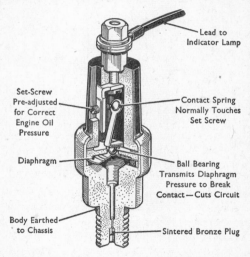

Lead to Indicator Lamp

Set-Screw Pre-adjusted for Correct Engine Oil Pressure

Contact Spring Normally Touches Set Screw

Diaphragm

Ball Bearing Transmits Diaphragm Pressure to Break Contact — Cuts Circuit

Body Earthed to Chassis

Sintered Bronze Plug

Fig. 32. An oil pressure switch, which breaks the circuit supplying the facia-mounted warning lamp when the diaphragm is raised by adequate oil pressure. (*By courtesy of Smith's Motor Accessories Ltd*)

OIL PRESSURE

The working pressure of the oil system varies from one engine make to another, but is usually of the order of 30–60 pounds per

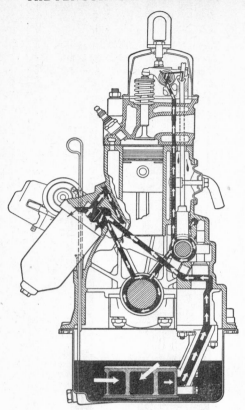

Fig. 33. A typical pressurized lubrication system (Austin).

square inch. The actual pressure may be indicated by a gauge mounted on the facia, but in many production cars the gauge has been superseded by a warning light which glows if oil pressure falls below a certain minimum, the light being controlled by an oil pressure switch (Fig. 32).

A feature of all pressure lubrication systems is that full flow of oil cannot occur until after the engine has been started. It is often

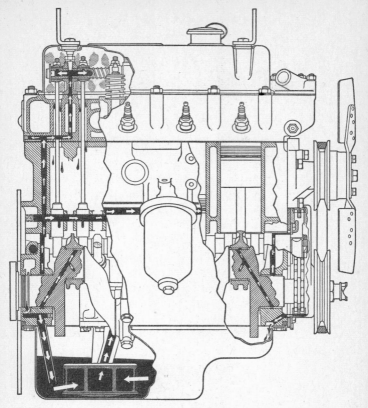

(By courtesy of the Austin Motor Co. Ltd)

asserted that for this reason the greater part of engine wear occurs in the first few minutes after starting. Clearly, if the oil is cold and thick, the initial circulation is restricted and could cause dangerously high pressure to be set up in the system if a release valve were not provided. This is an adjustable spring-loaded ball-valve which allows oil to escape into the sump without traversing the lubrication system, if a certain pressure is exceeded.

However, the flow through the release valve is itself limited in order to ensure that oil is forced to the vital bearing surfaces. For this reason, the indicated oil pressure is high when starting and falls off as the engine warms up. Usual pressures are about 15 pounds per square inch when idling, rising to a working figure as mentioned above as engine speed increases. Beyond a certain speed oil pressure remains constant as determined by the release valve setting.

As the engine wears the oil pressure falls because the working clearances at the bearings are increased and there is, therefore, less resistance to oil flow. The pressure may be restored to some extent by the use of a heavier grade of oil, but this will mean that there is a reduced flow of oil through the bearings, which depend upon this flow for cooling. However, since worn bearings are usually accompanied by worn cylinders, the change to a thicker oil is generally advantageous from the point of view of oil consumption, in that there is less tendency for oil to blow past the pistons.

OIL LEVEL

On the majority of cars the level of oil in the sump is determined by examination of a dipstick. In some quality cars, however, an indicator, similar to that used in the fuel tank, is made to show an oil level reading on the fuel gauge dial, when a button is pressed.

OIL VISCOSITY

An important factor in assessing the suitability of an oil is the viscosity/temperature characteristic. The viscosity of oil increases as the temperature falls, so that although an oil might have correct viscosity at normal engine temperature, at low temperatures it could become so thick that *oil drag* would place undue load on the starting equipment, and also the circulation of the oil would be retarded. For this reason it has been usual to specify a 'summer grade' S.A.E. 30 oil and a 'winter grade' of (say) S.A.E.20. However, the use of an oil which is reasonably thin at low temperatures may mean that at running temperatures the oil becomes so thin as to impair its lubricant properties. Both viscosity and oiliness contribute to lubricity.

Oiliness is an obscure term, but may be regarded as the ability of an oil to maintain an unbroken lubricating film between rubbing surfaces, and is related to the film strength of the oil. Oiliness is important with regard to the pressures under which the moving parts operate, and is a property not determined by the viscosity of the lubricant.

Over the past few years, *multigrade* oils have been introduced for which change of viscosity with temperature is not nearly so marked; they are sometimes referred to as 'flat curve' oils, because, if a graph is drawn with viscosity suitably plotted against temperature, the resultant curve is much flatter than for the normal type of oil. The table gives comparative viscosities at various temperatures for three grades of normal oils, and for a multigrade oil which is marketed by Alexander Duckham & Co. Ltd, and known as Q.5500. It will be seen that, while at engine-operating temperatures the viscosity of this oil is approximately the same as that of the S.A.E.30 grade, at freezing point (32°F) the normal oil is almost three times as thick as the Q.5500. At the exceptionally low temperature of 0°F (32° of frost) the viscosity of Q.5500 is of the same order as that of a normal S.A.E.10 oil, and these properties are denoted by the grading S.A.E.10W-30.

The obvious advantages of multigrade oil, with its free-flowing

TABLE OF COMPARATIVE VISCOSITIES

Temperature	Q.5500 S.A.E. 10W/30	S.A.E. 30 Engine Oil	S.A.E. 20 Engine Oil	S.A.E. 10W Engine Oil
0°F	9,500	54,000	24,000	9,500
32°F	2,400	7,200	3,800	1,600
70°F	580	1,250	750	360
100°F	260	440	285	155
140°F	110	160	110	70
210°F	52	56	47	40

properties, are the reduced drain on the starting battery and the very rapid circulation of the oil throughout the engine, which reduces cold-starting wear. In addition, the overall reduction in fluid friction means that more useful power can be developed during the warming-up period, and there is no longer any necessity for different grades of oil in summer and winter.

Besides the more satisfactory viscosity/temperature characteristic, multigrade oils possess improved anti-corrosive and detergent properties. Engine oil shows a tendency to oxidize (combine with atmospheric oxygen) especially when churned around at high temperature, forming sludge which may block oil-passages, and gums which may cause sticking valves and piston rings. The addition of oxidation inhibitors increases the resistance to oxidation; other additives are included in the oil to neutralize the corrosive acids produced in the sump oil by the products of fuel combustion and to a lesser extent by the products of breakdown of the sump oil itself. Other additives impart detergent properties which means that the deposits which would normally accumulate within the engine are held in suspension in the oil and eventually retained by the oil filter. The oil thus has a cleaning effect which is rather like that of detergent washing powders.

There is a general move by car manufacturers to extend the recommended period between routine overhauls, including engine oil draining and replacement, and there is also a tendency for engine designers to reduce the total oil capacity of engines. These factors, combined with the increased stress levels in modern engines, put constant pressure on the oil firms to develop higher performance oils capable of maintaining their lubricating properties at high temperatures for long periods; this has resulted in the marketing of new types of oil for which a 'life' of the order of 10,000 miles between changes is claimed.

OIL COOLING

In some high-performance cars the flow of air over the engine sump may be insufficient to keep the oil temperature below the point at which thinning becomes unacceptable and provision is then made for the oil to circulate through an *oil cooler*, which usually resembles a small radiator additional to the main cooling system radiator.

In the Kenlowe *Radomatic* system the oil cooler is incorporated as a tube passing through the bottom tank of the main radiator; this ensures that the oil is not over-cooled in cold weather and also assists in the rapid warming-up of the engine.

OIL FILTRATION

Various types of impurity are continually tending to accumulate in the lubricating oil. They include particles of metal worn from rubbing surfaces, carbon deposited from the oil itself, and dust drawn into the engine crankcase. The presence of these impurities can greatly increase the rate of engine wear, and modern engines are fitted with filters which maintain the oil in a clean state. The filter takes the form of a cylindrical container mounted on the outside of the engine and containing an element made from cloth or specially treated paper. The filter is situated in the output side of the oil pump. There are two main types of filter, the *full-flow* type (Fig. 34) in which all the oil is passed continuously through the

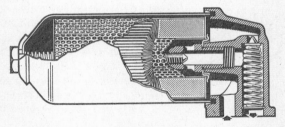

Fig. 34. Full-flow oil filter with valve to release pressure if filter becomes blocked. The element is replaceable (Purolator). (*By courtesy of Automotive Products Co. Ltd*)

element, and the *by-pass* type (Fig. 35) in which only part of the oil is 'bled off' and fed through the filter. The by-pass filter is the smaller and is simpler in construction; it can be installed quite easily on engines not originally equipped with a filter. The full-flow type must have its own release valve, otherwise, if the element became clogged, the oil flow would cease altogether.

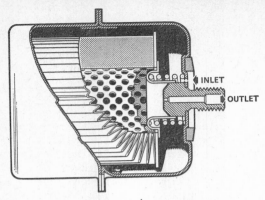

INLET

OUTLET

Fig. 35. By-pass oil filter of the throw-away type; the element is not replaceable (Purolator). (*By courtesy of Automotive Products Co. Ltd*)

Filter elements are usually replaced after about 9,000 miles, and this may be a matter of replacing the element itself or, in the case of the by-pass filter illustrated, the entire filter unit is replaced. In some cars a pressure-sensitive switch detects the excessive pressure drop across the filter when it has become clogged and lights a warning lamp on the instrument panel.

As a supplement to the oil filtration system, the engine may be fitted with a special type of sump drain-plug, containing a permanent magnet insert which attracts any ferrous particles such as manufacturing swarf which might otherwise cause blockage of the oil system or mechanical damage.

AIR CLEANER AND SILENCER

In order to prevent abrasive dust from entering the engine and also to silence the otherwise obtrusive 'hiss', it is standard practice to fit the carburetter air intake with a cleaner/silencer. The problem here is to extract the dust without obstructing the flow of air. In the 'centrifugal' type the air passes through a mesh filter and is then swirled in a long casing in such a way that the dust is thrown out. In an 'oil bath' filter the air passes over the surface of an oil pool, which collects the dust, and then passes through oil-wetted steel wool. A dry filter element of folded paper is also commonly used.

The crankcase of the engine has to be provided with an external opening or *breather*, since the movement of the pistons would cause a pumping action within the crankcase if a vent were not provided. The breather is a potential source of fumes from oil mist and from the blow-by of gases past the pistons; although many engines in the past have been fitted with a simple connexion between the breather and the engine air intake to encourage the engine to consume its own fumes to some extent, new 'anti-smog' legislation requires more positive steps to be taken to prevent the emission of fumes into the atmosphere. For this purpose, the Smiths' *crankcase emission control valve* has been evolved, this being a diaphragm valve fitted in a hose connexion between the crankcase and the inlet manifold; its function is to use the manifold vacuum condition to maintain a constant degree of suction on the crankcase and thus ensure that fumes are drawn back into the engine with the incoming mixture. The device incorporates a non-return valve to prevent a blow-back in the inlet manifold causing an explosion in the crankcase.

Cooling

Only a small part of the energy in the fuel used is converted into mechanical power, and the remainder of the energy appears as heat. Some of the heat is carried away in the exhaust gases, but that which passes to the cylinder head and walls must be dissipated by some form of cooling system.

AIR COOLING

Air cooling is almost universal in motor-cycle engines and is simply achieved by providing the cylinders with finning to increase the dissipating surface. In cars, direct air cooling is only rarely used, and since the natural draught is insufficient inside a closed engine compartment it is necessary to fit a cowling around the cylinders and use an engine-driven blower to gain the requisite air flow. Fig. 12 shows the arrangement used on the rear-mounted engine of the Volkswagen, including the oil cooler mounted in the air stream.

Air cooling has the advantages of simplifying engine construction and of providing immunity against freezing or boiling of the coolant. However, the blower tends to be noisy, besides itself consuming considerable power.

LIQUID COOLING

The vast majority of engines are liquid cooled with a coolant circulating in passages cast into the cylinder block and head. The liquid is, of course, water, but it may be necessary to use a glycol-based coolant ('anti-freeze') if freezing is likely.

Fig. 36 shows a typical water cooling system. The system is

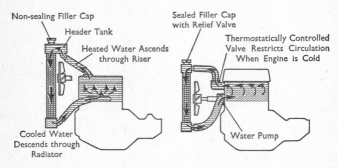

Fig. 36a. Cooling system with water circulation by thermo-syphon action.
   b. Modern cooling system with pump assisted circulation.

'closed', that is to say, the water circulates continuously without the addition of fresh water (except to make up slight losses). In older engines the circulation was entirely due to *thermo-syphon* effect; water expands when heated, so that its density decreases and it tends to rise, therefore the water in the jacket surrounding the cylinders flows upwards and is replaced by cold water entering from the radiator. The heated water passes down through the radiator and is cooled by the passage of air. A satisfactory thermo-syphon action is only obtained if there is a substantial *head* of water, which means that the top of the radiator must stand well above the engine.

However, the circulation is sluggish in a thermo-syphon system and the modern engine is invariably fitted with a pump to provide a positive water flow. An advantage of this is that the water passages can be arranged to direct the flow initially on to such hot spots as sparking plug bosses and the surrounds of the exhaust valves. The pump is usually of the centrifugal impeller type and situated

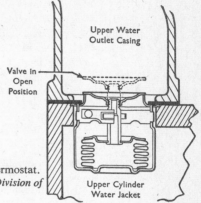

Upper Water
Outlet Casing

Valve in
Open
Position

Fig. 37. Cooling system thermostat.
(*By courtesy of A C-Delco Division of General Motors Ltd*)

Upper Cylinder
Water Jacket

in the flow of the water between the bottom of the radiator and the engine. It is driven by the fan belt and is occasionally mounted on the same spindle as the fan. The water is not fed into the bottom of the water jacket, as might be expected, but at a point higher up the engine. This is to prevent undue disturbance of the water at a point in the engine which does not become excessively hot and which would otherwise tend to be over-cooled.

In order to promote rapid warming-up it is standard practice to install a thermostat in the cooling system. The most common form of this (Fig. 37) is a valve located in the outlet from the engine, so that it restricts circulation of the coolant, and operated by a temperature-sensitive element. In the thermostat shown the element is a metallic bellows sealed with a partial vacuum and containing a mixture of methyl alcohol and water; at a pre-determined temperature the fluid evaporates and the vapour pressure allows the bellows to expand, thus lifting the valve off its seat and releasing the flow of coolant to the radiator. If the bellows should become punctured accidentally its springiness opens the valve fully, ensuring that the thermostat will 'fail safe'.

One disadvantage of the bellows thermostat is that in addition to responding to temperature it is also sensitive to the pressure within the cooling system and this becomes significant in the more recent compact systems with higher levels of pressurization. Therefore, for systems operating at pressures above about seven pounds per square inch a more suitable type of thermostat is that using a *wax pellet element*: this is very similar to the bellows thermostat but the valve is lifted by the expansion of a solid plug of wax trapped within a metal and rubber casing.

In another thermostat arrangement, fitted to thermo-syphon systems, the valve diverts the heated water through a pipe directly back to the engine entry, without passing it through the radiator.

PRESSURIZED COOLING SYSTEM

Another feature of modern cooling arrangements is the pressurizing of the entire system. If the pressure acting on the surface of a liquid is increased, the boiling point of the liquid is raised and *vice versa*. By sealing off the cooling system and providing the radiator cap with a valve, set to release at a pressure which is a few lb. per square inch higher than atmospheric pressure at sea level, it is possible to ensure that the water will not boil away, even at the high altitudes encountered in Alpine passes for instance.

COMPLETELY-SEALED COOLING SYSTEMS

In some cars the cooling system is entirely sealed off from the atmosphere and is filled 'for life' with an anti-freeze fluid containing corrosion-inhibiting chemicals. The object is to eliminate the continual small losses of cooling fluid which normally occur due to expansion or surge effects; this is achieved by including in the system an *expansion chamber* into which the fluid pushed out by expansion can escape via a relief valve and thus prevent the creation of excessive pressure as temperature rises. When the engine cools the expelled fluid is sucked back into the main circulating system. A sealed cooling system needs no topping-up maintenance and the anti-freeze mixture is always retained at correct strength, without deterioration due to constant exposure to air.

The Kenlowe Hermometic system provides a means of converting an existing cooling system to the fully-sealed type without the need for other modifications. It consists essentially of an expansion chamber which is coupled to the normal radiator overflow pipe, the usual pressure-relief radiator cap being replaced by a special sealed type. The chamber contains a quantity of chemicals which are released on the first occasion that fluid passes into the chamber; besides ensuring freedom from corrosion which might otherwise be caused over a long period by some types of anti-freeze solution these chemicals have an 'air-seeking' property such that they will seal off any minor leaks in the system, and they will incidentally eliminate the common complaint of squeaking noise produced by the water-pump.

ENGINE TEMPERATURES

Generally speaking, the operating temperatures of engines have been on the low side in the past, i.e. engines have been over-cooled. No harm is done by running an engine at temperatures as high as 200°F, and greater efficiency is obtained. The figure usually accepted nowadays is 185°F.

Rolls-Royce and Bentley cars are fitted with thermostatically operated shutters, which screen the radiator after the manner of a Venetian blind. The thermostat is set to maintain the engine temperature between 165°F and 185°F.

RADIATOR

In the modern car the radiator proper is invariably hidden behind a protective grille and sometimes ducting is provided to direct air on to the radiator core. Strictly speaking, the radiator should be referred to as a 'heat exchanger', since it never reaches a temperature at which a significant amount of heat is dissipated by direct radiation.

To induce a reasonable flow of air through the radiator block when the car is stationary, or moving slowly, a fan is almost invariably fitted immediately to the rear of the radiator. The fan may have as many as twelve blades, which in some designs are of moulded plastics material such as nylon or polypropylene, and it is driven directly from the engine by means of a belt, or belts, which also often serves to drive the electrical generator and the water-pump.

The fan has to be designed to produce an adequate air flow for cooling under the most adverse conditions as, for example, when the engine is idling in a traffic-jam on a hot day following a short burst of acceleration. However, with a directly-coupled fan the pulley ratio must be chosen such that the fan speed at idling is not too high otherwise the fan would be rotating at an impossible rate at high road speeds. Therefore, the fan tends to be large, and at high speeds when air flow due solely to forward motion of the vehicle is sufficient to make the fan unnecessary, the fan is absorbing power amounting to several horsepower. Considerable attention is being given to means of avoiding this waste of power and the attendant noise created by the fan, and various systems are available, either fitted as original equipment or installed in place of an existing conventional fan:

1. The fan is provided with *variable pitch* blades, each of which can twist about its own axis as in an aircraft propeller, so arranged that as the engine speed increases the pitch of the blades is progressively reduced automatically; the output of the fan therefore diminishes until at maximum speed the fan is virtually a flat 'disc'. This system is purely mechanical and the fan characteristic has to be carefully matched to the engine power output, thermostat setting, radiator efficiency and transmission gearing to ensure that cooling is still adequate under such conditions as when the vehicle is slowly climbing a long, steep hill in low gear on a hot day. The fan would then be in fine pitch because engine speed would be high, but must still deliver sufficient air, particularly in a vehicle with a transverse engine/radiator layout, so the compromise in

design means that there must be some power wasted. Variation of the blade pitch in this type of fan may be achieved either by a mechanism responding to the increase in centrifugal effects with speed or by sensing the increase in drag, or torque reaction, as speed rises.

2. A more refined system also uses a variable-pitch fan but the blade angle is adjusted by a mechanism responding directly to the cooling system temperature, either that of the water or of the air leaving the radiator; there are still some power losses with this method, due to 'churning' of the air at high speed.

3. Instead of being mounted directly on its spindle, the fan may be driven through a *viscous coupling*; this type of device is made by the Holset Engineering Company and resembles a miniature transmission-type fluid coupling, in which one element is driven by the engine whilst the other element carries the fan blades. As the engine speed rises the coupling commences to 'slip' progressively and the fan speed is thus kept down. In more elaborate versions the spacing of the elements is varied automatically by a mechanism sensitive to the temperature of the cooling system (either the water or the air) so that the degree of slip in the coupling is reduced if a greater flow of air is demanded to keep the temperature down.

4. The fan may be driven by the engine by way of an electro-magnetic clutch which is energized by a thermostat switch suitably located in the cooling system. The fan thus cuts in or out on an 'all or nothing' basis.

5. The fan may be driven and controlled electrically quite independently of engine speed. This is the principle of the Kenlowe 'Thermomatic' fan and this system would seem to offer the ultimate in power saving, the achievement of optimum engine operating temperature and flexibility of layout. The fan is driven at constant speed by an electric motor fed from the normal car electrical system and can therefore be designed to give the optimum air delivery at maximum efficiency at this speed, with the minimum of noise. The motor is switched on or off by a thermostat switch positioned in the radiator hose. It is particularly significant that under average driving conditions the total 'on' time of the fan is only about 5 per cent of the total motoring time. Apart from the obvious saving in power and reduction of noise, this system allows

the engine to be brought more quickly to optimum temperature for efficiency and minimum rate of wear, which is important for journeys of a few miles during which most conventionally-cooled cars never reach this temperature.

Three basic types of radiator construction are in use. The extremely robust *fin-and-tube* type is used, for example, on buses and some high-quality cars; the water passages are made from individual tubes to which fins are attached in various configurations. The *film* type of radiator was used at one time on the majority of quantity-produced cars; in this the water passages are formed by soldering the edges of metal strips to produce narrow tubes and corrugated strip is inserted between the tubes to increase the dissipating surface.

The *pack* type of radiator is commonly used nowadays for cars and is a compromise between the fin-and-tube and film types, utilizing lock-seam tubes packed with corrugated separating strips to form secondary cooling surfaces.

Carburation

The process of combustion which occurs within the engine is no different from any other type of burning, in that it is the combination of fuel with the oxygen in the air with which the fuel is mixed. The internal combustion engine is quite sensitive to the ratio of fuel to air in the mixture which is supplied to its cylinders, and it is the function of the *carburetter* to maintain this ratio at or near the correct value. The optimum is about 15 parts (by weight) of air to 1 part of petrol, and in this mixture the amount of oxygen present is just sufficient to burn the petrol completely. Mixtures in which the proportion of fuel is greater or less than the optimum are known as *rich* or *weak* respectively. It might be thought that the excess of air in a weak mixture would be advantageous in ensuring complete combustion, but any oxygen remaining in the exhaust gases tends to combine with other materials causing erosion of exhaust valves, etc., and hot running. On the other hand the incomplete burning of the petrol in a rich mixture leads to rapid build-up of carbon deposits.

Although the ratio quoted above is that which is chemically

correct, the power developed by the engine increases as the mixture is enriched up to a ratio of about 12 to 1, after which any further enrichment results in a reduction in power, accompanied by an increase in fuel consumption.

The complexity of the modern carburetters is due to the need to provide a suitable fuel/air ratio under a wide variety of conditions. To appreciate the problem it is necessary to understand that, basically, the carburetter consists of a spraying system which liberates petrol into a pipe along which air is drawn into the engine (Fig. 38)

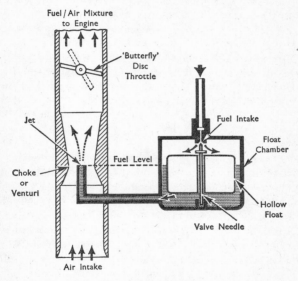

Fig. 38. Simple updraught carburetter.

The passage of the air breaks up the spray into a mist of fine droplets but does not necessarily vaporize the petrol. Since the power of the engine depends primarily on the weight of air which can be introduced into the cylinders, it is clearly preferable that this air should be cool and dense, and that the proportion of petrol should take up as little room as possible, both these conditions obtaining when the mixture is in the 'mist' state. The movement of the air along the induction pipe is entirely due to the partial vacuum which is created in each cylinder in turn by the descent of the piston, unless some form of forced induction is used (see section on 'Supercharging', pp. 115–16). The fall in pressure, or *depression*, which occurs in the pipe, causes air to flow inwards in an attempt to restore the pressure to atmospheric. This can never be achieved completely owing to the inertia, or reluctance to move, of the column of air, so that there is always a certain degree of vacuum in the induction pipe. (The existence of this vacuum is put to use in the operation of such devices as ignition advance mechanism, pneumatic windscreen wipers, windscreen washers, brake-servo mechanisms, etc.) If now a tube, connected to a petrol supply, is introduced into the induction pipe, the out-of-balance pressure on the surface of the fuel in the tank will cause petrol to be ejected. In practice, the vacuum at the point at which the fuel enters would be unsteady if the modification known as the *venturi* were not used. This is merely a carefully shaped narrowing of the induction pipe, and is sometimes referred to as the choke tube, although it is not actually the 'choke' with which every driver is familiar. Its effect is to cause the air to move faster at the narrowest point and to increase the degree of vacuum and make it more stable.

Note that the extent of the vacuum is decided more by the speed at which air is passing along the pipe than by the actual amount of air flowing. The speed of the air is decided by the speed of the engine, and therefore it would appear that the necessary conditions have been achieved, that is, as the engine speeds up correspondingly more fuel is provided; but this is complicated by the fact that although the engine may be running fast, it may only be required to produce low power, so that only a small amount of mixture is needed. The actual quantity of mixture supplied is controlled by a *butterfly throttle*, which is simply a pivoted disc arranged so that it blocks off the induction pipe, and is linked up to the accelerator pedal. Clearly with the throttle almost closed and the car running fast, the simple carburetter described will supply a small amount of air with a high proportion of fuel, i.e. a rich mixture, and conversely, it will supply a weak mixture when the throttle is wide open at low speed.

A number of different designs of carburetter have been developed, and some of these are described below. In all cases the object is to provide an enriched mixture when the demand for power is high (i.e. throttle open, speed low), progressively weakening the mixture as this demand falls off, with the ensuring of satisfactory slow running, and the provision of an enriched mixture for starting and sudden acceleration.

Common to all carburetters is the *float chamber*, which ensures a steady supply of fuel to the jet system, regardless of fluctuations in the feed from the tank. It consists of a small reservoir, usually an integral part of the carburetter (though it is mounted separately on the chassis in a few cases) and containing a hollow float. Fuel enters the chamber, via a needle valve, and upon reaching a critical level, i.e. just below that of the jet orifice, the float is raised far enough to close the valve. On some carburetters a spring-loaded 'tickler' knob is provided in the top of the float chamber. When this knob is held down the float is prevented from rising to close the needle valve, so that the carburetter is flooded, and supplies an abnormally rich mixture for starting. The use of the tickler is nowadays mainly confined to motor-cycles.

Also found on many carburetters is some means of restricting the air supply, again to provide a rich starting mixture. This is known as the *choke* or *strangler*, and in its simplest form comprises a pivoted flap, similar to the throttle butterfly, arranged partially to close the main air inlet to the carburetter when a hand control is operated.

A further point worth clarifying is the use of the term 'jet'. It does not necessarily imply that fuel is sprayed from the end of a pipe; in many cases the jet is a small orifice situated in a fuel passage (i.e. submerged), the size of the opening being chosen to meter the fuel at the required rate.

Carburetters are often classified according to the direction in which the inlet air is flowing when it passes through the mixing chamber (i.e. the point at which the fuel is introduced). Those in which the flow is directly upwards are termed *vertical* or *updraught* carburetters, but this type is almost unknown nowadays. Most common is the *downdraught* (*d.d.*) type in which the air passes vertically downwards; the progress of the mixture is here aided directly by gravity, and a large air-cleaner is easily installed in the most suitable position, at the top of the bonnet.

Also commonly used is the *sidedraught* carburetter, with the air entering directly sideways, a particular merit of this type being that it can be mounted to feed straight into the induction manifold, thus reducing the number of bends and twists which the mixture has to traverse. A compromise between downdraught and sidedraught is sometimes used, this being known as the *semi-downdraught* or *inclined* carburetter.

There are many proprietary makes of carburetter and they fall in two broad classes, the *fixed choke* type in which the size of the venturi throat cannot be altered, and those with *variable choke*, in which the air passage opens and closes automatically in response to mixture requirements.

Fixed Choke Carburetters

ZENITH CARBURETTER

The Zenith 'V' type carburetter is shown in its vertical form in Fig. 39, and the downdraught version in Fig. 40. The principle of this carburetter lies in the two submerged jets located in the base of the float chamber. The *main* jet supplies fuel continuously when the engine is running at speeds above idling, whilst the *compensating* jet feeds fuel to the *capacity tube* which is open to the air in the float chamber. At the lower speeds, fuel is drawn from both jets, but as the speed rises the amount of air passing through the capacity tube gradually diminishes the flow of fuel from the compensating jet, so that the mixture is progressively weakened. The mixture is fed into the venturi via the emulsion (i.e. mixing) block, and a bar placed just below the main nozzle assists in distributing the mixture evenly by creating a local vacuum across the venturi.

A strangler flap is fitted for starting and its control is interlinked to open the throttle slightly as the flap is closed. This provides a combination of fast idling and rich mixture for warming-up. In some models the flap incorporates a diaphragm, which opens automatically under induction pipe depression when the engine starts.

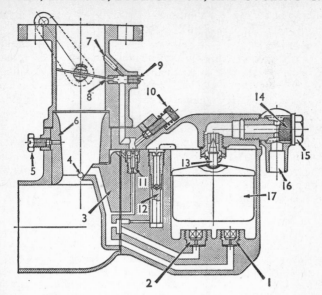

Fig. 39. Zenith 'V' type vertical carburetter (updraught).

1. Main jet.
2. Compensating jet.
3. Emulsion block.
4. Distributor bar.
5. Choke retaining screw.
6. Choke tube.
7. Slow running outlet.
8. Progression jet.
9. Progression jet cover or plug.

10. Slow running air screw.
11. Slow running jet.
12. Capacity tube.
13. Needle.
14. Filter.
15. Filter union.
16. Petrol union.
17. Float.

(*By courtesy of the Zenith Carburetter Co. Ltd*)

In others, the flap is mounted on an offset spindle and is held closed by a spring when the choke control is in use; here again, inlet pipe depression opens the flap when the engine fires, and reduces the degree of richness to a suitable level.

Slow running is provided for by an auxiliary outlet which opens into the induction pipe on the engine side of the throttle. Petrol is

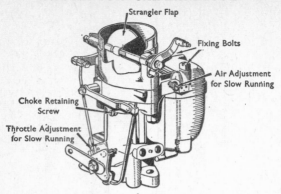

Fig. 40. Zenith 'V' type vertical carburetter (downdraught).
(*By courtesy of the Zenith Carburetter Co. Ltd*)

metered to this outlet by the slow-running, or pilot, jet and the necessary air is admitted by way of an adjustable needle valve. As soon as the throttle is opened, the suction on the slow-running outlet falls away, and to avoid a delay or 'flat spot' before the main jets respond, a further outlet, known as the *progression jet*, is provided in a position where it is just uncovered by the throttle butterfly when the latter is slightly open.

Some Zenith 'V' type carburetters are fitted with an automatic starting device. This is a miniature carburetter which operates only when the equivalent of the 'choke' knob is pulled out. The device feeds a rich mixture directly into the induction pipe, drawing its air through a tiny venturi and petrol from a tube which dips into a reserve well inside the main float chamber. The well provides sufficient fuel for a normal start, but, as this reserve is consumed, more air is admitted and weakens the mixture. A feature of the device is that neat petrol cannot enter the engine and tend to wash oil from the cylinder walls at the crucial moment of starting.

Additional fitments found on some Zenith models are the *economy* device and the *accelerator pump*. Since the full effect of the main jet is only required when the throttle is approaching the fully-open position, a reduction in fuel consumption is obtained by placing a restricted economy jet in the passage to the main jet.

When the throttle is opened wide an interconnected control releases a valve which allows fuel to flow directly to the main jet, by-passing the economy jet. The purpose of the accelerator pump is to enrich the mixture momentarily if the throttle is opened suddenly, i.e. it eliminates the slight delay in response which would normally occur. As its name implies, the device consists of a small piston-type pump, and this is coupled to the throttle linkage. The pump has no effect when its piston is moved slowly, but when the throttle is opened abruptly the piston forces a fine spray of neat petrol into the mixing chamber.

STROMBERG CARBURETTER

The Stromberg carburetter is produced in Britain by the Zenith Carburetter Co. Ltd, and is used in particular on certain cars made by Rootes Motors Ltd. All the models are of the downdraught type and incorporate automatic starting devices and accelerator pumps.

The fuel for normal running is supplied through a main jet which discharges into a small venturi situated centrally within, and just above, the narrowest part of the main venturi tube. This jet is built into the body of the carburetter as a long tube, with a series of holes to which air is admitted from a vent in the main air intake, known as the *high speed bleed*. This air has the effect of assisting in the atomization of the fuel, and of gradually compensating for the tendency for the mixture to become enriched as the airflow increases.

The idling and 'progression' arrangements are similar to those used in the Zenith carburetter, as is the economy device fitted on some models. On others, the by-passing of the normal economy, or 'lean-running', jet is accomplished by a valve which is controlled pneumatically, instead of by direct mechanical operation. The valve is linked to a piston which moves in a vacuum cylinder connected to the induction manifold. The relatively high degree of vacuum which occurs when the engine is running fast at small throttle openings holds the by-pass valve closed against spring tension, but when this vacuum is collapsed by the opening wide of the throttle, the spring is free to open the valve, allowing additional fuel to flow.

The special starting arrangements on the Stromberg carburetter comprise an automatic strangler mechanism and fast idling control. No normal choke control is provided, but when the engine is to be started from cold the accelerator is first depressed fully and released, thus allowing a thermostatic element, mounted on the exhaust manifold, to close the strangler flap and also set the throttle to a fast idling position. As soon as the engine fires, the inlet manifold depression operates a vacuum piston which opens the strangler slightly. The strangler flap is offset on its spindle so that, as the engine speed rises, the flow of air pushes the flap further open, and at the same time the thermostat element, in warming up, gradually releases its tension on the flap, allowing the latter to open fully and also returning the throttle to its normal idling position.

SOLEX CARBURETTER

The main spraying system of the Solex carburetter (Fig. 41) consists of a tube leading from the main fuel supply and supported in the centre of the venturi choke, with its open end facing into the air stream. Inside this tube is a smaller perforated emulsion tube which allows air, drawn through the air bleed, to mix with the fuel; the air/fuel emulsion is ejected through outlets in the sides of the assembly close to the narrowest part of the venturi.

The effect of increasing engine suction is to reduce the level of fuel within the emulsion tube, thus allowing more air to enter, and so achieving the desired weakening of the mixture.

The Solex carburetter is not provided with a strangler flap for starting; instead, a supplementary carburetter or *bi-starter* is built in especially to provide a rich mixture, which issues into the induction pipe between the throttle butterfly and the engine. This device is only brought into action by the rotation of a starter valve, operated by the driver pulling out the 'choke' control. A well provides a reserve of petrol for the necessary rich start, but as soon as this is exhausted a metering jet restricts the richness of the mixture to a suitable level.

Several types of accelerating pump and economy device are fitted to Solex carburetters, and in all cases a diaphragm type of

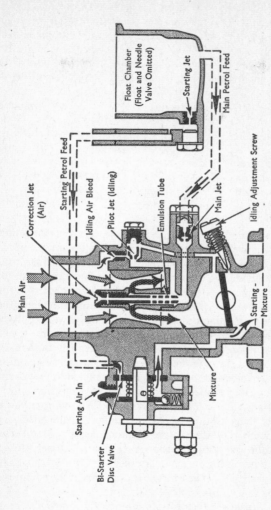

Fig. 41. In this *Solex* carburetter, mixture for starting is provided by the bi-starter (left) independently of the main carburetter. The bi-starter is hand-operated by a facia control corresponding to 'Choke'. (*By courtesy of Solex Ltd*)

The following labels appear in the figure:

Main Air

Correction Jet (Air)

Starting Petrol Feed

Idling Air Bleed

Pilot Jet (Idling)

Emulsion Tube

Main Jet

Idling Adjustment Screw

Float Chamber (Float and Needle Valve Omitted)

Starting Jet

Main Petrol Feed

Starting Jet

Starting Air In

Bi-Starter Disc Valve

Mixture

Starting - Mixture

pump is used. In some models the pump is operated directly by mechanical linkage to the throttle, and in others the pump is held ready charged by engine vacuum so that the sudden reduction in vacuum caused by opening the throttle allows a spring to force the diaphragm forward. With the valve fully open the pump is discharged and a by-pass valve is opened which releases additional fuel, enabling a smaller main jet to be used for part-throttle running.

Variable Choke Carburetters

S.U. CARBURETTER

The S.U. carburetter is a long-established design using a variable choke. The object of this is to maintain a constant air speed over the jet so that the suction effect is also constant. The additional rate of fuel feed required with the choke open wide is provided for by arranging that the size of the jet orifice is also increased.

The S.U. carburetter (Fig. 42) has a shouldered cylindrical dome. The wider part of this contains a large closely fitting piston which is extended downwards so that it forms a shutter in the main air intake. Attached to the bottom of the shutter is a tapered needle which slides into the orifice of the jet assembly mounted in the base of the carburetter. The interior of the chamber in which the piston slides is in communication with the region between the back of the piston and the throttle, through a passage in the engine side of the shutter, whilst the underside of the piston is vented to atmosphere. The position of the piston is therefore sensitive to the degree of depression in the above-mentioned region so that, if the demand is high, the shutter is automatically raised to admit more air, simultaneously opening up the jet orifice. The contour of the needle is such that a suitable ratio of air to fuel is maintained over the entire range. The depression within the piston chamber is balanced by the weight of the piston assembly, sometimes backed up by a light spring.

To provide a richer mixture for starting and cold running, means are provided for lowering the jet relative to the needle so that a wider orifice is exposed.

To cater for the enrichment required for sudden acceleration a

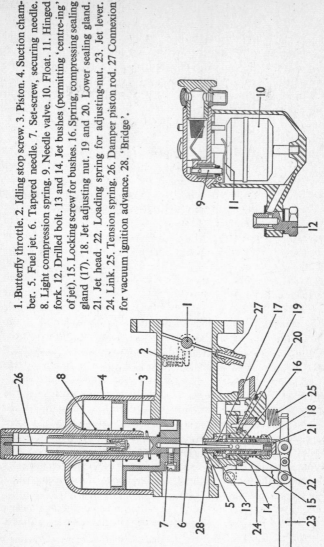

1. Butterfly throttle. 2. Idling stop screw. 3. Piston. 4. Suction chamber. 5. Fuel jet. 6. Tapered needle. 7. Set-screw, securing needle. 8. Light compression spring. 9. Needle valve. 10. Float. 11. Hinged fork. 12. Drilled bolt. 13 and 14. Jet bushes (permitting 'centre-ing' of jet) (17). 15. Locking screw for bushes. 16. Spring, compressing sealing gland (17). 18. Jet adjusting nut. 19 and 20. Lower sealing gland. 21. Jet head. 22. Loading spring for adjusting-nut. 23. Jet lever. 24. Link. 25. Tension spring. 26. Damper piston rod. 27 Connexion for vacuum ignition advance. 28. 'Bridge'.

Fig. 42. S.U. variable choke carburetter. *(By courtesy of the S.U. Carburetter Co. Ltd)*

piston damper is provided in the upper part of the dome. A cylin-drical oil-filled extension of the main piston assembly slides around a small fixed piston which incorporates a one-way valve. This is arranged to delay the lifting of the main piston when the throttle is snapped open, thus causing momentary enrichment.

An additional fitment on some S.U. carburetters is a starting device which consists of an electrically operated auxiliary carbur-etter. This may be controlled either thermostatically from the engine cooling system or by a manually operated switch, and it re-places the usual jet-lowering arrangement; it is a miniature version of the main carburetter, having a suction controlled needle and jet, and provides a degree of enrichment depending upon engine load-ing. A unique economy device is also fitted to some models and is known as the 'additional weakening device'. This utilizes engine suction to draw air through a small venturi tube which in turn applies a slight depression to the float-chamber and thereby reduces the rate at which fuel flows from the main jet at partial throttle opening.

STROMBERG CD CARBURETTER

The Zenith/Stromberg CD (constant depression) carburetter is a variable-choke design introduced comparatively recently. As seen from Fig. 43 it bears a superficial resemblance to the S.U. carburet-ter and its operation is similar in many respects. The choke area is blocked off by the piston or *air valve*, held down by its own weight and a light spring. The single fixed jet is partially blocked by a tapered needle carried on the air valve. The upper chamber is sealed off by a flexible diaphragm attached to the tip of the air valve, except for a small passage leading through the air valve; the partial vacuum created by engine 'suction' in the region between the air valve and throttle butterfly tends to cause the air valve to lift and open the choke area, at the same time withdrawing the needle from the jet and thus allowing more fuel to flow to balance the mixture ratio.

For starting, operation of the 'choke' control rotates a cut-away bar and slightly lifts the air valve so that the jet orifice is increased a little; at the same time the bar itself partially blocks off the air

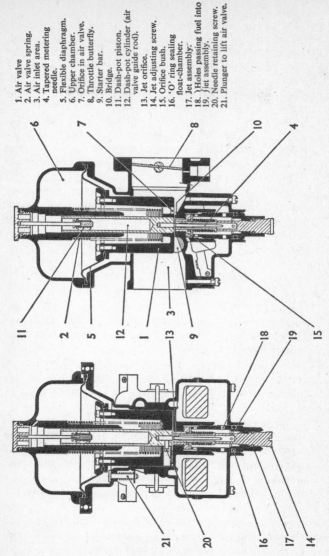

1. Air valve
2. Air valve spring.
3. Air inlet area.
4. Tapered metering needle.
5. Flexible diaphragm.
6. Upper chamber.
7. Orifice in air valve.
8. Throttle butterfly.
9. Starter bar.
10. Bridge.
11. Dash-pot piston.
12. Dash-pot cylinder (air valve guide rod).
13. Jet orifice.
14. Jet adjusting screw.
15. Orifice bush.
16. 'O' ring sealing float-chamber.
17. Jet assembly.
18. } Holes passing fuel into
19. } jet assembly.
20. Needle retaining screw.
21. Plunger to lift air valve.

Fig. 43. Stromberg CD (constant-depression) carburetter. (*By courtesy of the Zenith Carburetter Co. Ltd*)

passage revealed by the lifting of the air valve, the combined effect being to provide an enriched mixture.

A fixed piston and oil-filled cylinder above the air valve form a dash-pot which damps sudden movement of the valve and this provides momentary enrichment for snap acceleration.

A notable feature of the Stromberg CD carburetter is the arrangement of the float chamber, which is placed concentrically around the jet assembly; this ensures that if the fuel is displaced to one side by fast cornering or rapid acceleration the level at the centre remains constant with respect to the jet orifice and obviates momentary fuel starvation. The twin floats are made from expanded rubber and therefore not liable to leaks.

With this type of carburetter it is essential that movement of the air valve is perfectly free; a small plunger is provided as a convenient means of lifting the air valve by hand, to check that it can be heard to drop cleanly back on to its seat without binding.

Multiple Carburetters

Although the majority of family cars with engines having up to four cylinders (and, occasionally, those with six) have only a single carburetter, it is common practice to use twin or triple instruments on the larger engines; multiple carburetters are almost always used as a means of extracting extra power from sports engines. One reason for this is that there is a limit to the size of choke tube if stable flow conditions are to be maintained, and if a high volume flow of mixture is required then more than one carburetter must be used.

However, it is possible to combine the choke tubes into a single instrument to simplify the installation, and this produces the *multiple-barrel* carburetter. A particularly well-known example of this is the Italian-made Weber twin-choke carburetter, much used on competition engines; this is a fixed-choke type having two choke tubes fed from a single float-chamber. A feature of the Weber carburetter is that the main spraying nozzles feed into miniature venturi ducts placed within the choke tubes a little upstream of the main venturi restriction, so making use of the more stable air-stream at the centre of the choke tube.

In some twin-choke carburetters the two tubes feed a common inlet manifold but the throttle butterflies are linked together *differentially*, with the object of obtaining extra fuel economy under conditions of low power demand. Up to about half throttle, movement of the accelerator operates only on one butterfly, the *primary*, the other remaining closed so that the engine runs virtually as if fitted with a single carburetter; with further movement the *secondary* butterfly is taken up and is so linked to the first that they both reach the fully-open position simultaneously. The two chokes may not necessarily be of the same size, the primary barrel being the smaller of the two.

Multiple-choke carburetters are used on virtually all V-eight engines, some American engines having reached a degree of development where two four-barrel carburetters are fitted.

SUPERCHARGING

The power which can be obtained from a piston-type engine is largely dependent upon the amount of petrol-air mixture which can be introduced into the cylinders. In a *normally aspirated* engine the mixture is 'sucked in', or, rather, the partial vacuum above the descending piston induces the mixture to flow in under atmospheric pressure. Owing to the short time for which the inlet valve is open it is never possible to fill the cylinder completely, so that the full theoretical power output cannot be obtained. The problem is further aggravated by the fact that, in a multi-cylinder engine, the flow in the induction manifold is constantly changing direction in order to feed each cylinder in turn; this is a factor contributing to the erratic slow running of early side-valve engines.

It is possible to increase power output by pumping the mixture into the engine under pressure, this being known as *pressure-* or *super-charging*. The supercharger is a necessity on aircraft engines, since normal aspiration in the rarefied atmosphere at high altitude would not introduce sufficient oxygen for combustion. The application of forced induction to cars has been in the past confined mainly to racing engines, in which attempts to obtain maximum full-throttle power have usually involved the use of a noisy 'blower', accompanied by a marked increase in fuel consumption and a reduction in reliability. However, a moderate degree of super-charging can be applied to touring cars, without introducing these disadvantages, and an example of a compressor suitable for this purpose is that marketed by Messrs Shorrock Superchargers Ltd. Unlike the centrifugal blowers used in most aircraft and some racing car applications, this is a *positive displacement* compressor; it consists basically of a set of vanes rotating inside a cylindrical casing, in which they are eccentrically mounted. The dimensions are such that the volume of mixture delivered is equal to the swept capacity of the engine, plus one third. Thus it is ensured that there is always a positive boost pressure in the induction manifold, this pressure being usually five pounds per square inch. The super-charger, which runs very quietly, is driven by twin belts from the crankshaft pulley and is lubricated with oil metered from the engine system. Air is drawn through a carburetter mounted on the casing of the supercharger, which is simply fitted as a unit in place of the normal carburetter. It is customary, though not essential, to fit manual ignition timing control; there is, of course, no inlet manifold vacuum to operate the usual ignition advance device.

The smooth supply of uniform mixture which the supercharger affords results in remarkably flexible low-speed running. The much more efficient filling of the cylinders brings about a marked increase in power output, over 50 per cent in some cases, with corresponding improvement in performance. For example, the figures for a Series II Morris Minor saloon show that maximum speed was increased from 62 m.p.h. to 70 m.p.h., whilst acceleration times were reduced by nearly one half. The increase in fuel consumption was remarkably small, the overall figures being $36\frac{1}{4}$ m.p.g. unsupercharged and 34 m.p.g. with the supercharger (unsupercharged figures taken from *The Autocar* road test).

FUEL INJECTION

An essential feature of the normal carburetter is its choke tube or venturi, which creates a local vacuum in the induction pipe and thus 'draws' petrol from the float chamber. The choke tube must necessarily cause some obstruction to the air flow and therefore represents a considerable loss in power output.

To avoid the necessity for a choke, extensive development work has been carried out on direct *fuel injection* (*f.i.*) systems. As the name implies, petrol is sprayed into the engine under pressure and no carburetter is used. The throttle butterfly controls the air supply only but is interconnected to control the rate of fuel flow. In some systems, fuel is injected directly into the cylinder heads, using a timed pump similar to the Diesel arrangement. Also used is the constant delivery method in which fuel is sprayed continuously into the inlet ports, its entry being controlled by the normal valve timing.

Particular impetus has been given to the development of petrol injection in America, where the difficulties of providing adequate flow of mixture evenly to all cylinders in large V-eight engines have led to the use of very complex multiple-choke carburetter installations. However, for most smaller engines the conventional carburetter is quite satisfactory and is relatively simple to manufacture by ordinary production methods; fuel injection, on the other hand, requires exceptional degrees of precision in its pumps, fuel distributors and injectors and the higher cost is less easy to justify.

Petrol injection has been used in Europe for some years on racing engines and on some high-performance touring cars, but its introduction on medium price range cars has been comparatively recent. An example is the French-built Peugeot 404 saloon, which has a 1·6 litre four-cylinder engine offered with Kugelfischer petrol injection as an alternative to the standard carburetter, producing an increase in power of about 20 per cent. This system uses one injection pump to each cylinder, the pumps being actuated through rockers by a camshaft rotating at half engine speed. The accelerator pedal controls a butterfly throttle which regulates the air supply to the inlet manifold, and at the same time varies the return stop of each pump plunger to control its stroke and thus the rate of fuel delivery. This is done through an ingenious 'three-dimensional' cam which adjusts the pivot-points of the pump rockers; the same cam is also influenced by a governor device in accordance with engine speed to maintain correct mixture over the entire speed range. An electric fuel spray is used to introduce extra petrol directly into the inlet manifold for starting purposes, operating only whilst the starter motor is energized; a thermostatically-controlled valve responding to engine coolant temperature increases the pump stroke to enrich the mixture for cold-starting, at the same time admitting extra air to increase the idling speed.

Although fuel injection equipment is more costly than the conventional carburetter, it provides a means of substantially increasing the power output of an engine of given capacity and this is of particular value in those countries where taxation systems favour the use of engines of minimum size.

CHAPTER FOUR

ELECTRICAL SYSTEM

THE ease with which electricity can be distributed and controlled makes it ideal for the operation of many automobile components. The working of the electrical system is more easily followed if a few basic principles are understood. A flow of electricity may be considered as a transfer of energy which occurs between the particles of a material, i.e. it does not involve the movement of the particles themselves. This 'passing on' of energy occurs more readily in some materials than others. Those in which it occurs most easily we call *conductors*, examples of these being all metals, particularly copper, and carbon; and those which oppose the 'flow' of electricity are known as *insulators*. These include rubber, bakelite, polyvinyl chloride (p.v.c.), and many other plastic materials.

To cause electrical energy to flow in a length of material it is necessary to apply an *electromotive force (e.m.f.)* across the ends of the length, and as far as the automobile is concerned this force is obtained either *electromagnetically* or *chemically*. Whichever method is used the value of the e.m.f., which may be regarded as the pressure available, is measured in *volts*. The rate at which electricity flows when the source is connected to the conducting material is the value of the *current* and is measured in *amperes (amps)*. A current will flow no matter to what material the electromotive force is applied, but in the case of insulating materials the value is so low as to be negligible.

We are more concerned with what current will flow when a known voltage is applied to a conductor, and this is determined by the precise nature of the material and the dimensions of the conductor. These latter characteristics are accounted for in the term *resistance*, which is measured in *ohms*. For any specified material, such as copper in the form of a wire, the resistance increases as the wire is made longer, and also if it is made smaller in diameter, so that a long, thin wire will have a much greater resistance than a short, thick one.

The relationship between voltage, current, and resistance is expressed in Ohm's Law, and for our purposes this is probably best stated in the form

$$\text{Current (Amps)} = \frac{\text{Voltage (Volts)}}{\text{Resistance (Ohms)}}$$

In cars the voltage used is invariably either six or twelve volts, the latter value having become virtually standard on new cars.

Also worth knowing is the electrical equivalent of power, or rate of dissipation of energy, which is measured in *watts*.

$$\text{Power (Watts)} = \text{Voltage (Volts)} \times \text{Current (Amperes)}$$

From this simple relationship, knowing the wattage of a particular component, we can calculate the current which it will take. For instance, a 36-watt headlamp bulb will take 6 amperes when fed from a 6-volt supply.

It is useful to know the relationship between electrical power and mechanical power, as this enables us to appreciate how much of the engine output is being absorbed by the electrical system. This is given by:

$$746 \text{ watts} = 1 \text{ horsepower}$$

From this it is clear that such items as headlamps do not place any appreciable load on the engine, when taken individually.

The source of electromotive force must have two points of connexion, or terminals, and when these are joined by an external

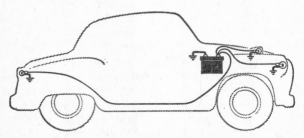

Fig. 44. In a car the metal bodywork is used as the common 'wire'; one terminal of battery and one connexion on each component are 'earthed'.

conductor a *circuit* is completed, allowing a current to flow. It is clear that this current passes not only through the conductor but also through the source itself (Fig. 45). The nature of the sources used in cars is such that the flow of current is always in one direction, which is taken conventionally as being away from the positive terminal, usually marked + or coloured red, and towards the negative terminal, marked — or coloured black. This unidirectional flow is referred to as *direct current* (*d.c.*), as distinct from *alternating current* (*a.c.*), which is used domestically and which changes its direction rhythmically many times per second.

Since it is essential to provide both flow and return paths between the source of electrical energy and the device which it is supplying, it is usually necessary to use two connecting leads, but in automobile wiring it is standard practice to use the structure of the car itself as one 'wire'. This becomes clearer if Fig. 45 is studied. Normally, each component would require a pair of leads, and of each pair, one lead would incorporate a switch controlling that component only. When parts are wired in this way they are said to be *in parallel*. Obviously, all the unswitched wires can be incorporated into one, and as the car is a good metallic conductor it can serve this purpose. One terminal of each electrical component is therefore connected to the bodywork, i.e. *earthed*. For the past thirty years or so, British cars have been earthed on the positive side since this helps to reduce certain problems of terminal corrosion and erosion of electrodes; however, these problems are less apparent with modern materials and there is now a trend to revert to the negative-earth system which is generally standard throughout the world. It is very important to be sure of the polarity of the electrical system when fitting certain kinds of accessories, since these may contain semiconductor devices such as transistors which can be irreparably damaged by even momentary connexion the wrong way round. Earthing can cause trouble, as the anchorage of the component is often also used to make the electrical connexion, which can become somewhat uncertain in time. It is more reliable to make the earthing connexion by means of a short wire (which need not be insulated) connected to some definite point on the bodywork. This is often done for such components as rubber-mounted side lamps.

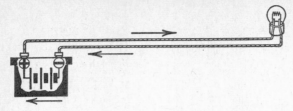

Fig. 45a. In this simple electrical circuit one wire is required to lead current to the lamp and a second wire to return the current to the battery. Note that the current flows through the battery itself.

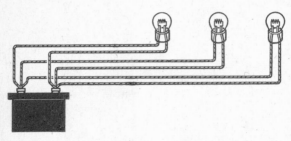

Fig. 45b. When a number of lamps are fed separately from the same source they are said to be connected *in parallel*.

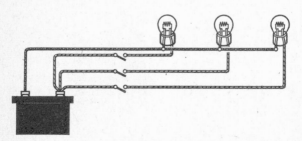

Fig. 45c. One wire of each pair can be replaced by a single common wire. Each lamp can still be controlled separately by including a switch in the other wire of the pair.

The individual wires which provide the unearthed connexions are stranded copper with braided coverings, coloured for easy identification. The installation of the wiring is done by a prefabrication method, all the wires being cut to the correct length, laid up together and braided into a *harness loom*, with each wire branching off at the appropriate point. Plastic sleeving may also be provided when special protection is required. The harness loom is then installed in the car and the individual connexions made, some of these being of the easily detachable push-on type.

An interesting development in the electrical installation is the application of printed wiring to the facia panel. Instead of jointing up the various electrical components by means of individual insulated wires, the items are mounted on an insulating board on which the entire circuit is 'printed' in copper. One method of producing such a circuit is by printing a suitable pattern on to a thin sheet of copper which is bonded to the entire surface of the board and then removing, by an etching process, those parts of the copper which are not covered by the printing. In this way it is possible to speed assembly and to eliminate errors. It is also practicable to 'print' such items as multi-position switch contacts and resistances; the printed circuit technique may also be applied to the production of heating elements such as those used for demisting.

SOURCE OF ELECTRICITY

The electricity used in the normal running of the car is derived from a generator or *dynamo* driven by the engine. This is a rotating device which utilizes the principle of *electromagnetic induction*. Around any magnet there is field of magnetic influence, and if a wire is caused to move within this field a voltage is set up across the ends of the wire, so that when the ends are joined by an external circuit an electric current will flow. In a dynamo there are a large number of moving wires, mounted in coils on an iron rotor known as the *armature* (Fig. 121) which revolves in between, and very close to, the shaped *poles* of an *electromagnet*. The latter works on the converse principle to electromagnetic induction; that is to say, if an electric current passes through a wire, then a magnetic field is set up around the wire. In this case the wire is built up in coils on an iron core, which greatly increases the magnetic effect. The internal connexions of the dynamo are such that the voltage induced in the rotating armature coils is applied to the stationary *field* coils so that in effect the dynamo provides its own magnet. The voltage is 'picked off' the armature by means of carbon blocks or *brushes* which press on to a drum mounted at one end and known as the *commutator* (Fig. 121). This consists of a number of small copper strips set parallel and close together to form a cylinder, with mica insulation between the strips. The purpose of the commutator, besides providing connexions to the armature coils, is to ensure that the *polarity* of the voltage at the terminals of the dynamo is such that a unidirectional current (d.c.) will flow. The output of a typical car dynamo is 250-300 watts (equivalent to about one half horsepower).

Of course, the dynamo is only capable of providing electricity whilst the engine is running, so that it is necessary to provide a standby source for such items as parking lights, and also for starting. This invariably takes the form of a storage battery of the lead-acid type. As its name implies, this is not in itself a primary source of electricity but depends upon the fundamental principle that when an electric current is passed through a cell containing two lead plates immersed in sulphuric acid (the electrolyte), chemical changes occur and electrical energy is 'stored' within the cell. This means that if the cell is connected to a circuit the chemical changes are reversed and current flows. A single cell of this type when fully charged with electricity develops an electromotive force of approximately 2·2 volts between the lead plates. To obtain the standard 6 or 12 volts it is necessary to connect 3 or 6 cells in *series*, as shown in Figs. 46a and b. These connexions may appear as external links, though in some 'link-less' batteries they are almost entirely concealed except for a portion left accessible for the testing of the individual cells.

It is important to note that the voltage obtainable from a cell does not vary with its size, the latter only determining its *capacity*. This is usually measured in *ampere-hours* (*Ah*), but it is a variable quantity which depends upon the rate at which electricity is drawn from the cell. For example, a typical capacity for a 12-volt car battery is 50-ampere-hour at the 10-hour rate. This means that the

Fig. 46a. This cut-away view of a 6-volt lead-acid battery shows the construction of the plates.

(b) A 12-volt lead-acid battery has six cells connected in series by external links. (*By courtesy of Oldham & Son Ltd*)

battery is capable of delivering 5 amperes for 10 hours; but it does not mean that the battery will be able to provide 10 amperes for 5 hours, since as the current rises the capacity falls and *vice versa*. If the current were 250 amperes the battery would be discharged ('flat') after a good deal less than the theoretical 12 minutes.

BATTERY VOLTAGE

As electricity is drawn from the battery, chemical changes occur and the voltage developed gradually falls off, but this reduction in voltage is not necessarily revealed simply by connecting a meter across the battery terminals. This is because as the battery discharges, its own internal resistance increases so that when a current flows through the circuit a certain proportion of the voltage is 'consumed' within the battery. This internal voltage drop varies with the current flowing and would only be very small for the tiny current taken by a voltage-reading meter. Therefore, in order to obtain a true measure of the battery voltage it is necessary to take a reading with the battery 'on load', i.e. passing a heavy current; a convenient method is by using a meter mounted on a pair of 'tongs' which bridge the battery terminals with a thick metal tape, allowing a high current to flow.

The most reliable way of determining the state of the battery is by measuring the specific gravity or strength of the acid. While the battery is discharging, part of the acid is converted into water, with the result that the overall strength of the liquid is lowered. The usual method of testing for specific gravity is by using an *hydrometer*; this resembles an outsize fountain pen filler, and is used to withdraw a sample of the liquid, the reading being taken by noting the depth to which a graduated float is submerged. Individual plugs are usually provided for access to the electrolyte though in some batteries these have been replaced by a single strip type plug and there are also various ingenious devices for ensuring that the electrolyte is automatically topped-up to the correct level.

It is claimed that the modern lead-acid battery is almost immune from damage by overloading, since the method of constructing the plates prevents buckling and disintegration. However, it is still true to say that if a battery is left in the 'flat' state for long periods its life will be much reduced, because the plate will become *sulphated*, i.e. gradually assume a fixed state, so that no chemical change occurs when a charging current is passed and therefore no electricity is 'stored'.

Before a new battery, which has been stored, can be installed in a car, it must be filled with acid and given a lengthy charge. This is because after the formation process, when dried in the usual way, the negative plates lose all their charge. The problem of constructing a battery which can be made available at short notice has been solved by special plate processing. One such process, exclusive to Messrs Oldham & Son Ltd, is 'Power Seal', incorporating a sealing treatment applied to the negative plates, which enables them to retain their dry charge almost indefinitely. As soon as the battery is filled with acid, current can be drawn from it at low rates, and within half an hour the battery is capable of starting a car engine without any charge being required.

ALTERNATIVE TYPES OF BATTERY

The lead-acid battery is subject to much criticism on account of its weight, relatively short life, and fairly strict demands in the matter of regular charging. Other types of battery exist, the best known of them being the alkaline batteries which are used extensively in electric traction and for stand-by applications (emergency lighting etc.). In one alkaline battery the electrolyte is caustic potash and the plates of nickel and cadmium. This combination yields a voltage of about 1·2 volts per cell, so that a 6 or 12-volt battery is rather larger than the lead-acid equivalent. The battery is very robust mechanically and almost fool-proof with regard to charging and discharging rates and lack of maintenance. It has a high internal resistance, so that it is self-protecting against heavy current surges, but this is one feature which is disadvantageous for automobile application, where electric starting demands a very large current from a relatively small battery.

There is a suggestion that the *silver-zinc* battery may eventually be used in cars, since it combines high capacity with small size and low weight. However, it is prohibitively expensive at present, and in point of fact the lead-acid battery is found on virtually every production car.

BATTERY CHARGING AND VOLTAGE CONTROL

The electricity which is drawn from the battery by the starter motor or by the use of parking lights must be replaced by the engine-driven dynamo during subsequent running periods. If, as is sometimes the case, the duration of running is insufficient, the battery will gradually lose its charge and have to be re-charged from an outside source.

Two facts have now to be considered:

(1) The dynamo cannot charge the battery unless it is generating a voltage greater than that of the battery.

(2) The battery must not be connected to the dynamo when the latter is not generating a sufficiently high voltage; if it were so connected, the battery would be trying to drive the dynamo as a motor.

(On some early cars the dynamotor was used, i.e. the same machine was used for both engine-starting and generating electricity, but the idea did not survive because, although it is generally true that an electric motor will act as a generator and *vice versa*, the two functions require widely differing characteristics which cannot be incorporated economically in one machine. However, a modern version of the dynamotor is used on some motor scooters and ultra-light cars.)

The device used to ensure the correct coupling of battery and dynamo is known as the *cut-out*, and is usually found housed in a small plastic box on the bulkhead of the engine compartment. It consists, in principle, of an electromagnetic switch which is sensitive to the voltages developed by the dynamo and battery; as the dynamo voltage rises, with engine speed, to a value slightly in excess of that of the battery, the switch 'cuts in' and couples the dynamo to the battery. The operation of the cut-out is indicated visually on the facia panel by a red lamp which, provided the ignition is switched on, is illuminated while the cut-out is open (i.e. while the battery is discharging). The extinction of the lamp then shows that the battery is receiving charge.

On some cars, but by no means all nowadays, an *ammeter* (i.e. ampere meter) is provided to indicate the actual current flow into or out of the battery. This is a centre-zero instrument; when the pointer swings to the + side the battery is being charged by the dynamo, while a − reading shows that the battery is discharging. In a healthy electrical system, with the battery well charged, the ammeter will show a slight + reading during normal running and a small − reading whilst the engine is stationary or idling slowly, this being the current drain on the battery due to the ignition coil. The ammeter is so wired that it does not register the heavy current taken by the starter motor (see page 135).

There are arguments for fitting a *voltmeter* rather than an ammeter, as a more informative indication of the health of the electrical system in general and that of the battery in particular.

This change has already been made on some cars but it requires the voltmeter reading to be interpreted carefully in relation to engine speed and electrical loading, and on most cars the simple warning light is still regarded as adequate.

Because the dynamo output voltage rises with engine speed it is necessary to ensure that the voltage is restricted to a value which cannot cause damage, particularly to lamps. On some cars of pre-1939 design the *third-brush* or *constant current* system is used, and this makes use of the special output characteristic of the three-brush dynamo to achieve a certain measure of control of voltage; however, it has the disadvantage that, if the dynamo is adjusted to give adequate output to cater for the full lighting system, the battery may be overcharged during daytime. It is sometimes necessary to provide a selector switch, operated by the driver, to control the charging rate.

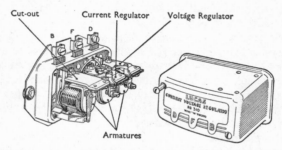

Fig. 47. Cut-out and Regulator (Lucas). (*By courtesy of Joseph Lucas Ltd*)

Most modern cars are fitted with the *compensated voltage control* (*c.v.c.*) system, which makes use of a *regulator* to govern the output of the dynamo. The regulator is also mounted on the bulkhead. Its mechanism, being sensitive, is pre-set by the manufacturer and then sealed, and consists primarily of an electro-magnetic device which controls the effect of the dynamo field coils by constantly switching a resistance in and out of circuit.

In some cases the cut-out and regulator unit are housed under the same cover, Fig. 47, together with a distribution panel and fuses for the various electrical accessories. The fuses are similar to those used in domestic installations in that they provide a 'weak link' to ensure that, should any fault occur, the resulting heavy current surge will blow the fuse rather than damage the wiring. However, for the sake of convenience the fuses are of the cartridge type, i.e. the fuse-wire is enclosed in a glass tube with metal end-caps; a blown fuse is normally regarded as expendable, though it may be rewired. Fuses are usually provided to protect certain auxiliary circuits such as those for horn and direction indicators, but the lighting system is not fused. Modern practice is to reduce fuses to the minimum or omit them altogether.

USE OF ALTERNATING CURRENT

At present the entire electrical system of most cars operates on direct current, but there are advantages to be gained from the use of alternating current. The a.c. system is used on many motorcycles, in which the magneto used to supply the ignition voltage is modified so that it also becomes a generator feeding alternating current to the lamps and other auxiliaries. A selenium or silicon rectifier is used to convert the output of the generator to the direct current required for charging the battery.

Alternator/rectifier systems have been used on commercial vehicles and omnibuses for some time and are being fitted to an increasing number of cars; conversion kits are available to enable an alternator to be fitted in place of an existing dynamo. The alternator is able to produce a greater output current than a dynamo of similar physical size and also generates a useful current at engine tick-over speed. It is therefore of particular value on vehicles which have an exceptionally heavily-loaded electrical system or which make repeated short runs at low average speeds with much use of the starter; such vehicles include ambulances, taxi-cabs and door-to-door delivery vehicles. With a normal generator the battery may not receive sufficient make-up charge and gradually become discharged during the course of the day.

The alternator has an outward appearance similar to that of a dynamo except that it is usually shorter; it has a smaller pulley, one of the advantages of the alternator being that its construction allows it to run at higher speeds than a dynamo and this is a feature which enables it to give its good performance at engine idling speed. A typical alternator is that produced by Joseph Lucas Ltd, in which three-phase alternating current is generated in the stationary outer windings; the winding on the rotor is fed by a brush system similar to that of a dynamo except that instead of a segmented commutator there are two smooth *slip-rings*, which, since they carry only a relatively light current, are subject to the minimum of wear and permit the alternator to run at high speeds. The alternating current produced in the stationary windings is *rectified* that is, changed to direct current, by being fed through six *silicon diodes* connected in a circuit arrangement known as three-phase bridge, housed in the end of the alternator; the resulting d.c. is not perfectly smooth but by using a three-phase system the degree of 'ripple' in the output is kept to an acceptably low level. The silicon diode is the electrical equivalent of a one-way valve and since it will not allow the battery to pass any appreciable current back into the alternator windings there is no need for a cut-out as used normally between a dynamo and battery. In addition, the alternator has an inherent characteristic such that it cannot produce current in excess of its designed output and therefore no separate current regulator is required. All that is needed is a means of controlling the output voltage and for this Lucas produce a control unit which operates in a manner rather similar to that of a normal voltage regulator, by rapidly switching on and off the current in the alternator rotor. However, this is done electronically by means of a transistorized circuit instead of an electro-mechanical switching device and since it has no moving parts whatsoever the unit requires no maintenance such as adjustment of contacts.

THE CHOICE OF VOLTAGE

The automobile electrical installation, apart from the high-tension ignition circuit, is essentially a low voltage system, being suitable for running from a battery providing only 6 or 12 volts. For this reason many items take considerable currents, in order to develop reasonable power, compared with the currents usual in domestic installations. For instance, a 36-watt headlamp bulb requires 6 amperes when fed from a 6-volt battery, whereas a 36-watt household lamp running on 240-volt mains requires only $\frac{3}{20}$ amperes.

It has been stated previously that the modern trend is towards the standardization of the 12-volt system in cars. In some cases the bulk of a 12-volt battery has made it necessary to use two 6-volt batteries connected in *series*. The advantages of the 12-volt system are apparent when we consider that, in order to transmit equal power, without excessive voltage drop, the cables in a 6-volt system need theoretically to be four times the thickness of 12-volt cables. Starting, in particular, is much improved by the 12-volt system since almost twice the power is available without increasing the starter motor size and more effective voltage is available for the ignition coil during the starting surge.

Despite its disadvantages, accentuated by their greater electrical requirements, American cars used the 6-volt system for many years, though the 12-volt system has now been adopted.

ELECTRICAL STARTING

Because the piston engine is not self-starting and is incapable of running below a certain minimum speed, it is necessary to provide some means of overcoming the standstill resistance and 'cranking' the engine to a speed at which it is self-supporting. A convenient method of providing the 'breakaway' torque is by means of a small series-wound electric motor which develops its maximum torque at standstill; this type of motor produces its greatest *power* when running at about 1,000 r.p.m., and since the average engine requires a cranking speed of between 75 and 100 r.p.m. it is necessary to provide reduction gearing between starter motor and engine. This takes the form of a small pinion mounted on the motor shaft, and engaging with a toothed ring which is attached to the rim of the engine flywheel. It is not practicable to keep these gears meshed permanently, as this could entail the starter motor revolving at speeds up to 50,000 r.p.m. when the engine was running at high speed. Therefore, it is necessary to arrange for the motor pinion to be brought into mesh only at the moment of starting; the method of engagement used on almost all British cars is that employing the *inertia* or *Bendix* pinion. The heavy pinion is loosely mounted on a coarse screw thread on the motor spindle (Fig. 48). When the motor begins to spin the weight of the pinion causes it to be 'left

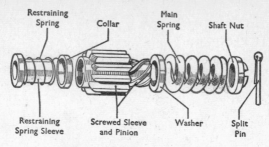

Fig. 48. The components of the Bendix pinion starter.
(*By courtesy of Joseph Lucas Ltd*)

at a standstill', momentarily, so that it runs along the spindle and engages with the flywheel teeth, the teeth of both pinion and flywheel ring being specially shaped to ensure clean meshing. As soon as the engine is running under its own power, at a speed greater than that of the starting motor, the pinion is spun back along the screwed spindle and out of engagement.

This somewhat brutal arrangement is used satisfactorily on the majority of car engines, but is not suitable for certain types of engine, including some Diesels, which need assistance to bring them up to the self-supporting speed even after they have commenced firing. In these cases a *pre-engaged* mechanism is necessary, i.e. the pinion is engaged with the flywheel before the starter motor is energized. This may be done mechanically, by a linkage incorporated in the starting control, by an electromagnet, or by using the 'Axial' starting motor; in the latter arrangement, the armature spindle can slide axially and has the pinion rigidly fixed to one end. The spindle is normally held off-centre with respect to the field-winding, but when the motor is initially energized the armature is drawn inwards by solenoid effect, thus engaging the pinion and closing contacts which apply full power to the motor. Pre-engaged starters are used occasionally in cars and are particularly valuable for cold-weather starting. One example, in which the pinion is engaged by an electromagnet and lever system, is shown in Fig. 49. This starter incorporates a braking mechanism to bring the motor and pinion rapidly to rest after disengagement so that it cannot be

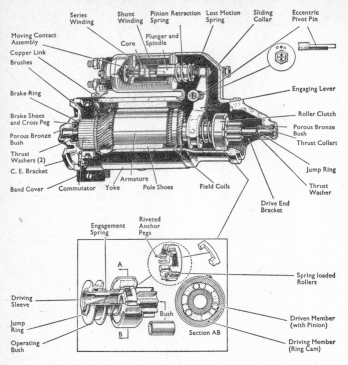

Fig. 49. Pre-engaged electric starter in which the pinion is engaged by a solenoid mechanism. *By courtesy of Joseph Lucas Ltd.*

re-engaged whilst still spinning and so cause damage to the teeth.

Pre-engagement also eliminates the trouble of premature pinion disengagement, which occasionally afflicts inertia-pinion type starters, i.e. the engine fires once and flicks the pinion out of mesh before the engine has had time to reach self-sustaining speed. This fault may be caused by excessive wear of the ring-gear teeth; because the engine always comes to a standstill in a position where one or other of the pistons is on compression, it follows that the starter pinion will always engage initially at any one of a number of points on the gear-ring according to the number of cylinders.

One cure for this is to remove the ring-gear and re-position it on the flywheel rim in such a way that engagement of the pinion will occur in between the already worn spots.

The electrical connexion to the starter motor is run direct from the battery, and because it is required to carry a current of as much as 450 amperes, without causing appreciable voltage drop, the cable must be of low resistance; for this reason stranded copper cable of large diameter (about half an inch) is used and the cable run is kept as short as possible. The cable used to 'earth' the battery to the chassis is of similar type.

The direct wiring of the starter motor means that the starting current is not registered on the dash-board ammeter. This is obviously desirable, since a meter capable of indicating currents of this magnitude would be insensitive to the relatively low battery-charging currents.

Since it is necessary for the starter switch to be situated in the cable between battery and motor, the switch must be remotely operated. In some cars the switch is mounted on the motor casing and is actuated mechanically by a Bowden wire control. In many modern cars the switch is solenoid-operated, i.e. the heavy current-carrying contacts are brought together by means of an electro-magnet which is energized from the battery by an auxiliary circuit. The latter circuit is closed either by push-button or by rotating the ignition key past the normal 'on' position, against spring-loading.

On some American cars no starter hand control is fitted; instead, the starter is automatically operated when the accelerator pedal is depressed initially.

An 'aid-to-driving' device used on some pre-war British cars operated the starter when the ignition was switched on and subsequently immediately re-started the engine if it happened to stall.

The Ignition System

We have seen that an essential part of the operation of the normal type of car engine is the firing of the combustible mixture at a closely defined point in the cycle of events. This is achieved by an electric spark which occurs between the *points* or *electrodes* of a *sparking plug*, and the voltage necessary to cause the spark can be derived in one of two ways. The method which we shall consider first is rarely used in the touring car, this being the *magneto* system of ignition. The magneto can be considered as a specialized form of rotating electric generator which is driven directly from the engine and is capable of producing very high electrical pressure, or voltage, without the application of an exterior source of electrical energy. This means that, as long as there is provision for rotating the engine (e.g. by starting handle), then the engine can be started and run without a battery. However, the magneto is at its best when running at high speed, hence its use in racing and some sports cars, but produces a relatively weak spark at low speed. Therefore it may be difficult to start an engine with magneto ignition if it is only possible to rotate the engine slowly by hand, or if the battery is so 'low' that the starter-motor will only just turn the crankshaft.

The ignition system used almost invariably nowadays is that, known as the *Kettering* inductive system, employing a *coil* which is capable of producing a high voltage, under the right conditions, even though the voltage applied from the battery is only six or twelve volts.

Here again it is as well to remember that the battery must be in a reasonable state of charge, so that if an engine with coil ignition is obstinate in starting it may be necessary to resort to hand-winding in order to leave enough charge in the battery to enable the coil to function. If the battery is completely flat it will be impossible to start the engine, by hand or otherwise.

The essential parts of a coil ignition system are shown in Figures 50 and 51, which indicate the basic circuit and also the positions in which the various components might be found in a typical under-bonnet layout.

The coil itself consists, in fact, of two coils which may be considered as separated electrically, although they are both wound on the same iron core and share a common terminal. One coil, known as the primary, is fed from the battery, and the principle of operation depends upon the fact that, if the supply to this coil is suddenly interrupted, then a voltage is created or *induced* in the other coil, known as the secondary. The voltages in the two coils can be considered for our purposes to be in the same ratio as the numbers of turns of wire on the two coils, so that by providing relatively few

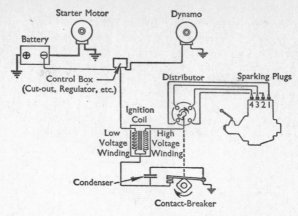

Fig. 50. Diagram of basic electrical system for four-cylinder engine with coil ignition.

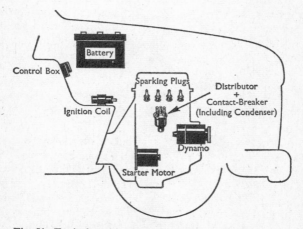

Fig. 51. Typical positioning of major components in coil-ignition system.

turns on the primary winding, and a very large number on the secondary, the necessary high voltage is obtained.

The voltage required to cause a spark between the sparking plug points depends upon both the pressure of the mixture within the cylinder and the gap between the points. Under average conditions a voltage of the order of 7,000 volts is needed. Although the precise mechanism of the spark is not perfectly understood it has been established recently that a 'big fat spark' is not necessarily a guarantee of perfect ignition and that other characteristics, such as the electrical constants of the ignition circuit, must be considered.

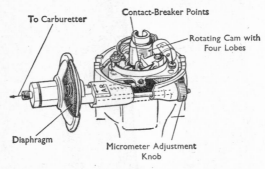

Fig. 52. Contact breaker for four-cylinder engine with vacuum advance device. (*By courtesy of Joseph Lucas Ltd*)

Earlier it has been stated that the development of the higher voltage in the secondary winding of the ignition coil only occurs when the electricity supplied to the primary winding is suddenly interrupted. This interruption is arranged to take place at the correct instant by a special type of rotary switch which is positively driven at half the engine speed (i.e. the same speed as the camshaft). This switch is known as the *contact-breaker* (Fig. 52) and consists simply of a spindle upon which is mounted a cam with as many lobes (i.e. projections) as the engine has cylinders. As the cam rotates, each lobe, in turn, causes the momentary separation of a pair of contact points which form part of the circuit to the ignition coil primary winding. The amount by which the points are separated and the precision with which they remake contact is of great importance.

Mounted alongside the contact-breaker will also be found a cartridge-shaped *condenser* or capacitor, whose function is to ensure a rapid interruption of the circuit when the contact-breaker points separate and also to reduce burning and pitting of the points. The rotation of the contact-breaker cam at half engine speed, and the number of lobes on the cam, ensures that the correct number of sparks per engine revolution are available at evenly spaced intervals, but some provision has to be made to lead each spark towards its correct sparking plug. This is the function of the *distributor*, which is located in the top of the contact-breaker housing and is readily distinguished by the bunch of heavily insulated leads springing from its cap (see Pl. 1a). The latter, which is usually a bakelite moulding, has around its inner surface a number of strips, to each of which is attached a heavily insulated cable leading to one or other of the sparking plugs, the order of the connexion being the same as the firing order of the cylinders. The cables are usually referred to as H.T. (High Tension) leads. Sweeping round close to the strips is a rotor arm which is driven from the top of the contact-breaker spindle (Fig. 53). (To immobilize your car it is only necessary to unclip the distributor cap and lift out this rotor arm.) A lead is brought from the ignition coil to the centre of the distributor cap and thence to the centre of the rotor arm via a spring-loaded carbon rod, and as each high voltage impulse is produced the spark jumps across to the correct strip and thence to the plug. (The spark can jump the distributor gap quite easily since the surrounding air is only at atmospheric pressure.)

As was mentioned earlier, it is desirable to be able to vary, within limits, the precise point at which ignition occurs, whilst the engine is running. This is provided for by varying slightly the relative positions of the contact-breaker operating arm and the lobed cam, by rotating the entire body of the instrument a few degrees. For instance, if, as is usual, the cam spindle rotates clockwise when viewed from above, then by twisting the casing slightly in the clockwise direction all the sparks will be made to occur a little later in the revolution, i.e. the ignition timing will be retarded. At one time it was usual for the driver to vary the ignition timing, by means of a

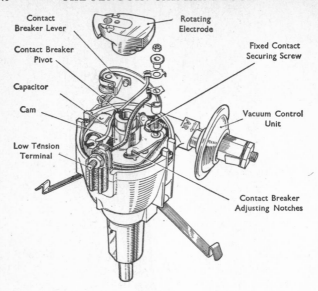

Contact Breaker Lever

Rotating Electrode

Contact Breaker Pivot

Fixed Contact Securing Screw

Capacitor

Cam

Vacuum Control Unit

Low Tension Terminal

Contact Breaker Adjusting Notches

Fig. 53. 'Exploded' view of distributor with cap removed, showing the rotating electrode arm. (*By courtesy of Joseph Lucas Ltd*)

manual control, according to the demands made upon the engine, but this is rare nowadays as automatic advance and retard mechanisms are almost invariably used. These usually consist of two separate devices. The first, which varies the ignition according to engine speed, is a simple arrangement of spring controlled weights mounted on a small platform attached to the spindle underneath the contact-breaker cam (Fig. 54). As the speed of the spindle rises the weights are thrown outwards and cause the cam to be rotated relative to its spindle, thus altering the timing. This provides the desirable characteristic of advancing the ignition for continuous high speed cruising, but also means that the timing will be unsuitable for sudden acceleration, when retarded ignition is required. This situation is provided for by the second device which is known as *vacuum advance*. This depends upon the fact that when the engine is running fast with the throttle almost closed (i.e. the engine is only

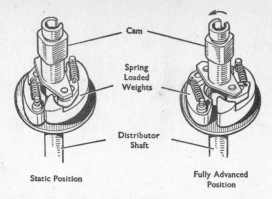

Fig. 54. Centrifugal advance mechanism (housed in case of distributor). (*By courtesy of Joseph Lucas Ltd*)

lightly loaded) there is a high degree of vacuum in the induction manifold. A narrow pipe connects the manifold to a circular case, containing a thin sealed diaphragm, mounted on the side of the distributor (Fig. 52); variation of pressure within the pipe causes movement of the diaphragm which is translated into a slight rotation of the distributor body. Sudden opening of the throttle causes a collapse of the inlet manifold vacuum so that the diaphragm returns to the 'retard' position under spring pressure.

Electronic Ignition Systems

The long-established electro-mechanical inductive coil ignition system has two particular features which restrict its performance. One of these is that the contact-breaker 'points' are rapidly switching on and off an inductive current of several amperes and are therefore subject to burning and wear so that they require regular cleaning and re-setting; the second restriction is due to both mechanical and electrical limitations of the contact-breaker and the inductive circuit, which prevent it producing sparks satisfactorily at rates above 400 sparks per second. This means, for example, that in a six-cylinder engine the ignition system imposes a speed limit of about 8,000 r.p.m., which is not considered especially high nowadays in racing engines.

Both of these drawbacks are being overcome by the use of 'solid-state' electronic devices from the *semiconductor* family, which are rugged components capable of switching electricity without the opening and closing of contacts. A well-known example is the *transistor* though there are other similar devices such as the *thyristor* which may be used ultimately. The transistor is a small capsule with three electrical connexions; in this application, two of the connexions carry the main circuit current in and out of the device and this current can be virtually turned on or off by switching a much smaller control current on or off at a third connexion. The transistor thus behaves in the same way as a relay but its special feature is that it can operate as a switch at speeds far higher than those required for an ignition system and since there is, of course, no mechanical movement or sparking, the question of maintenance does not arise.

Electronic devices have been used in ignition systems in two distinct phases. Firstly, there is a hybrid system known as the Lucas *T.A.C.* or *Transistor-Assisted Contacts*, in which a transistor is interposed between the contact-breaker and coil in an otherwise conventional ignition system. The contact-breaker points are only required to carry the very small non-inductive control current of the transistor. There is therefore a very much reduced rate of wear at the points and the absence of arcing means that the low-speed performance is improved, thus assisting starting. Also, because the transistor can handle a much higher main current than could the contact-breaker points when used in the normal way, the design of the coil can be modified to improve its performance at high speeds. The contact-breaker condenser can be dispensed with and contact adjustments are required only at 25,000-mile intervals, solely to compensate for mechanical wear of the operating mechanism.

The more advanced stage in electronic ignition is a fully-transistorized system used in racing engines. Very briefly, the Lucas system employs two stages of transistor switching in conjunction with a special form of coil; however, instead of using a contact-breaker, the transistors are 'triggered' by electrical pulses produced by an electromagnetic pick-up responding to pole-pieces accurately spaced around the engine flywheel. The system is capable of producing precisely-timed sparks at rates up to 1,000 per second, sufficient to operate a V-eight engine at 15,000 r.p.m.

SPARKING PLUGS

An essential part of the ignition system is the provision of electrodes, within the engine cylinder, across which the igniting spark can discharge. It is desirable to arrange that these electrodes shall be easily accessible and they are therefore mounted on a screwed-in plug.

A sparking-plug consists essentially of a steel body which bears the earthed electrode, an insulator, and a central rod which forms the other electrode, fed from the distributor. The lower part of the body is threaded to suit a screwed hole provided in the engine, the length of the threaded portion being known as the *reach* and varying with the plug design. The body of the plug seats on to a soft copper washer when it is screwed into the engine.

The insulator operates under particularly arduous conditions, since not only must it withstand the high ignition voltage, but its lower end is subject to the full heat of combustion and it is also liable to mechanical shock. At one time the insulator was made from porcelain but modern plugs use ceramics based on sintered aluminium oxide.

The central electrode is sealed into the insulator and is provided with a screwed terminal at the upper exposed end, often shaped to accept a snap-on connector. The tip of the electrode, at which the spark occurs, usually has an insert of heat-resisting metal such as nickel.

The earthed electrode protrudes from the plug body and in some designs three electrodes are provided, spaced around the body. The distance between the central and earthed electrodes is about $\frac{1}{40}$ inch or slightly more and is adjusted by bending the outer electrode.

The construction of the sparking plug differs according to whether the plug is of the *detachable* or *non-detachable* type. These rather misleading terms refer to the manner in which the insulator is sealed into the plug body, and do not imply that the plug can or cannot be detached from the engine, since all plugs are, of course, 'detachable' in this sense. In a detachable plug the insulator is secured in the body by a threaded sleeve and can be removed for cleaning (Fig. 55). In a non-detachable plug the top edge of the body is turned over to lock the insulator permanently in position (Fig. 56b).

HEAT VALUES

It is generally held that the working temperature of a sparking-plug must be within the range 450° to 850°C. since this ensures that carbon which tends to accumulate on the nose of the insulator is

burned away. Below 450°C. the carbon forms an alternative path (i.e. short circuit) for the electric discharge; in other words, the plug is *fouled* and ceases to fire. Above 850°C. the plug points may become incandescent and cause pre-ignition.

The temperature of the plug can be controlled by designing the insulator and central electrode arrangement so as to provide a suitable path along which heat must travel in escaping to the cylinder head. The terminology often used in referring to heat value is somewhat misleading. A *hot* plug (Fig. 56a) has a long heat path and tends to run hot; it is therefore suitable for a cool-running engine and is sometimes called a *soft* plug. Conversely, a *cold* or *hard* plug (Fig. 56b) has a short heat path and is intended for hot running such as would occur in racing or high-speed touring. When plugs of given heat value are used under conditions for which they were not designed they are liable to fouling or overheating.

Fig. 55. A 'detachable' type sparking plug dismantled. (*By courtesy of K.L.G. Sparking Plugs Ltd*)

Although sparking-plug manufacturers publish lists indicating the plug suitable to a particular vehicle, the recommendation is usually applicable only to normal touring conditions. If a car is to

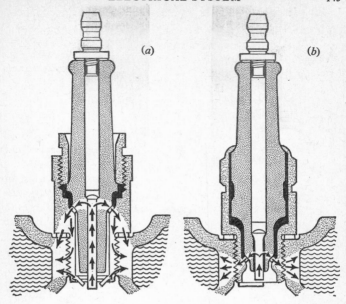

Fig. 56a. A 'hot' or 'soft' plug has a long heat flow path and is intended for cold-running engines. This is a detachable design.

b. A 'cold' or 'hard' plug has a short heat flow path and is intended for hot-running engines (e.g. in competition motoring). This is a non-detachable plug.

be used for high-speed work or other abnormal duty, the plug manufacturer should be specially consulted.

PLATINUM-POINTED PLUGS

The platinum-pointed sparking plug originally was developed for aircraft application, but is now available for car engines. It is of non-detachable construction and features an elaborate central electrode assembly in which the platinum tip is gold-soldered into a copper core. This provides efficient heat transfer and enables the plug to operate over a much wider heat range than a conventional plug.

Because platinum has a high resistance to spark erosion and chemical corrosion it is possible to make the points about one-third the size of the usual nickel type. These smaller electrodes have less tendency to shield the spark from the surrounding mixture and so give improved starting, smoother running, and lower fuel consumption. The plug has incorporated into it a resistor which limits the current through the electrodes and reduces wear.

The platinum-pointed plug is more costly than the normal type, but its life is three to five times as long.

SURFACE DISCHARGE IGNITERS

It seems possible that over the next few years there may be a trend away from the conventional sparking plug with air-gap electrodes towards the use of the *surface discharge igniter*. This device is similar to the ordinary plug in appearance, having a central electrode and an outer ring of electrodes but the intervening space is filled with a solid semiconductor material, across the surface of which the spark discharges. The claim for the surface discharge igniter is that a much 'fatter' spark is produced and that starting, fuel economy and power output are improved; since the electrodes are massive they do not burn away and the performance is not lessened by carbon deposits. At present the cost is higher than that of the sparking plug but it is to be expected that some type of surface discharge igniter will be needed to exploit fully the improved performance of electronic ignition circuitry in certain types of engine.

Lighting Equipment

HEADLAMPS

The requirements of a headlamp system differ from those of a domestic lighting installation in that whereas the latter is normally required to provide an adequate illumination over a wide area, a headlamp is needed to produce brilliance over a confined area and therefore requires only relatively low power. This is, in any case, desirable because a high power demand would involve the use of an unduly large generator.

A typical headlamp bulb would take 36 watts, the light produced being concentrated into a suitable beam by means of a parabolic reflector. This has the property that if a point source of light is placed within the reflector at a position known as the *focus*, the resulting reflected beam is parallel. As opposed to the domestic lamp bulb, which has a relatively long and fragile filament, the low voltage headlamp bulb necessarily has a low resistance filament which is short and thick; besides being inherently robust and therefore suited to withstand vibration, the filament is sufficiently compact to approximate to the point source of light necessary for accurate focusing. In a modern lamp the bulb is *pre-focused*, that is, the manufacturer places a collar around the bulb cap in the correct position relative to the filament so that the bulb is accurately located within the reflector. On older lamps provision was made for adjusting the bulb in its holder.

The headlamp bulb has two filaments, the *main beam* filament being mounted centrally whilst the *dip* filament is offset so that a deflected beam is produced. In practice, a perfectly parallel beam is not desirable, since some side illumination is required, and also some 'cut-off' of light above the horizontal to prevent dazzle. This is achieved by means of a suitable design of front glass lens, which is usually of the *block* pattern and arranged to give correct light distribution. Modern practice is to combine the reflector and lens into what is sometimes loosely referred to as a *sealed beam light unit*. In fact, the true 'sealed beam' is a comparatively recent innovation in which no separate lamp bulb is used; all-glass sealed beam headlamp units are available from Joseph Lucas and can be fitted as replacements in existing headlamps. The unit (see Fig. 57) consists of a front lens and an internally-aluminized glass rear reflector, fused together to form a single envelope which is fitted with a double-filament assembly; the whole unit is in effect a very large lamp bulb. The object of this construction is that the unit can be manufactured very accurately so that headlamp adjustment and aiming can be more precise; also, because of the large internal surface there is none of the gradual blackening which occurs with small bulbs due to deposition of metal evaporating from the filaments, and a longer life is claimed. The precise location of the filaments relative to the lens and reflector enables the lamps to

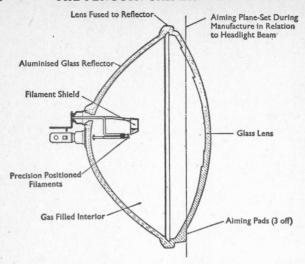

Fig. 57. The sealed beam light unit is made almost entirely from glass and is virtually a large lamp bulb with built-in lens and reflector. (*By courtesy of Joseph Lucas Ltd*)

give improved range and illumination and the accurate aiming results in less glare and dazzle from the 'dipped' beam.

TUNGSTEN/IODINE LAMPS

A new type of bulb which is being introduced in car headlamps is the tungsten/iodine quartz bulb, sometimes known simply as the iodine quartz (I.Q.) bulb. This is basically an incandescent lamp with a tungsten filament enclosed in a small envelope containing a little iodine. The principle of the lamp is that the tungsten which evaporates from the filament, and which would normally be deposited as a blackening of the inside of the lamp, reacts with the iodine to form volatile tungsten iodide; near the filament the iodide is broken down by the high temperature and the tungsten is re-deposited on the filament. The rate of loss of tungsten from the filament is thus very much reduced so that the life of the bulb is greatly extended; it also becomes possible to reduce the size of the envelope and to increase the working temperature of the filament, but the envelope must be made from a special glass or from quartz. The tungsten/iodine lamp produces a high light output within small dimensions; for example, a Philips 62 watt bulb, producing 1,550 lumens, is less than half an inch across at the filament region and such bulbs can be used in very powerful headlamps of no greater than usual dimensions.

Double dipping (deflection of both off- and near-side headlamp beams) is standard practice nowadays and is achieved by the use of twin-filament bulbs in both lamps. Continental practice is to hood the dip filament within the bulb to cut off all direct (unreflected) light but this system has not been generally adopted in Britain. Some older cars are fitted with the 'dip-and-switch' system in which the offside lamp is extinguished and the nearside beam deflected, the latter often being achieved by tilting the reflector itself by means of a solenoid device.

FOUR HEADLAMP SYSTEMS

Although most headlamp systems combine the main-beam and dipped or 'meeting' beam functions into single lamps, the lighting requirements for the two conditions are considerably different and this arrangement must therefore be a compromise. This is the reason for the adoption of four-headlamp, or 'dual', systems with the headlamps arranged in pairs either side by side, one above the other, or diagonally. In a typical system, one lamp of each pair is a double-filament unit having a 50 watt filament positioned at the focal point of its optical system, which is designed for optimum meeting-beam lighting. The second filament is of $37\frac{1}{2}$ watts, arranged below the first filament to give a fan-shaped spread of illumination at relatively close range, and is switched on as supplementary main- or driving-beam lighting, the 50 watt filament then being switched off; the major part of the main-beam illumination, however, is provided by a single 50 watt filament in the other lamp of each pair, which is designed for long-range lighting. Thus, in the 'dipped' condition two lamps provide a total illumination of 100 watts whilst on 'main beam' all four lamps are on, giving a total of 175 watts.

Automatic Dipping. Some American cars make use of a photo-electric device known as the 'Autronic Eye' which is sensitive to the glare from approaching cars and dips the headlamps accordingly. The system has been investigated in Britain, but the twisting nature of the roads and the lack of uniformity in vehicle lighting are factors which render automatic dipping impracticable here at present. Of interest, however, is the Lucas automatic anti-dazzle driving mirror, which is an elaboration of the prismatic mirror principle by which the setting of the mirror can be flicked to a different angle to present a reduced intensity reflection from following vehicle headlamps. In the automatic mirror, light detected by a photo-cell in the corner of the mirror causes a transistor circuit to energize a solenoid which tilts the mirror to its anti-dazzle position; the circuit includes a delay feature to prevent the mirror 'flapping' in fluctuating light conditions.

OTHER LAMPS

Reference is made in Chapter 12 to the legal requirements concerning automobile lighting. In general, two white side lamps are required, to indicate the width of the vehicle, and two red rear lamps. Also, the rear number-plate must be illuminated. Brake warning lights are not obligatory but are standard fitments. (See also Chapter 8.)

Pass-lamps may be fitted to supplement the normal headlamps and are designed to give flat topped beams which, whilst not being entirely suitable for continuous driving, do give non-dazzling illumination when passing on-coming vehicles.

A fog lamp, to be most useful, should be trained upon the kerb a short distance ahead of the car and should be of a type which throws no light upwards to be reflected from the fog bank. It is held by some that a yellow tinted light has greater powers of fog penetration; incidentally, in France the law requires all headlamps to be amber tinted. British law puts special restrictions upon the use of lamps placed less than two feet from the ground.

Reversing lamps giving a white light to the rear are standard fittings on some higher priced cars. They may be arranged to be illuminating automatically by the engagement of reverse gear.

Lamps other than those used for driving include those for illuminating the instrument panel, the car interior, step boards, and the engine and luggage compartments. In a few cases the so-called 'black' light is applied, as in aircraft, to instrument panels; the light source is an ultra-violet lamp which causes green fluorescence of the specially treated dial markings and pointers.

A recent development is the use of 'piped light' or fibre optics, in which the light is distributed from a central source to various points on the facia panel along flexible bundles of glass or plastics fibres.

SWITCHING OF LAMPS

Since lamps are normally used in connexion with one another it is usual to control certain of them by a combination switch; for example, if headlamps are required then side and tail lamps will also be illuminated. Similarly, lamps normally used only at night, such as reversing lamps, will only be operative if side and tail lamps are switched on. Pass- and fog-lamps are usually switched individually.

It is becoming the practice to combine the control of all lights into a single multi-position switch mounted on a 'stalk' projecting from the steering column.

In some cases, a rheostat (variable resistance) is provided to allow adjustment of the brilliance of the instrument lighting.

Headlamp dipping is almost always controlled by a foot switch, although steering column controls are also used. Often a small lamp is illuminated on the facia panel to indicate when the headlamp main beam is in use, i.e. when the lamps are undipped.

An increasing number of cars are equipped with a steering column switch which is spring-loaded ('biased') and used to flash the headlamps off and on, this being the recognized warning of approach for use in the 'silent' hours.

Some cars are now being fitted with the Lucas *Two-level Signalling* system, in which specially designed lamps, giving about twice normal illumination (but without increasing the bulb wattage), are used for the front and rear flashing direction indicators and for the brake warning lamps, so as to give increased visibility during daylight; at night, however, switching-on of the side and tail lamps connects resistors in series with the rear signalling lamps to reduce their intensity to about one quarter since otherwise their extra brilliance would cause dazzle. The resistors are not used for the front indicators as these have to be readily visible against the glare of headlamps.

It is becoming usual for the side- and tail-lamp circuit to be provided with additional switching positions such that the lamps on only one side or the other may be switched on for all-night parking (where the law permits this), thus reducing battery drain; there are also available photo-cell devices which may be used to switch these lamps on or off automatically at nightfall or sunrise by responding to the surrounding natural light conditions.

DIRECTION INDICATORS

Up to a few years ago, direction indicators or 'trafficators' were required to alter the profile of the vehicle and the electric semaphore type of indicator became standard equipment. This is a solenoid device in which an iron plunger is drawn into a cylindrical coil when the latter is energized. The semaphore arm is secured in its lowered position by means of a spring, but when the plunger begins to move it withdraws the abutment for this spring which is thus rendered inoperative; this means that the electromagnet is not lifting the arm against spring pressure. As the arm rises a pair of auxiliary contacts are closed to illuminate a tubular bulb within the arm.

The semaphore indicator was subject to some criticism because of the vulnerability of the arm, the troubles caused by wind pressure if the indicator was raised at high road speeds, and the difficulty of accommodating the mechanism in certain types of coachwork. Nowadays, flashing indicators or 'winkers' are invariably fitted. These have also been criticized because, in some circumstances, the signal is not readily visible, particularly when a red lamp is used in close proximity to red tail lights and brake lights. In the more commendable installations the direction indicator is an amber lamp which is far more readily distinguished. Investigations by the Road Research Laboratory have shown that the type of indicator known as the 'blushing ear', i.e. a semi-circular flashing amber light projecting from the door pillar, gives the most rapid recognition. Most installations comprise lamps mounted front and rear in such a way that they are also visible from the side but it is also becoming usual to fit small 'repeater' lamps on the sides of the vehicle, where they are particularly easily seen by cyclists riding alongside and by traffic on roundabouts.

The frequency of flashing is also a factor in the ready identification of a turn signal. One type of flasher unit for producing the interrupted signal is sealed within a metal can and uses the 'hot wire' principle. Current passes through a thin wire which heats up and expands, causing contacts to separate and break the circuit. The wire then cools and allows the contacts to reclose, thus repeating the cycle.

Direction indicators may be operated by a switch mounted on the steering wheel boss, by partial rotation of the horn-ring, or by a 'stalk' type switch projecting from the steering column. In many cases the indicators are self-cancelling, being either switched off automatically when the steering is straightened up, or controlled by a clockwork time-switch. In some cases, the indicator switch is mounted above the facia panel and is itself illuminated when either indicator is in use. Some flasher installations are arranged to emit a ticking sound to indicate that the signal is functioning.

A facility which may be expected to become more common is a special control for switching on *all* the flashers simultaneously as a warning signal when the vehicle is placed in a particularly hazardous situation, for example, obstructing a motorway lane due to breakdown, or at the scene of an accident.

ELECTRIC HORNS

Warning instruments used on cars are invariably electrically operated and fall into two classes, *high frequency* (*H.F.*) horns and the *windtone* types.

The high frequency horn is used singly and its operating principle resembles that of an electric buzzer; an iron armature is attracted towards an electromagnet and its movement causes the separation of two contacts, thus interrupting the supply to the magnet. The armature being attached to a springy, flexible diaphragm then flies back and recloses the contacts, the process being repeated at a rate which depends upon the natural frequency of the diaphragm assembly, usually around 360 cycles per second. The sound from a high frequency horn is due solely to vibration of the diaphragm.

The windtone type horn (Fig. 58) uses a similar electromagnetic device to vibrate a diaphragm which in this case is situated at the inner end of what may be regarded as a curled-up trumpet, part of

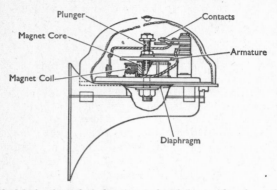

Fig. 58. Mechanism of windtone type electric horn. (*Based on a drawing supplied by Messrs Clear Hooters Ltd*)

which is formed as a cavity in a die-casting. The sound is produced by the resonant vibration of the air column within the horn, just as the instrumentalist's lips vibrate the air column in, say, a French horn. The pitch of the note produced is determined by the length of the horn cavity. The usual practice is to use windtone horns in pairs, tuned to a pleasant musical interval such as the minor third given by E Flat (307 cycles per second) and F Sharp (364 cycles per second).

Electric horns require a considerable operating current; for instance, a pair of windtone horns operating at 6 volts will take a total of 16 amperes. Therefore, in order to reduce the voltage drop in the cables it is usual to minimize the length of cable run to the horns by the use of relay switching; the relay is simply an electromagnetic switch mounted near the horns and is closed remotely by the operation of the horn push. Only a light current is required to operate the relay and the cable to the horn-push can therefore be small in section.

SPEEDOMETER

Although the speedometer is, strictly speaking, a mechanical device, one form of it incorporates an interesting electrical principle. The drive to the speedometer is taken, by means of a flexible cable, from a pair of gears situated in the output end of the gearbox. The cable has an armoured casing and a revolving inner core. At the instrument end, the latter engages with a train of gears which operate the mileage recorder or *odometer*. In some cases an additional *trip recorder* is provided, which can be reset to zero after any particular journey. The revolving cable also causes the rotation of a permanent magnet which is positioned close to an aluminium disc, similar to that found in the domestic electricity meter. An electromagnetic effect causes the disc to try to rotate, but it is restrained by a hair-spring. The actual movement is related to the speed of the magnet, so that a pointer attached to the disc indicates road speed, provided that the instrument is properly matched to the transmission system. Obviously, a change in the axle gear ratio or in the effective diameter of the road-wheels affects the accuracy of the readings.

The speedometer cable needs regular lubrication, otherwise the inner core may tend to stick. This results in a rhythmic winding-up and unwinding of the core, causing swinging of the pointer.

REVOLUTION COUNTER

The higher-performance car is often fitted with a revolution counter, more accurately described as an engine speed indicator. In competition work the rev-counter is a much more valuable aid to efficient driving than the speedometer in that it tells the driver when the engine is working at optimum speed and when it is approaching the safety limit in terms of revolutions per minute. In any case, changes in wheel and tyre size or in final drive ratio may cause the speedometer to give false indications unless it has been re-calibrated. The rev-counter is arranged to indicate engine speed directly, regardless of the gearbox ratio in use, and is usually calibrated in 'hundreds of r.p.m.' e.g. 30 denotes 3,000 r.p.m. The mechanism of the instrument may resemble that of the speedometer described above, or it may be an electrical type in which the voltage developed by a small generator coupled to the engine is shown on a voltmeter calibrated in terms of engine speed. A new type of engine speed indicator introduced recently uses electronic circuitry to count the rate of ignition pulses, which give, of course, a direct measure of engine speed, provided the number of cylinders is taken into account.

CHAPTER FIVE

TRANSMISSION SYSTEM

THE transmission system is the train of components required to transmit engine power to the driving wheels, and in the piston-engined car it may be considered as consisting of the following:

(*a*) A clutch, which couples the transmission system to the engine, when required.

(*b*) A gearbox, or other means for increasing engine torque.

(*c*) A propeller shaft connecting the gearbox to

(*d*) the final drive unit, which combines three functions:

    (1) It further reduces the speed of the engine to a value suitable for the road wheels.

    (2) It turns the line of the drive through a right-angle, i.e. from a longitudinal axis to a transverse axis. (This feature is not required, of course, if the engine is set transversely, as in certain B.M.C. cars, for example.)

    (3) It provides for the difference in speed of the inside and outside road wheels when traversing bends.

(*e*) The wheel suspension arrangements which couple the final drive unit to the road wheels and transfer the driving thrust to the chassis.

The above requirements present themselves in all cases, including rear-engined and front wheel drive cars, except that in some arrangements the propeller shaft is not required.

The clutch and gearbox arrangements conform essentially to a set pattern on the majority of cars; this department of the car probably arouses the most criticism from the user because whereas the actions of starting, steering and stopping each comprise an essential part of directing the vehicle, performed at the will of the driver, clutch operation and gear selection are ancillary functions which only result from basic deficiencies in engine characteristics, namely the inability of an internal combustion piston engine to start instantly from rest under load or to maintain adequate torque over its entire speed range. There have been many developments aimed at simplifying or eliminating clutch and gearbox manipulation; four basic types of mechanical transmission have evolved, though only two of these can be said to be predominantly successful, as described below:

(a) Foot-operated friction clutch and manually operated gearbox, still used on the majority of cars outside North America; an overdrive unit may be included.

(b) Manually selected gearbox with automatic operation of the clutch, which has been quite extensively developed but which has not found any great favour with motorists.

(c) Pre-selector gearbox, with fluid coupling or centrifugal clutch, which has been used successfully on a limited number of cars.

(d) The fully automatic transmission system, which is becoming virtually standard on the largest cars and is gradually extending into the medium-power range.

It may be deduced from the limited success of 'semi-automatics' that the motorist will only pay the extra cost for a transmission system which is fully automatic; also, although a number of European car manufacturers have attempted to develop their own automatic transmission systems, the present trend is towards the adoption of virtually standard proprietary transmissions made by a limited number of specialists, with the attendant benefits in cost reduction resulting from quantity production.

FRICTION CLUTCH

This is invariably installed between the engine and gearbox and is almost always mounted directly on the output end of the engine, though occasionally both it and the gearbox are incorporated in the final drive unit. The clutch is always foot operated, the pedal being linked either by a direct mechanical linkage or, very often nowadays, by a hydraulic system (Fig. 20), similar to that of hydraulic brakes. The latter method facilitates the accommodation of the considerably transverse movement of rubber mounted engines.

A very common form of clutch is the dry single plate type, as manufactured by Messrs Borg & Beck Ltd. Fig. 59 is a diagrammatic illustration to show the operating principle and it can be seen that there are three main elements. In the centre is the *clutch*

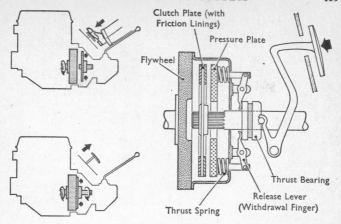

Fig. 59. Principle of dry plate friction clutch.

a. Clutch pedal depressed – interrupts drive between engine and gearbox.

b. Pedal released – spring pressure restores drive.

plate, which is a steel disc to both sides of which are attached rings of special friction material, similar to that used for brake linings. This is mounted so that it can slide on the front end of the input shaft to the gearbox. The clutch plate is normally pushed firmly against the machined rear face of the flywheel by a spring-loaded *pressure* (or *presser*) *plate*. The depression of the clutch pedal moves the pressure plate back slightly and relieves pressure on the clutch plate, allowing slip to occur. Since all three main parts are normally revolving together, the movement of the clutch linkage is transferred to the pressure plate by a thrust bearing, which is either a heavy ball-race or a thick carbon ring, the latter type requiring no lubrication. The forward movement of the thrust bearing or collar is 'reversed' by three levers known as *release levers* (Fig. 60). To aid the smooth take-up of the drive, the clutch plate is usually made with a flexible centre, i.e. the outer portion is mounted upon a separate hub, with springs or rubber interposed to allow a limited amount of angular movement which absorbs torsional vibration.

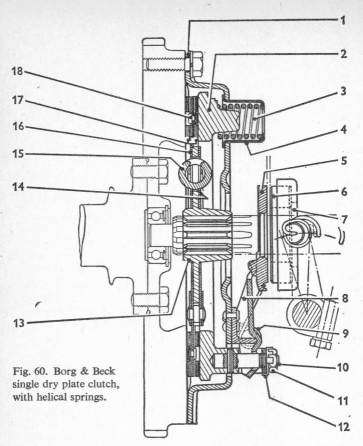

Fig. 60. Borg & Beck
single dry plate clutch,
with helical springs.

1. Pressed steel cover.
2. Cast-iron pressure plate.
3. Thrust springs (six).
4. Spring cups.
5. Release lever plate.
6. Thrust block.
7. Bearing cup.
8. Release lever (three).
9. Anti-rattle springs.

10, 11, and 12. Release lever stud
assembly.
13. Splined hub.
14. Driven plate.
15. Coil springs (providing flexible
centre to driven plate).
16. Disc of driven plate.
17. Facings (friction linings).
18. Rivets.

(*By courtesy of Automotive Products Co. Ltd*)

A further refinement in some friction clutches is the use of centrifugal force to exert pressure on the clutch plate. Pivoted weights are used in conjunction with weaker springs than usual. By this means only a light pressure is required to disengage the clutch at low engine speed, but as the engine speed rises the weights are thrown outwards and, by suitable leverage system, provide additional force on the pressure plate.

This principle is extended further in the fully automatic centrifugal clutch in which the speeding up of the engine automatically engages the clutch in the manner described above. A device is incorporated to limit the centrifugal force applied, since otherwise it might be impossible to disengage the clutch at high engine speeds. This type of clutch is not suitable for use with the normal type of gearbox, since drive is only completely disconnected from the box when engine speed falls to idling.

A special clutch suitable for transmitting the high torque of racing engines is also made by the Borg & Beck Co. Ltd. This is a three plate clutch, i.e. it has three friction-lined discs, and the spring pressure is reinforced by the use of centrifugal bob weights. Positive take-up rather than cushioned drive being an important requirement of a racing clutch, the clutch plates do not have sprung centres; the diameter of this clutch is only one and a quarter inches greater than that of the smallest touring car clutch.

DIAPHRAGM SPRING FRICTION CLUTCH

The well-known friction clutch with multiple coil springs is likely to be superseded by the *diaphragm spring clutch*; this operates on a virtually identical principle, but the coil springs and release levers are replaced by a single large disc spring, with its centre portion pierced to form a number of radial fingers, which is substantially flat in the engaged position and which flexes into a saucer shape (see Fig. 61) when the clutch pedal is depressed and so withdraws the pressure plate. This clutch occupies a smaller depth and can accommodate a larger clutch plate within a given housing diameter; its simple construction results in reduced friction in the mechanism and means that substantially lower operating effort is required. The diaphragm spring clutch can be operated at high engine speeds without effect on its 'clamping' force and accurate balance can be

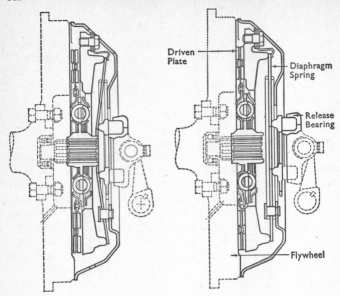

Fig. 61. These views of a diaphragm spring clutch show the shape taken by the disc spring in the freed and engaged positions. (*By courtesy of Automotive Products Co. Ltd*)

maintained. In the Borg & Beck *strap-drive* diaphragm spring clutch illustrated, friction is further reduced by the use of a number of short, slightly flexible links (not shown) arranged near-tangentially to transmit drive from the clutch housing to the pressure plate and the release plate; both of these have to be able to rotate with the housing but also to move axially by a small amount during clutch operation.

The Gearbox

This is more correctly termed a variable-ratio gearbox; that is, it allows the ratio of the speed of the input and output shafts to be varied as required. All modern gearboxes provide three or four forward ratios, and reverse gear; one of the forward ratios (top gear) is normally direct drive, in which the propeller shaft runs at engine speed. However, in some Continental cars top gear is an *overdrive* gear, i.e. the propeller shaft runs faster than the engine. This may seem irrational, since this gearing-up appears to be cancelled out by the gearing-down in the final drive unit, but it is intended that the car shall normally be driven in third gear, which gives a ratio close to direct drive, top gear being used only when sustained fast running under easy conditions is possible. The engine then runs more slowly but maximum speed is usually little, if any, higher than the maximum possible in third gear.

Manufacturers appear to disagree on the merits of three- and four-speed boxes. The three-speed arrangement is simpler and cheaper to construct and is easier to arrange for remote control from the steering column than the four-speed version, but the latter gives more freedom in choice of gear ratios, and in particular allows the use of a very low ratio first gear for starting from rest on hills etc.

Five or more forward gears have occasionally been provided, mainly for competition work.

CHOICE OF GEARBOX RATIOS

The automobile designer decides upon the ratios of the various gear combinations in order to make the best possible use of the engine characteristics, having regard to the power, weight, and type of the car in question.

In the average touring car a small engine is required to propel a relatively heavy vehicle, demanding a low gear ratio for starting. On the other hand, the engine itself is designed to give a reasonable pull at fairly low speed so as to make possible the use of top gear over a wide range of road speeds; so it is permissible to provide a third gear which gives only a relatively low road speed at maximum engine speed. Typical gear ratios for this class of car could be:

1st	4 to 1
2nd	2·5 to 1
3rd	1·5 to 1
Top	1 to 1

These ratios are well spread out over a wide range, and this type of gearbox is known as *wide ratio*.

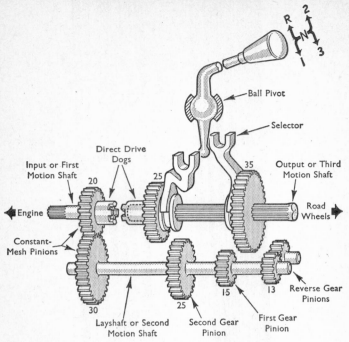

Fig. 62a. Simple sliding-pinion or 'crash' gearbox.
Sideways movement of the lever swings the lower projecting portion into
engagement with either of the gear selectors and the subsequent forward
or backward movement slides the gear into mesh.

In a competition car the engine is so designed that it produces
tremendous power at high engine speeds but the power drops off
sharply if engine speed falls. Therefore, it is necessary to provide
gearbox ratios which permit engagement of a lower ratio without
overspeeding the engine, as soon as road speed begins to drop.
Typical ratios for this application would be:

1st	2·9 to 1
2nd	2·0 to 1
3rd	1·3 to 1
Top	1 to 1

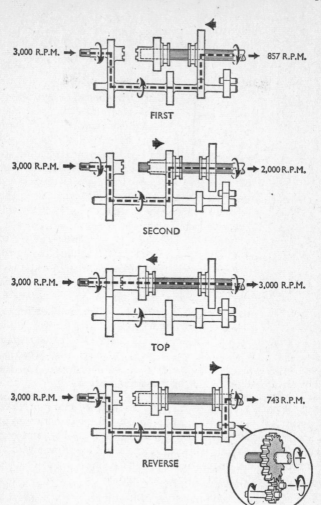

3,000 R.P.M. →   → 857 R.P.M.

FIRST

3,000 R.P.M. →   → 2,000 R.P.M.

SECOND

3,000 R.P.M. →   → 3,000 R.P.M.

TOP

3,000 R.P.M. →   → 743 R.P.M.

REVERSE

Fig. 62b. The transmission path for each ratio is shown for a simple three-speed and reverse gearbox.

A gearbox with these ratios would be termed *close ratio*. (See page 200 for further points on this topic.)

The way in which movement of the gear lever causes engagement of the gears is more easily followed in the early type of 'crash' box having, for simplicity, three forward gears and reverse (Fig. 62). The gearbox contains three parallel shafts, two of them being in line and the third lying to one side or below them. The short input shaft, driven from the clutch, is known as the *primary* or *first-motion shaft*, and it carries a gearwheel which meshes with a larger gear on the offset shaft or *layshaft*, also known as the *jackshaft* or *second-motion shaft*. These two gears are always meshed together and are therefore termed *constant mesh* gears or pinions. The layshaft also carries three other fixed gears, and each of these can be meshed with one of two gears on the output shaft or *third motion shaft*. The output shaft gears can slide along the shaft, being splined to it, and they are controlled by *selector forks*. In the neutral position both sliding gears are out of mesh, but when the gear lever is moved to the first gear position it picks up a selector fork and slides the appropriate gear forward into mesh with its counterpart on the layshaft. In the example shown, this means that between the input and output shaft there are two gear reductions, one (constant mesh) 30 to 20 (1·5) and the other 35 to 15 (2·33). These multiplied together give a total gear ratio of 3·5 to 1. In other words, if the engine is rotating at 3,000 r.p.m., the layshaft turns at 2,000 r.p.m. and the output shaft at 857 r.p.m. Subsequent selection of second gear firstly disengages the first gear pinion and then meshes the second gear sliding pinion by moving its selector fork towards the rear. The meshing gears here give a 1 to 1 ratio so that the overall reduction is that of the constant mesh gears, 1·5 to 1.

If top gear is selected the second gear pinion is moved forwards but does not mesh with a layshaft pinion; instead coarse, square, endwise teeth or *dogs* on its front face engage with similar teeth on the rear of the input shaft, so that the input and output shafts are now locked together, giving a total of 1 to 1 ratio, and 'by-passing' the constant mesh pinions. None of the gears is working under load and this explains why the transmission system of the average car sounds quieter when operating in top gear. (Also, if 'howling' is heard from the transmission when running in top gear, especially on the over-run, it follows that this is generated by worn gears in the rear axle and not by the gearbox.)

For reverse gear, the first gear pinion is moved backwards to engage with a pinion which is not mounted directly on the layshaft, but is itself in constant mesh with a third pinion on the layshaft. In this way the reversal of rotation is obtained. In the example, the ratio of the reverse pinions is 2·69 to 1 (the intermediate gear not affecting the ratio), the overall reverse ratio being 4·04 to 1.

In practice, the engagement of sliding gears requires considerable skill, since the two gears need to be revolving at similar peripheral speeds if they are to be brought together in any degree of silence. The art of double de-clutching arose from this necessity; i.e., after the initial declutch, neutral gear is selected and the clutch re-engaged, so that the engine is again driving the layshaft in neutral. The engine speed then being adjusted according to the driver's judgement, the clutch is again depressed and the appropriate gear engaged. It was found that this procedure was considerably eased by re-designing the gearbox so that the pairs of pinions for each gear ratio were kept permanently in mesh and only engaged with the output shaft as required, by means of sliding dogs similar to those used for top gear. This meant that the noisy straight teeth essential in sliding gears could be replaced by quieter-running helical teeth.

However, the constant mesh gearbox with sliding dogs still required a fair amount of skill in manipulation, and in the early 1930s an automatic means for matching the speeds of engaging dogs was introduced. This is termed *synchromesh*, and the principle of one type is shown in Fig. 63. It is seen that the dog clutch is in three parts, the sliding member being a ring with internal teeth. This slides on the outside of the driving member but is normally held in place by spring loaded balls. As the selector moves this assembly towards the driving member (attached to the output shaft pinion) tapered projections (*synchromesh cones*) on the approaching faces come into contact and the friction between them rapidly causes the two parts to rotate together. Further pressure on the selector causes the outer ring to override the sprung balls and form a rigid connexion between the two toothed members.

At one time it was common practice to provide synchromesh, or

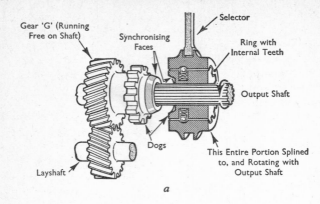

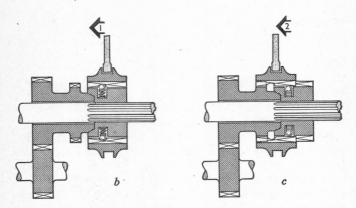

Fig. 63. Synchromesh.

a. During a gear-change, output shaft is positively driven by the road wheels. Clutch is disengaged, so input shaft, layshaft, and gears are 'running free'.

b. First part of movement of gear selector brings conical synchronizing faces into contact and frictional drag rapidly speeds up or slows down the gear G to output shaft speed.

c. Further pressure on gear lever causes toothed ring to overcome spring-loaded balls and to bridge both sets of dogs, locking gear G to the output shaft.

'synchro', on all gears except first gear; the justification for this was that first gear (and, of course, reverse) is almost always engaged with the car at rest so that matching of engine speed to road speed does not arise. These gears were therefore engaged by the sliding of straight-tooth pinions with no synchronizer units. However, engagement of first gear whilst on the move on a gearbox of this type, even of modern design, is a matter requiring some skill; also, the selection of first gear from rest tends to be difficult occasionally and the pinions run noisily. Therefore, it is now more usual for gearboxes to be 'all-synchromesh', with helical gears and syn-chronizers on all forward ratios, including bottom.

The changing of gears on a simple synchromesh box calls for a slight pause as the synchronization takes place, and the mechan-ism can be completely over-ridden if force is used. With a modified type of synchromesh, known as *baulking-ring*, the gears cannot be engaged until completely synchronized. In a typical baulking-ring mechanism the conical face of the synchronizer is formed on a separate ring attached to the synchronizer with a limited amount of rotational 'play'; this ring has external dogs matching those on the pinion and will not allow the outer bridging ring to move until both sets of dogs are in line, which can only occur when the cones have brought the synchronizer and pinion to the same speed so that there is no relative rotation between the two.

In any manually controlled gearbox the initial selection of a gear ratio requires two movements, one across to engage the appro-priate fork and one forward or backward to mesh the dogs. On early gearboxes the movement of the lever was guided by a 'gate' which might or might not be exposed, the cross-wise movement sometimes entailing sliding the lever bodily, and being termed moving 'across the gate'. This mechanism was superseded by the *ball-change*, in which the gear lever is pivoted in a ball joint; in-advertent selection of reverse gear is prevented either by a spring-loaded catch, released by suitably manipulating the gear lever knob, or in the case of some floor-mounted levers, by the necessity of lift-ing the lever bodily before reverse can be engaged.

The gearbox incorporates an interlock to prevent the accidental engagement of two gear ratios simultaneously. If this were to hap-pen the gearbox would be locked immovably.

There are still considerable variations in the disposition of the gear lever. Mounting the lever directly on top of the gearbox gives precise control, but may mean a long 'whippy' lever if the driving seat is set far back from the box. In this case a short lever is mounted on a rigid extension to the rear of the gearbox and coupled by a remote control linkage. The post-war fashion which dictated clear floor space at all costs caused the lever to migrate to the steering column, with a tendency towards a loss of 'feel' due to the complicated linkage required. This may be particularly so in the case of a four-speed box where the asymmetrical reverse gear position entails an additional control connexion, often of the cable type. The movements of the steering-column gear lever are similar to those of the floor mounted lever, but on a different plane. Usually the lever is spring-loaded towards the line of the third and top gear position.

Most manufacturers have now reverted to the floor-mounted lever as standard practice or as an optional alternative.

On the Riley 'Pathfinder' and the closely related Wolseley 6/90 a floor mounted lever was used, but set to the right of the driver's seat as was also the practice on Rolls-Royce and Bentley cars for many years.

OVERDRIVE

As mentioned previously, the term overdrive implies that the speed of the output shaft from the gearbox is higher than that of the input shaft; in top gear, of course, these speeds are normally the same. In the case of a car with three forward gears it may be necessary, in order to preserve flexible top gear performance, to use a final drive gear of low ratio, and this means that at high speed the engine will be running faster than is desirable. On American cars where the use of large engines favoured the three-speed gearbox, the overdrive unit became popular. This geared up the drive and was normally arranged to engage automatically when a given speed was attained and disengage when the speed fell. Since the extra high gear resulted in reduced torque being available for overtaking and hill climbing, a 'kick-down' device was provided, by which full depression of the accelerator disengaged the overdrive.

Overdrive units are now available as standard or optional equipment on many British cars, including those with four forward gears, a well-known example being the Laycock-de-Normanville. This is a compound epicyclic gear (see pp. 173–4) which is fitted to the rear of the gearbox. It is engaged by hydraulic pressure derived from a pump within the unit, the application of this pressure being controlled by a valve which may be operated in one of several ways. The engagement and disengagement may be entirely automatic, being controlled by a governor set to operate at a certain speed, if so required, or it may be manually controlled, either by an additional movement of the normal gear lever or by an electric switch. Important features are that no operation of the clutch is required and power drive is sustained during the change into or out of overdrive. Also, the design ensures that the braking effect of the engine is always available. This unit may be applied to both second and top gears of a three-speed box, making available five forward gears.

The overdrive does not necessarily provide an increase in maximum speed but it does mean that at any given road speed the engine revolutions may be reduced by about 20 per cent; apart from reduction in noise and vibration, this allows the engine to work at a more economical speed and brings about an improvement in fuel consumption.

AUTOMATIC CLUTCH OPERATION

A system in which gear selection is entirely in the hands of the driver but in which the clutch is operated automatically would appear to be an attractive one, especially for use on the smaller engined cars which have no spare power to waste on fluid couplings and which require frequent gear changes.

An example of such a system was marketed by the Automotive Products Co. Ltd and known as the 'Manumatic' system. The mechanism is fairly complex, since it not only provides the requisite operation of the clutch when a gear change is made, but also adjusts engine speed accordingly, and incorporates a centrifugal clutch for moving away from rest.

Basically, the system consists of a clutch servo mechanism operated by vacuum obtained from the engine induction manifold, a vacuum reservoir also being installed. The gripping of the gear lever knob closes a switch which controls the vacuum valve so that as the lever is moved the clutch is automatically disengaged. The gear is then engaged manually with the assistance of the normal synchromesh mechanism, but a throttle control unit, acting in conjunction with a two-part switch built into the clutch, ensures that the clutch does not re-engage until the engine speed is synchronized with that of the driven clutch plate. The actual rate at which the clutch re-engages is determined by the position of the accelerator pedal, that is, if the car is being driven in an enterprising manner, then the re-engagement is correspondingly rapid.

A feature of all centrifugal clutches is that they will not engage to drive the engine when the car is towed, no matter what the speed. To overcome this, an optional feature of the Manumatic Transmission System is a 'tow-start' device which allows for manual engagement of the clutch by a lever resembling the hand brake lever, and this can also be used as a supplement to the normal parking brake if the car is left in gear.

'NEWTONDRIVE'

A two-pedal transmission system using manual operation of the standard gearbox, with automatic clutch control, was produced by Messrs Newton & Bennett Ltd, and known as 'Newtondrive'. It formed the basis of the inexpensive 'Standrive', which was fitted to certain Standard vehicles, and also of Ford two-pedal control.

A new Newton centrifugal clutch is used, which engages or disengages as the engine speed rises or falls, the critical speed of engagement being 800 r.p.m. The clutch incorporates a novel arrangement which uses only one set of springs both for disengaging the clutch and for maintaining driving pressure; this permits a simpler and lighter construction than has been possible in previous centrifugal clutches, using two sets of springs. The clutch is also equipped with an over-riding withdrawal mechanism of conventional type, which is operated by a vacuum cylinder and piston, no clutch pedal being provided.

For starting from rest, a low gear is engaged in the usual way and the accelerator is depressed, causing the centrifugal clutch to engage smoothly as engine speed rises.

In grasping the gear lever for subsequent changes a switch incorporated in the knob is closed and applies a vacuum to the clutch operating cylinder, so that the clutch is disengaged during the change. Simultaneously a linkage to the throttle automatically provides a suitable adjustment of engine speed. The clutch subsequently re-engages when the gear lever is released, the speed of engagement being determined by the extent to which the accelerator is depressed. This is achieved by means of an interconnexion which controls the rate at which air is admitted to destroy the vacuum in the clutch cylinder; if the car is being driven hard the clutch re-engages quickly and *vice versa*. Vacuum is obtained from the engine induction manifold and is stored in a reservoir. An extension to the choke control is provided to ensure that increased engine idling speed does not cause the clutch to engage prematurely, use of the choke causing the clutch to be held out by the vacuum servo until the accelerator is depressed.

The design of the centrifugal clutch allows for the inclusion of a tow-starting device when this is considered necessary.

CITROEN DS SALOON TRANSMISSION SYSTEM

In common with several other controls on the Citroen DS saloon, hydraulic power operation is applied to the clutch and conventional type gearbox. Selection of gears is entirely under the control of the driver, but the actual work of engaging the gears is performed by hydraulic cylinders. An interconnected mechanism provides for automatic disengagement and re-engagement of the clutch during gear changes, whilst a further mechanism disengages the clutch when engine speed drops below a certain figure, and *vice versa*. The speed of engagement of the clutch is dependent upon the degree of throttle opening, and is therefore automatically adjusted to meet the needs of gentle or spirited driving. No clutch pedal is provided, but a manual control allows for engagement of the clutch when the engine is stationary, for tow-starting etc.

EPICYCLIC GEARBOX

The principle of epicyclic gearing is explained on page 358, and it will be seen that a simple epicyclic gear train has three main members, namely a centre sun wheel, a planet carrier bearing a number of freely rotating planet gears which run around the sun wheel, and an annulus or ring gear which embraces the planet gears. A number of gear ratios can be obtained according to which of the members is driving, driven, or held stationary.

In motor car gearbox applications a series of epicyclic gear trains are used and brought into action by locking the annulus of each train in turn. An example of this is the *Wilson pre-selector gearbox*, which was used in particular on Daimler and Lanchester cars for many years. In this case the locking of each annulus is by a friction band brake which is applied by a foot pedal corresponding to the usual clutch pedal. To engage a gear, a steering column mounted lever is first moved to the required position, thus selecting the gear in advance. The actual change is made by depressing the foot pedal which releases any brake band already in use, and on being allowed to return, contracts the pre-selected band. Top gear is obtained by means of a multi-plate clutch which locks all the gear trains together to give direct drive. The slight amount of wear in the brake bands is provided for by automatic adjustment.

In the Cotal gearbox the annulus gears are locked by means of electromagnets, these being energized in turn by a small multi-position switch. In the Armstrong Siddeley Preselectric gearbox the pre-selection of the gears is also achieved by electromagnets, but the brake bands are contracted by foot pedal.

A noteworthy feature of epicyclic gearboxes is that gear changes can be made whilst torque is being transmitted, so that the drive from the engine need not be completely uncoupled during a change. To take advantage of this it is almost always employed either with an automatic centrifugal clutch or with a *fluid flywheel*. The latter consists of two parts, the *rotor*, which is driven by the engine, and the *runner*, which is connected to the gearbox and which is embraced by the rotor in such a way that an oil-tight box is formed. Each member of the wheel is divided up by radial vanes into a series of cells. The wheel is almost entirely filled with a light mineral oil. As the engine driven rotor revolves, the oil in the cells is thrown outwards and is directed by the shape of the cells into the cells of the stationary runner, the transfer of energy causing the runner to rotate in the same direction. At engine idling speed the drag on the runner is very small, but as the engine is speeded up the coupling effect increases rapidly until there is very little slip between rotor and runner. The oil itself circulates in a curved helical path in that it follows the shape of the cells whilst it also traverses the circle of the wheel. The fluid flywheel inevitably absorbs a certain amount of power in the churning of the oil which is heated up in the process; however, this slight disadvantage is offset by the ability of this type of coupling to absorb transmission shocks.

A fluid coupling is used in the Hydra-Matic automatic gearbox and can be seen at the left-hand end in Plate 3.

MAGNETIC POWDER TRANSMISSION

A new type of transmission utilizing a novel form of coupling was introduced by Smiths Motor Accessories Ltd. The coupling, which is based on an American patent, is illustrated in Fig. 64; it operates on the principle that two parts which rotate one within the other can be coupled together by causing magnetized powder to bridge the gap between them. In this application the outer part, which is bolted to the engine flywheel, is made from a suitable steel in two halves which are joined together to enclose an annular coil of wire. The second part, which is mounted on splines on the gearbox input shaft, is located by a sealed ball-race so that there is a small gap between it and the outer part. When an electric current is passed through the coil of wire the outer part of the coupling becomes magnetized and the path of the magnetism passes through the inner part as shown in the illustration. About an eggcup-ful of 'magnetic' powder, which is contained within the coupling, is attracted into the gap between the two parts. It thus forms a bridge capable of transmitting torque to a degree which can be controlled by variation of the current supplied to the magnet coil. Centrifugal force on the powder prevents it escaping via the centre bearing whilst the coupling is rotating, and a labyrinth system of traps catches any powder which falls towards the centre when the coupling stops rotating.

The intrinsic advantages of this new coupling are:

(1) Its operation is entirely electrical and requires no mechanical linkages.

(2) The torque transmitted can be varied, simply and progressively, by varying the current in the coil.

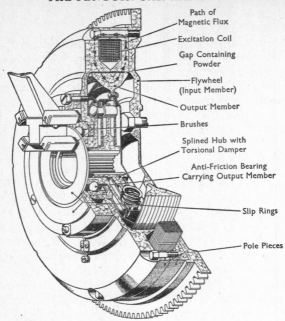

Path of Magnetic Flux

Excitation Coil

Gap Containing Powder

Flywheel (Input Member)

Output Member

Brushes

Splined Hub with Torsional Damper

Anti-Friction Bearing Carrying Output Member

Slip Rings

Pole Pieces

Fig. 64. One form of the magnetic powder coupling. (*By courtesy of Smiths Motor Accessories Ltd*)

(3) 'Pick-up' is perfectly smooth, without 'judder' or snatch.

(4) When fully 'engaged' there is no slip, as with a fluid coupling, nor is there any appreciable drag with the coupling de-energized.

The magnetic powder coupling formed an essential part of a fully automatic transmission system developed by Smiths and marketed for a time by Rootes Motors Ltd under the name 'Easidrive'.

FULLY AUTOMATIC TRANSMISSION SYSTEMS

A fully automatic transmission system would seem to be more desirable on a car with a small engine demanding frequent gear changing but until a few years ago the complexity, weight and cost of such systems had limited their application to the largest cars. Automatic transmissions, mainly of American derivation, have been available on the more powerful British cars for some years as standard or optional equipment; more recently, lighter transmissions have been developed and most cars in the medium range are now offered with fully automatic transmission as an alternative to the manual gearbox, at extra cost. This facility is also becoming available on small cars with engines below 1-litre capacity.

A general criticism which has been directed against all automatic gear-change systems concerns their inability to anticipate those situations which arise frequently on hilly or twisting roads, such as the need for a rapid change down for overtaking or for the negotiation of a fast bend. For this reason, some degree of over-riding manual control of the gears has usually been retained in the automatic systems used on British cars.

Automatic transmission systems fall generally into two classes, namely, those which utilize the automatic selection of gears in a fairly conventional gearbox, and those which employ a *torque converter* in conjunction with an automatic gearbox. In the first type, an example of which is the *Hydra-Matic* transmission, described in more detail below, the gearbox is of the epicyclic type, and the automatic locking of the appropriate annulus gears is carried out by a hydraulic servo mechanism; this is controlled by a device which is sensitive to engine speed, road speed, and throttle opening. In the torque converter transmission an epicyclic gearbox is again used, but in some cases this may only provide one intermediate gear ratio, direct drive and reverse gear. The range of torque multiplication which is obtained from a conventional gearbox is from 1 to 1 in top gear to about $3\frac{1}{2}$ to 1 in bottom gear, and this range is provided, in part, by the hydraulic torque converter, which resembles an elaborate fluid flywheel, see Fig. 65. An engine-driven impeller or *pumping-rotor* throws fluid into a turbine disc which drives the gearbox input shaft, the fluid then passing through a fixed blade system or *stator-ring* which re-directs it into the impeller; the re-direction of the fluid may be performed in stages by a split pumping-rotor/stator-ring system, the device then being known as a *polyphase* converter.

The property of the hydraulic or hydro-kinetic torque converter is that it causes the torque of the input shaft to be multiplied at the output shaft, to a degree which depends on the relative speeds of

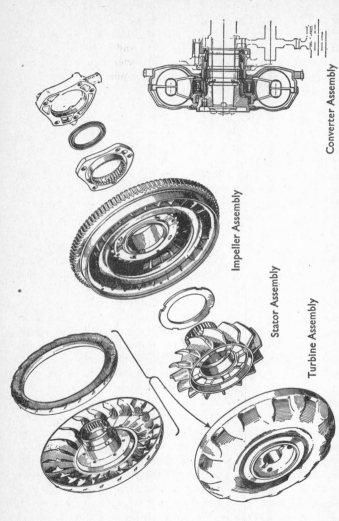

Impeller Assembly

Stator Assembly

Turbine Assembly

Converter Assembly

Fig. 65. Torque converter used in the Automotive Products/B.M.C. automatic transmission system. (*By courtesy of Automotive Products Co. Ltd*)

the two shafts. At *stalling-point*, i.e. with the output shaft stationary, the output torque is increased 2 to 2½ times, and as the output shaft gathers speed this magnification is reduced until, with the shafts running at almost equal speed, the input and output torques are also nearly equal. In other words, the converter simulates the effect of a conventional gearbox with an infinite number of ratios and changing gear as the circumstances demand. The range of torque conversion thus provided is sufficient for normal driving requirements, when used in conjunction with a suitably large engine, but for emergencies, such as moving away on a steep incline, the single gear ratio mentioned above is brought into action to supplement the converter, being engaged by manual selection. By this means, the overall torque range is increased to about 4 to 1. Some torque converter transmission systems are designed so that an intermediate gear is always used for moving off, the transition to direct drive being made automatically at an appropriate speed.

An additional refinement found in some torque converter systems, is a friction clutch which automatically 'locks up' or bypasses the converter and gearbox to give direct drive during top gear working conditions and thus eliminates 'churning' losses during the greater part of running time. These losses can be considerable, especially when the converter is working near stalling-point, and it is necessary to provide means for cooling the fluid; in some designs a water-cooled heat exchanger is used for this purpose.

HYDRA-MATIC TRANSMISSION SYSTEM

The American Hydra-Matic automatic gearbox was introduced in 1939 by General Motors, and a modified form of it is now manufactured in Britain by Messrs Rolls-Royce Ltd, and fitted as standard equipment on Rolls-Royce and Bentley cars (Plate 3). The system utilizes an epicyclic gearbox, having four forward and one reverse ratio, with a fluid coupling. The box contains three planetary gear trains, two of these each providing two forward ratios, and the third giving reverse gear. Each of the forward gear trains has a band brake operating on the annulus and a plate clutch to lock the train, both brake and clutch being hydraulically actuated. Reverse gear is brought into action by means of a cone clutch.

An interesting feature of this gearbox is that though the fluid coupling is located between the engine and the planetary units, torque from the engine actually passes through the front planetary unit before it reaches the fluid coupling. This characteristic has two advantages – the first of reducing the tendency of the car to 'creep' with the engine idling in first gear, and the second, in conjunction with the intermediate shaft of the gearbox, of reducing the power loss in the fluid coupling in third and fourth gears. In these gears the torque after passing through the first planetary unit to the intermediate shaft is divided, approximately 40 per cent passing forward to the fluid coupling, the remaining 60 per cent going to the rear clutch and thence to the rear annulus gear. That part of the torque transmitted by the fluid coupling is applied by the main shaft to the sun gear of the rear planetary unit. With torque applied in the direction of engine rotation to both the annulus and sun gear of the rear planetary unit, its planet carrier and the output shaft are carried round with the sum of the two applied torques. This 'Split Torque' characteristic results in far less slip in the fluid coupling than would be the case if the full engine torque passed through the fluid coupling, with a consequent increase in the gearbox efficiency.

The automatic selection of the gears is determined by a 'gear change control unit' mounted on the near-side of the gearbox (not shown in Plate 3); besides being supplied with oil under pressure from pumps driven by the input and output shafts, the unit is also connected to the throttle linkage and to a manual selector lever which is mounted on the steering column. The latter can be placed in five positions, N (Neutral), 4, 3, 2, and R (Reverse). The engine cannot be started unless the lever is in the neutral position. (If reverse gear is engaged whilst the car is stationary with the engine switched off, positive locking of the transmission is provided by means of a pawl engaging with a coarsely toothed wheel incorporated in the reverse gear train. This is used when the car is parked, the customary safeguard of leaving a car 'in gear' being ineffective when the transmission includes a fluid coupling.) The lever is moved to position 4, and depression of the accelerator causes the car to move off in first gear, the upward changes being made automatically. The actual speeds at which the changes occur vary according to the degree of throttle opening; for instance, if the accelerator is fully depressed the final change to top gear does not occur until 70 m.p.h. is reached. This feature is referred to by some as *throttle modulation*. Downward gear changes also occur automatically according to speed and throttle opening.

When the car is in top gear and not exceeding 68 m.p.h. the driver can change down to third gear by selecting position 3, and thereby obtain extra acceleration and hill climbing ability. However, if 75 m.p.h. is exceeded, top gear will re-engage automatically.

In position 2 second gear is held permanently up to maximum engine speed (45 m.p.h.). A further feature is the 'kick-down' device; full depression of the accelerator produces an immediate change down to third gear, if speed is below 68 m.p.h., or second gear below 25 m.p.h., thus providing increased acceleration for overtaking.

BORG-WARNER TRANSMISSION

Borg-Warner fully automatic transmission systems are of American origin and have been outstandingly successful in their adoption as optional or standard equipment on a wide range of European cars, including models by most of the major British manufacturers; in particular, the Borg-Warner Model 35 transmission has been developed for quantity production at a cost and weight such that it is a practical proposition for relatively small cars with four-cylinder engines of capacity as low as only 1 litre.

Borg-Warner transmissions employ a single-stage torque converter, giving a torque multiplication variable up to a maximum of about 2:1 at stall, in conjunction with an epicyclic gearbox giving two indirect forward ratios, 'direct' drive and reverse gear. An additional feature of the type of transmission used on some large cars is that in direct drive, which is in use during the greater part of normal driving, a plate clutch automatically couples the engine directly to the mainshaft of the gearbox, thus by-passing the torque converter and planetary gear sets; there are, therefore, negligible losses in the transmission when direct drive is in use.

The engine can only be started when the manual selector lever is at the N (Neutral) or P (Park) positions; in all other positions a starter inhibitor switch incorporated into the selector lever prevents operation of the engine starting circuit. In position P a mechanical parking pawl is engaged and locks the gearbox against rotation of the output shaft, thus duplicating the function of the conventional handbrake. For ordinary driving conditions, position D (Drive) is selected and on depressing the accelerator pedal the car moves away smoothly in the lower of the two indirect gear ratios. Changes into the intermediate gear ratio and top gear (direct drive) are made in succession automatically under the control of a governor device which is responsive to road speed, engine speed and the degree of throttle opening, gear changes occurring at relatively low speeds if pressure on the accelerator pedal is light and at high speeds for heavy pedal pressure. Downward gear changes occur automatically as road speed drops but can also be made at the will of the driver by a kick-down of the accelerator into what is termed the *forced throttle* position, unless road speed is so high that a change-down would cause overspeeding of the engine.

The control mechanism is so designed that there is a differential between the road speeds at which upward or downward changes occur for each ratio; this is called *shift speed hysteresis* and is incorporated to obviate the system 'hunting' in and out of a given gear ratio at certain critical road speeds. As an indication of the effects of throttle opening and hysteresis, the average speeds at which gear changes occur automatically in a typical Borg-Warner transmission for a family saloon car are given below:

Accelerator position	Upward Changes		Downward Changes	
	1st gear to 2nd gear	2nd gear to top gear	Top gear to 2nd gear	2nd gear to 1st gear
	m.p.h.	m.p.h.	m.p.h.	m.p.h.
Minimum throttle	4½	6½	—	2
7/8 throttle	22	35½	12½	2
Kick-down ('forced throttle', fully open)	33½	51	47	27

It will be noted that if the car is brought to a low speed in top gear the automatic change down is made directly to 1st gear, without passing through 2nd gear.

A further selector position is provided, this being L (Lock-up). This is for use in exceptional circumstances where automatic gear changes are not desirable, and it locks the transmission in 1st or 2nd gear, depending on road speed. This is a valuable feature in that it allows full use of engine braking for hill descents. By manipulation of the selector lever between the Lock-up and Drive positions it is possible for the driver to retain manual control over gear changes.

In some Borg-Warner transmissions for the more powerful cars two Drive positions are provided, identified as D2 and D1. With D2 selected, only second and top gears are operative and this position is used when the fierce acceleration of first gear is either not needed or would be hazardous because of road surface conditions. In the D1 position all three forward gears are operative.

Another special feature incorporated into some cars with Borg-Warner transmission is an *anti-creep* device. When the car is braked to rest on hills or at traffic-signals, for instance, the rear brakes are held on automatically by trapping of the hydraulic pressure in the brake lines, until such time as the accelerator pedal is again depressed.

ROOTES 'EASIDRIVE'

This two-pedal system was used for a time by Rootes Motors Ltd and is of interest in that it incorporated the Smiths automatic transmission, using magnetic powder couplings (see page 175). The latter are of a modified form in which a separate member driven by the engine rotates between a fixed outer part carrying the magnetizing coils, and the inner member which drives the gearbox. In effect, the rotating part is magnetized indirectly and no slip-rings are necessary to carry current to the coils.

Two couplings are used in conjunction with a three-speed and reverse layshaft gearbox of basically conventional layout. One coupling provides direct drive (Top gear); when the other coupling is energized it either drives through a constant-mesh gear train giving Low gear or through an alternative gear train, engaged by a solenoid-operated dog clutch, to give Intermediate gear. A free-wheel incorporated in the Low gear train allows the latter to be over-run when Intermediate gear is engaged. Reverse gear is engaged manually by sliding pinion.

Automatic engagement of the three forward gear ratios is controlled by a mechanically driven governor fitted with electrical contacts and working on much the same principle as a speedometer (see page 155). The governor is biased by a linkage to the accelerator pedal to vary the speeds at which gear changes occur, according to the driving technique. The transmission also permits the driver to select and hold Intermediate gear at will and provides 'kick-down' facilities for shifts from Top to Intermediate and from Intermediate to Low gear.

DAF VARIOMATIC TRANSMISSION

The *Variomatic* transmission (Fig. 66) fitted as standard by the Dutch firm of DAF (Van Doorne's Automobielfabriek) in their 'Daffodil' cars is a fully automatic system operating on quite different principles from those normally used. It provides a continuous range of ratios between 16·4:1 and 3·9:1, automatically adjusted in accordance with driving requirements by means of variable-diameter cone pulleys and flexible belt drive.

The drive is taken from the front-mounted engine by an automatic centrifugal clutch, which operates in two stages, to a 'power-divider'; this is a bevel gearbox which includes a simple sliding-dog clutch to allow the drive to be reversed when required. The power-divider carries on each side a large cone pulley, each pulley being split in two halves, one fixed and one sliding sideways; each sliding half-pulley is controlled by a built-in centrifugal device and by a vacuum chamber which can be connected to the engine manifold vacuum, or to a vacuum reservoir, or opened to atmosphere. Drive from the two pulleys is taken towards the rear by large vee-belts passing over two more cone pulleys which are also split, the halves being thrust together by spring pressure. The rear pulleys take the drive via reduction gears to the rear wheels, which are suspended by a type of swing-axle system.

When the car is at rest the halves of the front pulleys are at their widest spacing so that they present the smallest effective diameter

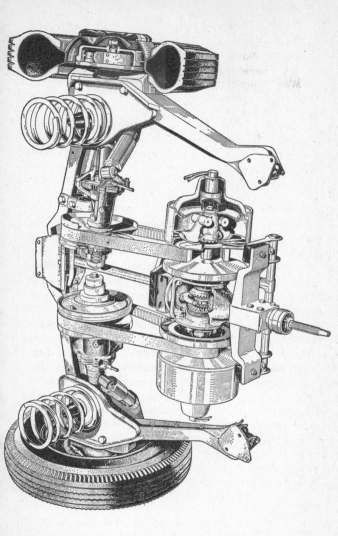

Fig. 66. The DAF *Variomatic* transmission system provides a continuously variable range of drive ratios by a combination of belts and split cone pulleys, controlled automatically by centrifugal and vacuum effects. (*By courtesy of Van Doorne's Automobielfabriek N.V.*)

to the belts, and the sprung rear pulley halves automatically push the belts outwards to the maximum diameter to give the correct belt tension, thus providing a low-ratio drive. When the engine is speeded up the centrifugal clutch engages and as the front pulleys gather speed the centrifugal device starts to pull the halves together, thus forcing the belts on to a larger diameter; this effect is aided by the vacuum chambers, the outer ends of which are automatically connected to the vacuum reservoir. The rear pulley halves are forced apart by the belt tension so that they present a smaller effective diameter and thus the drive ratio is gradually reduced and 'changes up' smoothly. For any steady accelerator position the drive will settle to the most economical engine speed as determined by the vacuum in the reservoir, so giving an automatic 'overdrive' effect.

If the accelerator is 'kicked down', the outer vacuum chambers are opened to atmosphere, thus collapsing the vacuum assistance and causing the driving pulleys suddenly to open out to a smaller diameter; this gives immediate availability of a lower ratio for acceleration. Also, if the accelerator is released the outer chambers are connected to atmosphere and the system gradually 'changes down'.

If the brakes are applied vigorously not only are the outer vacuum chambers opened to atmosphere but the inner ends of the chambers are also connected to the inlet manifold vacuum, which counteracts the centrifugal device and gives an immediate change-down to provide maximum engine braking effect. For hill descents a similar result can be obtained by operation of a hand control on the dashboard.

The Variomatic system also gives an automatic differential effect since the two pulley systems can operate at different ratios to give the necessary rear wheel speed difference for cornering; also, because the two systems are independent, slipping of one rear wheel does not affect power transmission by the other and thus a 'self-locking' differential effect is obtained.

AUTOMOTIVE PRODUCTS/B.M.C. TRANSMISSION

The automatic transmission developed by Automotive Products Company Ltd. in conjunction with the British Motor Corporation

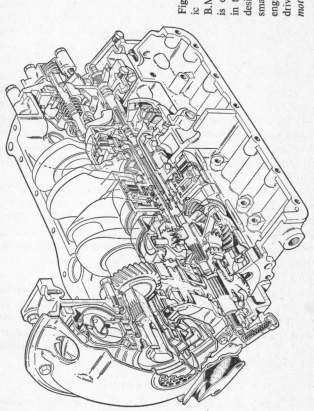

Fig. 67. The fully-automatic Automotive Products/B.M.C. transmission system is entirely contained within the engine outline; it is designed specifically for the small car with transverse engine and front-wheel drive. (*By courtesy of Automotive Products Co. Ltd*)

is of particular significance since it is specifically designed for integration with the transverse engine-cum-gearbox layout used on many B.M.C. models and is conceived for use with small engines in the 'mini' class.

Fig. 67 shows the lower half of an engine having this transmission contained within the crankcase, the layout resembling that of the usual B.M.C. front wheel drive 'manual' transmission (see Fig. 68). A torque converter (Fig. 65) is mounted directly on to the crankshaft in place of the normal flywheel and clutch, and the power is transmitted downwards by a gear-train to the variable-ratio gear system. The output is thence taken by final-drive gears to the usual differential and the output shafts; the power flow is shown diagrammatically in Fig. 69.

The four forward gear ratios (top gear being direct drive), and reverse, are provided by an extremely compact cluster of eight bevel pinions which make up two planetary gear sets, resembling two differentials, one built inside the other. The locking of the various elements to give the required gear ratios is achieved by three external-type brake bands and two multi-disc clutches operated in the appropriate combinations by hydraulic servo pistons.

The system can be used as a fully automatic transmission, with 'kick-down' facility to engage a lower ratio for greater acceleration, or the selector lever may be operated manually to engage and hold any of the gear ratios. The valve system directing the supply of hydraulic fluid to the brake band and clutch servos is controlled either by a mechanical governor for automatic gear shifts or directly by the selector lever for manual gear changing.

A high-output engine-driven pump circulates oil throughout the entire engine and transmission system for both lubrication and control purposes, also maintaining a low-pressure flow through the torque converter to dissipate the heat generated therein; an auxiliary pump driven from the output end of the system is provided to enable the transmission to operate for tow-starting, since the main pump is not delivering when the engine is not running.

HOBBS TRANSMISSION

This British two-pedal fully automatic transmission system is possibly unique in that it is entirely mechanical in operation; it

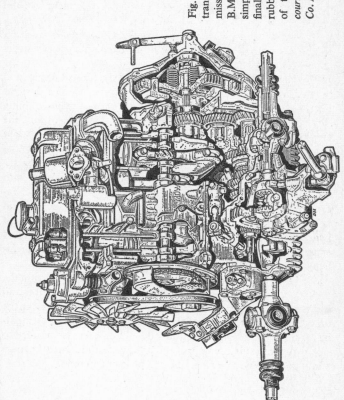

Fig. 68. The combined transverse engine and transmission system of the B.M.C. 'mini', showing the simple spur gears of the final drive and one of the rubber-bushed Hooke joints of the drive shafts. (*By courtesy of the Austin Motor Co. Ltd*)

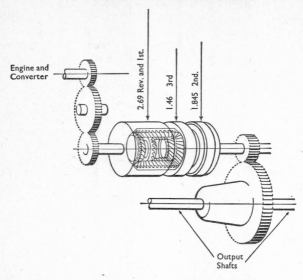

Fig. 69. Basic layout of the Automotive Products/B.M.C. automatic transmission system. (*By courtesy of Automotive Products Co. Ltd*)

makes no use of the vehicle electrical or vacuum systems and does not contain a hydraulic coupling or torque converter. Basically, it consists of a four-speed and reverse gearbox using planetary gear sets of the type shown in Fig. 128. These are controlled by three plate-type brakes and two clutches which are engaged as required by the admission of hydraulic pressure to flexible diaphragms. The automatic selection of gears is achieved by a hydraulic governor, with throttle bias and 'kick-down' facilities. In addition, over-riding provision is made for manual selection of any gear ratio. The Hobbs transmission was available as an alternative on certain cars, either as original equipment or as a conversion.

FREE WHEEL

The free wheel, so widely used on pedal cycles, has been fitted to some cars, notably by Rover. It is placed on the transmission between gearbox and final drive unit and is not a ratchet ('click') device but consists basically of a drum containing wedging rollers. The rollers jam into shaped recesses to provide a solid drive when the engine is pulling, but if the car tends to over-run the engine, the rollers are freed. Obviously then the effect of engine braking is lost and a hand control is provided to allow the driver to lock the free wheel if desired.

The free wheel allows the car to 'coast' economically and also permits 'clutchless' gear-changing under some conditions, since the gear teeth are relieved of load on the over-run.

CHAPTER SIX

POWER TRANSMISSION CONTINUED
FROM GEARBOX TO DRIVEN WHEELS

THE manner in which power is transmitted onwards from the gearbox to the driven wheels is determined largely by whether or not the road wheels are independently suspended. On a great many rear-driven cars they are not so, and are mounted, at the ends of a rigid axle casing, so that any up and down movement of one wheel necessarily affects the other.

There are basically two ways in which a rigid rear axle may be arranged. The more common of these is known as *Hotchkiss drive* (Fig. 70), in which the rear axle casing is suspended by leaf springs,

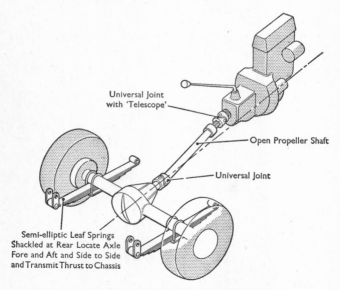

Fig. 70. *Hotchkiss drive*, in which leaf springs provide both springing and axle location.

1a. The Vauxhall Viva 'oversquare' 1057 c.c. engine (bore 74.3 mm, stroke 61.0 mm) uses inclined overhead valves operated by short push-rods and rockers. (*By courtesy of Vauxhall Motors Ltd*)

1b. This is the rear engine, transaxle and suspension of the Hillman 'Imp', in which power is taken forward to the gearbox and then back to the differential; drive is taken to the wheels by half-shafts with Metalastik 'doughnut' couplings at the inner ends and Hooke couplings at the outer ends. The wheel hubs are carried on massive trailing arms. (*By courtesy of Rootes Motors Ltd*)

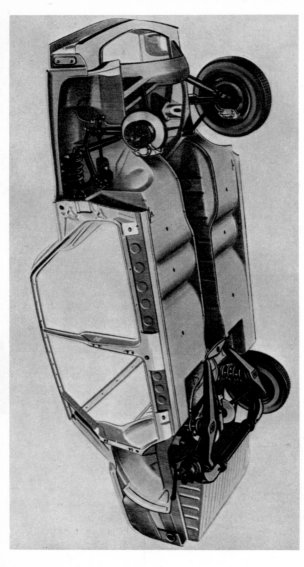

2. The partially-completed base unit of the Rover 2000, showing the layout of the suspension systems. (*By courtesy of The Rover Co. Ltd*)

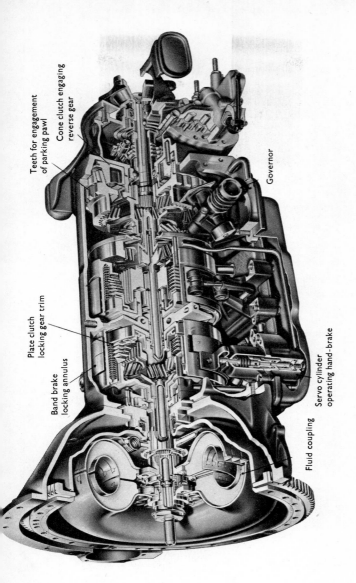

Teeth for engagement
of parking pawl

Cone clutch engaging reverse gear

Governor

Plate clutch
locking gear trim

Band brake
locking annulus

Servo cylinder
operating hand-brake

Fluid coupling

3. The Rolls-Royce form of the Hydra-Matic automatic gear box. (*By courtesy of Rolls-Royce Ltd*)

4a. Assembling a coach-built limousine body (Austin 'Princess'). (*By courtesy of Vanden Plas (England) 1923 Ltd*)

4b. Morris 'Oxford' Series V Traveller. (*By courtesy of the Nuffield Organization*)

5a. Jaguar 'E' type fixed-head coupé. (*By courtesy of Jaguar Cars Ltd*)

5b. Jaguar 'E' type open two-seater. (*By courtesy of Jaguar Cars Ltd*)

6a. Austin 'Princess' long wheelbase limousine. (*By courtesy of Vanden Plas (England) 1923 Ltd*)

6b. Sunbeam 'Rapier' two-door hard-top saloon.

7a. Morris 'Mini Minor' two-door saloon with 848 c.c. front engine driving front wheels. (*By courtesy of the Nuffield Organization*)

7b. Hillman 'Imp' two-door saloon with 875 c.c. rear engine driving rear wheels. (*By courtesy of Rootes Motors Ltd*)

8a. The Austin 1800 four-door saloon with transverse front engine driving front wheels. (*By courtesy of the Austin Motor Co. Ltd*)

8b. Bond 'Equipe GT 4.S', with fibreglass reinforced plastics bodywork. (*By courtesy of Fibreglass Ltd and Sharps Commercials Ltd*)

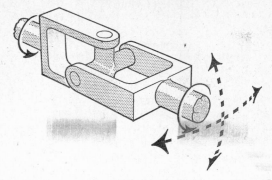

Fig. 71. In the simple Hooke (or Cardan) universal joint, the end of each shaft is forked and pivoted on a common cross-piece.

almost always of the *semi-elliptic* type. The transmission of power from the gearbox to the final drive is by means of a tubular *propeller shaft*; because the axle is able to move up and down relative to the chassis, whereas the gearbox remains fixed, it is necessary to provide means for accommodating the swing of the shaft whilst it is rotating. This is provided for by means of *universal joints* (u.j.'s) at each end of the propeller shaft. Fig. 71 shows the working principle of a universal joint, whilst Fig. 72 shows the well-known

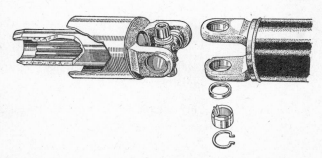

Fig. 72. Hardy Spicer universal joint with needle-roller bearings. (*By courtesy of Hardy Spicer Ltd*)

Hardy Spicer joint which utilizes needle-rollers to reduce friction.

The flexing of the semi-elliptic springs means that the distance between the gearbox and rear axle is always changing slightly, and this is allowed for by a splined telescopic joint at the forward end of the propeller shaft. The simple universal joint shown, known as a Hooke or Cardan joint, has an *inconstant velocity* characteristic, i.e. if one half of the joint is running at constant speed, the other half, when it is running at an angle, tends to 'flick' round. In this particular application, however, the angle between the line of the gearbox and the line of the propeller shaft is always so small as to make this effect unimportant. In cases where two shafts are revolving at considerable angles as in some front wheel drive arrangements, more complex universal joints of the *constant velocity* type are necessary. In the Hotchkiss drive arrangement the propeller shaft only performs in a rotating capacity. All the work of transmitting the forward thrust and also the rearward braking drag from the axle to the chassis is done by the leaf springs. The ability to act in the dual role of springing medium and suspension member is a primary reason for the retention of the somewhat antiquated 'cart spring'.

On some of the longer and more expensive cars with rear wheel drive from a front-mounted engine, a *divided propeller shaft* is used, having an additional resiliently-mounted universal joint near its centre. Advantages gained from this arrangement are that there is less tendency for the shaft to 'whip' and it also enables the shaft to follow a lower path, which reduces the intrusion of humps and tunnels into the floor space of the passenger compartment.

The modern leaf-spring has tended to lose any resemblance to the semi-elliptical shape. It is usually almost flat when loaded and may even take on a slight upward curve. The spring is slung underneath the axle and attached to it by means of U bolts. A typical spring consists of six steel leaves with three zinc interleaves; the spring has a reasonably controlled amount of friction between the leaves which gives it an inherent damping property. In some cases the spring is enclosed in a leather 'gaiter' to retain the grease and exclude grit.

The spring is attached to the chassis by the rolled ends of the longest leaf. Since the spring must be able to vary in length in order to flex, it is not possible to anchor both ends rigidly, and a typical practice is to 'hinge' the rear end by means of a *shackle* (Fig. 73). Usually this is of the rubber bush type which needs no lubrication. The change in length which occurs when a deeply curved spring flattens is one reason for the adoption of springs which are substantially flat under all conditions. It is clear that if one spring only were to 'lengthen' (for instance, with the weight thrown outwards on a bend), then the axle would become slightly askew, as seen in

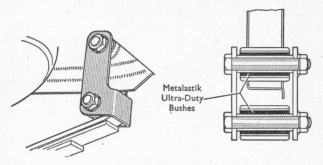

Metalastik
Ultra-Duty
Bushes

Fig. 73. Rear spring shackle with rubber bushes (Metalastik). (*By courtesy of Metalastik Ltd*)

plan, and would then be steering the rear end of the car. Fig. 74 shows how this would contribute to *oversteer* (see Chapter 7).

In order to combine soft suspension with adequate resistance to heavy loads the springs are sometimes reinforced with *helper leaves*. Fig. 75 shows how the additional leaf performs no function until the spring is loaded beyond the flat stage (i.e. has negative camber), when it reinforces the stiffness.

The second and rarely used method of rigid axle suspension is that known as *torque tube* drive. It differs from Hotchkiss drive in that the leaf spring is used only for the purpose of springing, the location of the axle being maintained by *radius* rods which, together with the axle, form a triangle. The propeller shaft rotates within the torque tube, which is rigidly attached to the axle casing and hinged by a ball-joint at the rear of the gearbox. The *transverse leaf spring*, placed above the axle, is most often used with torque

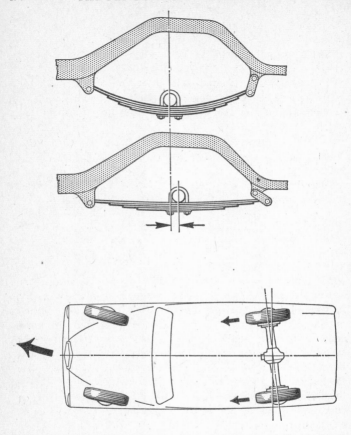

Fig. 74. When a leaf spring with positive camber is flattened under load, it 'lengthens', and the axle is moved slightly rearwards.

Since load is transferred to the outside wheel during a turn, the lengthening of the spring may cause the rear axle to 'skew' and so steer the car into a sharper turn than that determined by the attitude of the front wheels, this being termed *roll oversteer*. (In the latest arrangements the spring is given negative camber and forward slope, with the axle placed forward of the spring centre, in order to promote *roll understeer*.)

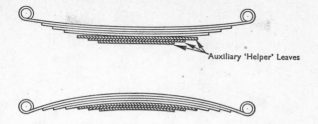

Fig. 75. Progressive Leaf Spring.

When the spring is only partially loaded the auxiliary leaves are inactive.

When the same spring is fully loaded, the auxiliary leaves come into full contact and stiffen the spring.

tube drive. It is worth noting that if a semi-elliptic transverse spring is used it must be shackled at *both* ends in order to allow symmetrical flattening of the spring under load; this means that the axle is not positively located laterally. For this reason a *Panhard* rod is sometimes used with this type of suspension; this is simply an arm with one end hinged to the side of the chassis and the other end hinged to the opposite end of the axle casing (Fig. 76), thus limiting sideways movement of the axle. The Panhard rod should not be confused with the *anti-roll* or *anti-sway* bar, often used in the front suspension and sometimes on the rear axle. This is a spring-steel bar which is attached, through rubber bushes, to the underside of the body, with its ends bent round and connected to the ends of the axle. If the body simply moves up and down the bar has no effect, but if the body tends to roll to one side the bar is twisted and resists the roll (Fig. 91).

Shock absorbers (spring dampers) of a similar pattern to those used in the front suspension (see Chapter 7) are used on the rear springs. If of the telescopic pattern they are sometimes tilted inwards so that they resist more directly any tendency towards sideways roll.

Besides the possible movements of the axle already mentioned there are other less obvious tendencies. Firstly, the driving torque at the road-wheels induces a reaction which tends to twist the axle

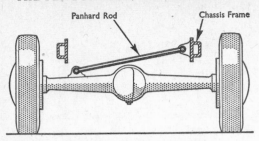

Panhard Rod   Chassis Frame

Fig. 76. The purpose of a *Panhard Rod* is to restrict sideways movement of the axle.

bodily. In the Hotchkiss drive this is readily resisted by 'wind-up'
of the springs and it is rigidly opposed in the torque-tube arrangement. However, it has to be catered for by specific means in certain
other suspension systems. A second and more obscure tendency
is concerned with reaction at the crown wheel and pinion in the
final drive unit (see later in this chapter). When accelerating there
is a reaction which tends to twist the entire rear axle assembly
about the longitudinal axis of the car. This means that one road
wheel tends to 'lift', so that if the torque is sufficiently great and
the load on the rear wheels is comparatively small, that wheel
may spin. In certain sports/racing cars using rigid back-axles it
has been necessary to make special provision against this occurring, since it can seriously affect the 'standing start' performance.

THE REAR AXLE

As stated previously in Chapter 5, the rear axle assembly has
several functions to perform, which may be summarized as follows:

(1) To carry the rear road wheels.
(2) To gear down the drive from the gearbox and to turn this drive
through a right angle.
(3) To transmit the power to the rear wheels.
(4) To compensate, by means of a differential gear, for the difference in speed of the inner and outer wheels when traversing a
curve.

We have already seen the different ways in which the rear axle may be suspended, and the methods used to transmit the drive from the gearbox. In the majority of cars the propeller shaft lies along the centre line of the car and the rear axle gearing is enclosed in a 'swelling' or *banjo* at the centre of the axle casing. However, in certain cases the banjo may be offset to one side or the other.

The necessary speed reduction and change in direction of the drive is obtained by a simple gearing as shown in Fig. 77. At one time the expensive worm drive was used, but it is rarely found nowadays other than on certain models by Peugeot. The two usual forms of gearing are the *spiral bevel* and the *hypoid bevel* (i.e. hyper-

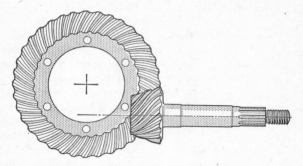

Fig. 77. Hypoid-bevel crown-wheel and pinion, in which the teeth are specially shaped so that the gears can mesh off-centre, thus permitting a low propeller shaft line.

boloid), a small toothed wheel or *pinion*, rotated by the propeller shaft, engaging with a large *crown-wheel*. The teeth on the crown-wheel and pinion (c.w.p.) are curved, so that the load is transferred smoothly and quietly from one tooth to the next. In the case of the spiral bevel the pinion engages at a point level with the centre of the crown-wheel, whilst with hypoid bevel gears engagement occurs below the centre line. Hypoid bevel gearing thus permits the lowering of the line of the propeller shaft and minimizes the extent to which its 'tunnel' obstructs the floor of the passenger compartment.

In either type of final drive gearing the pressures occurring between the teeth are very high and require special lubricants. In the spiral bevel type the action occurring between the teeth is largely 'rolling' and *extreme pressure* (*e.p.*) oil is used; with hypoid gears there is also a degree of sliding of one tooth over another, and it is essential that a special 'hypoid' lubricant should be used in this type of axle.

The gear ratio of the crown-wheel and pinion is of the order of 4 to 1 and is not normally variable unless the axle is stripped and the gears replaced. The ratio is sometimes quoted as the relative numbers of teeth on pinion and crown-wheel, for example 10:41 (ratio 4·1 to 1). The ratio is determined initially by the designer, having regard to the gearbox ratios, engine characteristics, and the type of car. On a small saloon the ratio would be about 4·75 to 1, which would provide a reasonable performance at low road speed in direct drive. However, top speed would be limited because the maximum speed of the engine would soon be reached with this axle ratio. Therefore it is sometimes considered advantageous to equip the gearbox with an 'overdrive top' gear, not so much to increase maximum road speed as to reduce the rate of engine rotation when cruising under light conditions.

On more powerful cars the additional low speed torque permits a higher axle ratio, say 4 to 1, without sacrificing top gear flexibility, whilst on a competition car the ratio may be as high as 3·5 to 1; this allows of very high road speeds without overspeeding the engine, the extensive use of the closely spaced intermediate gear ratios compensating for the reduced top gear performance at low engine speed. Some makes of sports cars are offered with a choice of back axle ratio, according to whether the car is required for touring or competition motoring.

OVERALL GEAR RATIO

The relation between the rotational speed of the engine and that of the driven wheels is given by the *overall gear ratio*. This is found by multiplying each gearbox ratio in turn by the crown-wheel and pinion ratio. For instance, taking our example gearbox (page 166) used with a final-drive unit in which the pinion has 12 teeth and the crown-wheel 48 teeth (ratio 4 to 1), we have:

	Gearbox Ratio	Final-Drive Ratio	Overall Ratio
1st gear	3·5 to 1	4 to 1	14 to 1
2nd gear	1·5 to 1	4 to 1	6 to 1
Top gear	1 to 1	4 to 1	4 to 1
Reverse gear	4·04 to 1	4 to 1	16·16 to 1

When, as in this case, top gear is given by direct drive, the overall top gear ratio is that of the crown-wheel and pinion; however, if an 'overdrive top' gearbox is used, as on the Volkswagen, the final drive ratio (4·38 to 1) does not necessarily appear in the overall gear ratio figures, which in this case are:

	Gearbox Ratio	Overall Ratio
1st gear	3·80 to 1	16·65 to 1
2nd gear	2·06 to 1	9·02 to 1
3rd gear	1·32 to 1	5·78 to 1
Top gear	0·89 to 1	3·90 to 1

(There is no direct drive in this particular gearbox.)

The relation between engine speed and road speed is, of course, dependent upon the effective size of the tyres. It is usual to state this relationship as 'miles per hour per thousand r.p.m. of engine speed, in top gear', and this assumes that standard size wheels and tyres are used. Speeds obtained in practice may be influenced by such factors as tyre 'growth' (under centrifugal force) and wheel slip.

THE DIFFERENTIAL

The drive from the centre of the back axle is taken to each road wheel by a *half-shaft* which revolves within the axle casing. The inner ends of the half-shafts cannot be attached directly to the crown-wheel, owing to the necessity for differential gearing (Figs. 78 and 79). It will be seen that the crown-wheel is in the form of a ring bolted to a carrier or *cage* on which are mounted two (or, in some cases, three or four) small bevel gears known as *star pinions*. These pinions are sandwiched between larger bevel gears

splined to the inner ends of the half shafts (Fig. 78). The action of
this apparently complicated arrangement may best be understood
by examining Fig. 79b which shows a plan view of the two half-
shaft bevels and one star pinion only. The star pinion is being
carried forward by the rotation of the crown-wheel and, as long as
there is no tendency for either half-shaft to 'lag behind', then the
function of the star pinion is simply as a 'bridge piece'. That is,

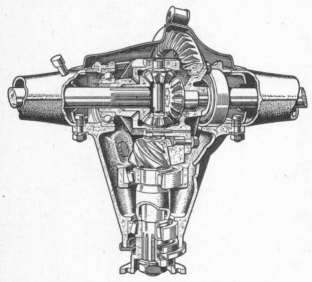

Fig. 78. Complete final-drive unit. (*By courtesy of the Austin Motor Co.
Ltd*)

the heavily lined portion in Fig. 79b may be regarded as a solid
bar with the points A, B, and C moving forward together. However, if one half-shaft tends to lag then the point A will trail
behind and the pinion will start to revolve slowly about its centre
B while the point C moves forward. It can be shown that the *average* speed of the two half-shaft bevels is the same as the crown-
wheel speed. In the extreme case, with one half-shaft locked, the
point A will be stationary, and for any distance moved forward by

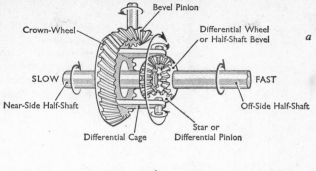

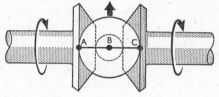

Fig. 79 Basis of the Differential.

During straight running both half-shafts revolve at the same speed as the crown-wheel. The star or differential pinions remain stationary on their own spindles and merely serve to bridge the differential wheels. On a left-hand curve the near-side half-shaft slows down but the differential cage continues to revolve at the same speed. The star pinions therefore rotate on their own spindles and impart additional speed to the off-side differential wheel.

the centre B the point C moves twice as far, i.e. the right-hand half-shaft revolves twice as fast as the crown-wheel. Conversely, if one road wheel is able to slip, on boggy ground for instance, it may revolve at twice crown-wheel speed while the other road wheel remains stationary. For this reason some heavy vehicles are fitted with a device enabling the differential gear to be locked so that both half-shafts revolve together as a solid axle.

Some of the more powerful touring cars, and, of course, racing cars, in which high engine torque is combined with relatively low weight on the driving wheels, are fitted with *limited slip* differentials.

If a conventional differential is fitted to such a car, the loss of drive due to one wheel slipping would not only impair get-away at starting but would also adversely affect the practice of *four-wheel drifting*, which involves deliberate spinning of the driven wheels. The Salisbury *Powr-Lok* is an example of a limited slip differential, in which the differential action essential for traversing curves is preserved in the normal way but in which the half-shaft bevel gears are artificially loaded by means of friction clutches built into the differential mechanism between the rear face of each gear and the cage. Consider again the extreme case in which one road-wheel is entirely clear of the ground; the crown wheel rotates the cage and the 'free' half-shaft would normally rotate at twice the cage speed with the other half-shaft and its bevel pinion remaining stationary and no torque could be transmitted. Note that the 'free' half-shaft is revolving faster than the differential cage but if its rotation relative to the cage is partially braked by the friction clutch between its bevel pinion and the cage, it now becomes possible for torque to be transmitted to the other bevel pinion and road wheel. In the Powr-Lok differential the basic clutch loading is provided by dished springs incorporated into the clutches but the loading is also increased as torque increases, due partly to the tendency for the bevel pinions to be forced apart by the star pinions under load and also because of the special method of mounting the star pinions within the cage.

The function of the limited slip differential is to so proportion the input torque that at all times the road wheel having the greater adhesion transmits the greater portion of the torque, thus controlling wheel spin.

MOUNTING OF THE ROAD WHEELS

In considering the methods used to mount the road wheels upon the rear axle it must be appreciated that they have several duties to perform; not only must the wheels carry the driving torque but they must also support the downward load of the rear of the car and resist sideways thrust due to centrifugal force or striking obstructions.

Ideally, the rear wheel should rotate on bearings outside the axle

casing, with the half-shaft driving the wheel through a splined connexion. This arrangement, known as a *fully floating axle*, is rarely
used because of its cost, but it has the advantage that the half-shaft
does not carry any vertical or side loads, merely serving to transmit driving torque to the wheel.

In the more common *three-quarter floating axle* the outer end of
the half shaft is shaped to form a mounting plate for the road
wheel, but the vertical load is taken by a single bearing placed over
the axle casing (Fig. 81).

Another popular arrangement is known as *semi-floating*, and
here the entire load is taken on the half-shaft bearings which are
located within the axle casing (Fig. 82).

The wheel bearings themselves are of the ball or roller type. The
hub invariably incorporates some kind of oil-seal which prevents
lubricant from leaking out on to the brake linings.

INDEPENDENT REAR SUSPENSION (I.R.S.)

The classic system of mounting the rear wheels at the ends of a
rigid axle has numerous advantages in that it ensures that the
wheels are maintained parallel to each other and fundamentally
perpendicular to the road surface whilst providing a convenient
support for the wheel bearings and a means of accommodating the
drive shafts; the axle casing also serves to transmit driving, braking and cornering forces to the car structure via the suspension
system. This method of construction is well understood and relatively cheap because of its simplicity and basic standardization.
Nevertheless, it also has certain drawbacks and there are cases
where it cannot be used conveniently. It introduces a considerable
weight which is *unsprung*, that is, which moves up and down with
the wheels so that its inertia compared with that of the sprung
main structure permits road shocks to be transmitted to the car as
a whole; also, the 'lever' effect of the axle tends to cause the vehicle
to tilt bodily sideways if one wheel is lifted by a bump (see Fig. 86
for the equivalent effect in the front wheel suspension). In rear-
engined cars the short length available for drive shafts makes it
virtually impossible to use a rigid axle.

For these reasons, *independent rear suspension* (*i.r.s.*) is the rule for rear-engined cars and it is becoming common on cars of other-wise 'conventional' layout; it should be borne in mind that in an i.r.s. system the wheel suspension arrangement has to meet basic requirements in respect of wheel attitude, torque transmission and thrust loading and the problem of achieving this at a reasonable cost has delayed the introduction of i.r.s. on medium-priced cars.

There are a variety of ways in which the rear wheels can be in-dependently suspended but they tend to share common features; especially important is the mounting of the differential unit directly on the car structure so that it forms part of the sprung mass, thus achieving the desired reduction in un-sprung weight. It is also possible further to reduce the un-sprung weight by placing the brakes *inboard* at each side of the differential unit though this introduces other problems of cooling and of access for servicing, and also means that braking torque must be transmitted from the brakes to the wheels via the half-shafts.

One of the earliest forms of i.r.s. is that known as *swing-axle*; this can be visualized as a normal back axle with the outer parts of the casing hinged each side of the final drive housing. Clearly, as each wheel moves up or down it changes its *camber*, that is, its angle of inclination to the vertical, in a way similar to that in divided-axle front wheel suspension (Fig. 87a); since change in camber alters the resistance of the wheel to side-slip the use of swing-axle suspension does not always confer the best of handling qualities under extreme conditions.

Somewhat more elaborate i.r.s. systems are used, in which the geometry is designed to produce predicted changes of wheel cam-ber to give the desired handling characteristics under all condi-tions. An example is shown in Fig. 80; the wheel revolves on a stub-axle supported in a hub-carrier which is linked to the final drive casing by the lower arm, pivoted at both ends. The Cardan shaft, transmitting drive to the stub-axle, is of fixed length and is provided with a Hooke-type universal joint at each end; the shaft also acts as the upper link of the suspension system. Springing is by means of a *spring strut*, comprised of a telescopic damper sur-rounded by a coil spring. Not shown in the illustration is a further pivoted link running forward from the outer end of the lower arm to the car structure, to maintain the fore-and-aft location of the

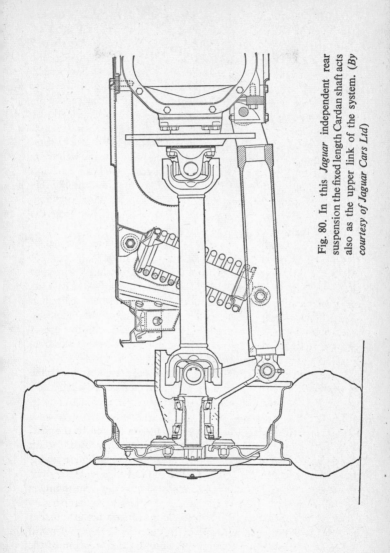

Fig. 80. In this *Jaguar* independent rear suspension the fixed length Cardan shaft acts also as the upper link of the system. (*By courtesy of Jaguar Cars Ltd*)

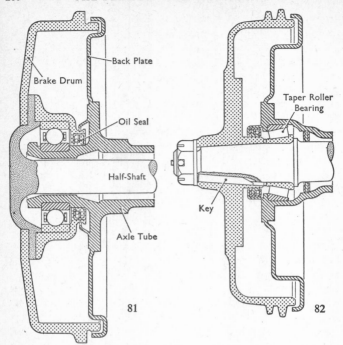

Fig. 81. In a *three-quarter floating* axle the axle tube is extended and the bearing is mounted on the *outside* of the tube. The end of the half-shaft is shaped to form a hub and is 'returned' to house the outer bearing race. (Cross-hatched parts remain stationary.)

Fig. 82. In a *semi-floating* axle the bearing is housed within the axle tube and vertical loads are borne directly in the half-shaft. In this example the wheel hub is keyed to the half-shaft on a taper fitting. (*Based on drawings supplied by Salisbury Transmission Ltd*)

wheel; the braking disc can be seen mounted inboard, adjacent to the final drive unit.

An example of a type of independent rear suspension used in a rear-engined car is shown in Plate 1b; the road wheels are again supported on hub carriers which are mounted on massive trailing arms with widely spaced pivot points. Drive is transmitted to each hub by a fixed length shaft with a Hooke-type universal joint at the outer end but with a Metalastik *Rotoflex* flexible coupling at the inner end. The latter is sometimes called a 'doughnut' coupling and comprises a bonded rubber and steel 'ring' with a three-armed spider bolted to each side; it acts as a universal joint for small angular misalignments, with a slight degree of endways flexibility, and has the ability to absorb transmission shocks and vibration but requires no lubrication since it has no parts subject to wear. The suspension operates against upright coil springs accommodated in pockets in the links; drum-type brakes are mounted outboard, within the roadwheels. The power path may be deduced from the illustration, the drive being taken forward to the gearbox and then back to the final drive unit. The entire transmission system is built up as a single assembly, referred to as a *transaxle*.

The Ford 'Zephyr' i.r.s. is another example of the use of semi-trailing wishbones but the drive-shafts are of fixed length (to avoid the need for sliding splines in the universal joints) and a novel method is used to accommodate the resulting small sideways movements of the wheel hubs as they rise and fall; the inner ends of the transverse limbs of the wishbones are mounted on short shackles, similar to those used with leaf springs, which allow the wishbones to swing sideways by a small amount. In the Ford system the suspension and final drive is mounted on a sub-frame which is in turn attached to the car by rubber mountings to minimize the transmission of road noise to the bodywork.

Cars with front wheel drive usually have their rear wheels independently suspended but since, of course, no power transmission is involved, the suspension is commonly a simple form of trailing link (see Chapter 7).

DE DION SUSPENSION

A method of rear wheel suspension used on racing cars, but only rarely on touring cars, makes use of the De Dion axle (Fig. 83), which dates back to early motoring history. This is usually in the form of a large tube which passes across the car either in front or behind the final drive unit, and has its ends rigidly attached to the

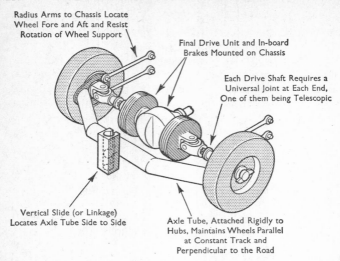

Radius Arms to Chassis Locate
Wheel Fore and Aft and Resist
Rotation of Wheel Support

Final Drive Unit and In-board
Brakes Mounted on Chassis

Each Drive Shaft Requires a
Universal Joint at Each End,
One of them being Telescopic

Vertical Slide (or Linkage)
Locates Axle Tube Side to Side

Axle Tube, Attached Rigidly to
Hubs, Maintains Wheels Parallel
at Constant Track and
Perpendicular to the Road

Fig. 83. Use of the *De Dion rear axle* results in a reduction in unsprung weight since final-drive unit and brakes are mounted on the chassis. In the form shown it does not provide independent suspension of the wheels.

road wheel hubs. The tube can move up and down but is constrained from moving from side to side, often by a swinging link system or by a ball sliding in a vertical guide. The tube performs the same function as the outer casing of a rigid axle, i.e. it supports the wheels, and maintains them at constant *track* (distance apart) and at right-angles to the road. The drive is taken to the hubs by means of Cardan shafts from the rigidly mounted final drive unit and the hubs are prevented from twisting by means of pairs of parallel radius arms which run forwards (or backwards) to hinge points on the chassis.

In this form, the De Dion axle does *not* provide independent suspension, but it does enable a big reduction in unsprung weight to be made and obviates wheel-lift due to torque reaction. However, a De Dion system can be made to give more nearly independent suspension by *articulating* the main tube, as in the Rover 2000

(Fig. 84). In the latter case the splines in the drive shafts, which normally tend to introduce unwanted friction when attempting to slide endways whilst transmitting torque, are omitted; this means that allowance must be made for the slight 'change in length' effect of the shafts as they move up or down and so the De Dion tube is divided near the centre and provided with a large telescopic joint. This joint also allows rotational movement of the two parts

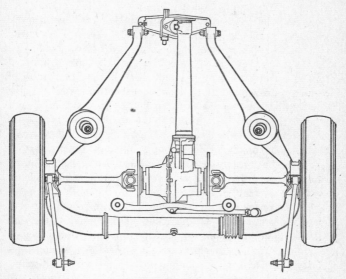

Fig. 84. The De Dion tube incorporating a sliding joint. (*By courtesy of the Rover Co. Ltd and the Iliffe Marketing Co. Ltd*)

of the tube relative to each other to take up slight differences in the attitudes of the respective hub carriers. The telescopic joint is only required to accommodate small movements and can be made relatively friction-free. Articulated De Dion suspension does not give constant track but it still provides the important features of maintaining the wheels vertical and parallel, and minimizes unsprung weight.

FRONT WHEEL DRIVE

Front wheel drive has been used in conjunction with a front-mounted engine for many years, notably by Citroen; it has come into greater prominence in recent years with the introduction of the British Motor Corporation range of cars, starting with the 'mini', having engines mounted transversely, this trend being followed by other manufacturers.

A front wheel drive system is arranged in basically the same way as a rear-engined car, the gearbox and final drive arrangements being built 'in unit' with the engine, with power transmitted to the road wheels by universally-jointed shafts, but with the additional problem that the joints at the road wheels have to be capable of operating satisfactorily at the large angles of displacement arising when the wheels are turned for steering. The joints at the inner ends of the shafts have only to operate at the small angular deflections which occur due to wheel suspension movements and they can be of the simple Hooke type, for example, but at the outer ends they must be of the constant-velocity type otherwise a 'flicking' effect will occur when the wheels are turned to full steering lock. In B.M.C. front wheel drive cars the inner joints are similar in appearance to the normal Hooke type but the centre cross-piece is of rubber reinforced with steel and anchored to each side of the joint by U-bolts, providing a slightly flexible coupling requiring no lubrication. The outer joints are the *Birfield-Rzeppa* constant-velocity type. The Rzeppa coupling is essentially a ball-and-socket joint in which the drive between ball and socket is transmitted through a ball-race built into the coupling. The constant-velocity characteristic is obtained by ensuring that the ball-race always takes up a position exactly bisecting the angle of deflection of the coupling; in the original Rzeppa design this was achieved by a guide pin controlling the angle of the ball-race cage but in the Birfield version the same effect is secured without the use of the guide pin by precise shaping of grooves in the ball and socket which control the positions taken up by the ball bearings.

A particularly important feature of the B.M.C. transverse engine arrangement (Fig. 68) is that the whole of the transmission system, including the 'gearbox', final reduction gears and differential, is incorporated into a single unit with the engine, a common lubricating oil supply being used throughout. This results in an incomparably compact layout, and since the line of drive is parallel with the crankshaft the final drive can comprise a simple pair of helical gears which involve neither the loss of power or the need for special lubricants arising with the bevel or worm gears used in conventional arrangements where the line of drive has to be taken through a right angle.

CHAPTER SEVEN

THE CHASSIS

In the early days of automobile development, when almost every car was a unique model, it was necessary that the basis of the car should be a framework to which the various components could be attached and subsequently modified as required.

The traditional construction of the car was therefore based on a *chassis frame*, originally of timber reinforced with steel plates and subsequently of steel channels. Once the wheels were attached to this frame the whole formed a conveniently mobile carriage, which with the addition of engine, transmission, and steering, became a roadworthy vehicle, the bodywork being added later as a separate construction. The carriage unit, i.e., the car, complete apart from its bodywork, is known as the *chassis*. The system of building a chassis and then fitting it with suitable coachwork is quickly becoming restricted to the more expensive cars, often supplied in chassis form to specialist coachbuilders, and to sports and racing car construction. Commercial vehicles also are almost invariably built as separate chassis, and indeed these may often be seen on the road in this form, on the way from manufacturer to coachbuilder. However, the majority of modern production cars are built to an entirely different system, known as unit or integral construction, and a more detailed description of this will be found in Chapter 8. Basically it implies that the body is made rigid enough, by the use of a welded assembly of steel pressings, to perform the functions of both coachwork and chassis frame.

THE MODERN CHASSIS FRAME

When a separate chassis is used nowadays it is usually composed of steel girders of 'channel' or 'box section' with welded cross-members and body supports, etc. Often, a cross-shaped bracing is used at the centre-section, producing what is known as a cruciform chassis frame. The main side members of the frame are swept upwards at the back to clear the rear axle. For maximum rigidity, these main girders must be made as deep as possible, and obviously, apart from the disadvantage of added weight, this increases the overall height of the car. On some cars this has been overcome by bringing the side-members to the full width of the body and lowering the floor of the passenger compartment between them. This necessitates a 'step-down' at the doors. Incidentally, this deep door sill is also a feature of certain unit-construction cars.

There are many variations on the girder chassis frame, including the 'A' frame, of pre-war Austin Seven fame, and the development of the cruciform principle by Lagonda in which the crossbracing becomes the main chassis member.

Special sports and racing car chassis frames are often constructed from steel tubes with two large-diameter, but thin-walled, tubes as the main members; these are united by a number of cross-members to form a 'ladder' frame. Also widely used in sports cars is the 'space' frame, composed of a large number of small tubes welded together to form a basket-like structure.

A type of construction which has been used particularly on the Continent is the 'backbone' frame which uses a single tubular member as the central foundation of the car. This again suffers from disadvantages regarding the mounting of the body and engine, etc. It will be seen that the steel floor pressing of an integral construction car combines with the transmission tunnel to form a type of 'backbone'; in fact, the replacement of a separate girder frame by the provision of channel sections pressed into a steel floor was one phase in the development of unit construction proper. In the rear-engined Volkswagen a complete steel underpan forms the foundation of the car, but there is, of course, no propeller-shaft in this case.

Springing

Obviously it is not practicable to attach the road-wheels directly to the chassis frame or body-construction, since major shocks, caused by road surface variations, would be transmitted immediately to the vehicle and its occupants. It is the prime function of the wheel suspension and springing arrangements to absorb these shocks and to allow the car to proceed on a level course regardless of road conditions. Ideally, when a wheel strikes a bump in the road the wheel should be thrown upwards and its energy entirely absorbed by the suspension system. The extent to which this occurs in practice depends very largely upon the weight of the wheel and its appendages, relative to the weight of the car, and in general these components are made as light as possible by such means as the use of small wheels and, in extreme cases, by mounting the brake drums on the chassis instead of on the wheels. Such measures are expressed in general terms as 'reduction of un-sprung weight'.

To appreciate the advances made in suspension systems it is only necessary to watch old and new cars taking a bumpy stretch of road at a fair speed. The front end of the older car will be thrown bodily upwards by a bump, or drop heavily into a pot-hole, whilst the wheels of the modern car 'flip' up and down the irregularities without seriously affecting the ride. Incidentally, whenever we are considering a suspension system it is helpful to imagine the wheels moving relative to the car, rather than to think of the car springing up and down on its wheels.

TYPES OF SPRINGING

Before we actually consider the manner in which the wheels are attached it will be as well to review the various types of spring in current use.

We have already come across the laminated or leaf spring in Chapter 6, where we saw that it is almost universally used for the rear springing. Most pre-war cars also used half-elliptic leaf springs at the front, either mounted in a similar manner to those at the back, or arranged across the car, i.e., transversely. The latter method is a particular feature of the older Ford designs.

There are two other types of 'conventional' spring which are widely used. These are the torsion-bar and the coil or helical spring.

The torsion-bar consists of a straight steel rod which may be either tubular or solid, or built up from several leaves into a bar which is square in cross-section (Fig. 85). The springing effect is obtained by holding one end of the rod and twisting the other. The coil-spring is quite familiar, and may be thought of as a torsion-bar 'wound up'.

Other forms of spring which have been adopted quite recently

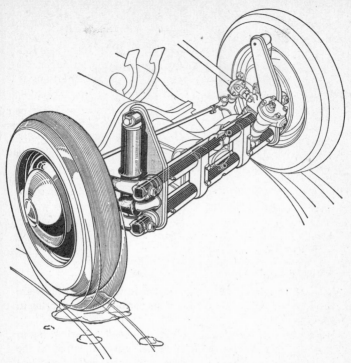

Fig. 85. The independent front suspension of the Volkswagen is by trailing arms with square-section laminated torsion bar springs. (*By courtesy of Volkswagenwerk G.m.b.H.*)

are the rubber spring, which utilizes rubber either to resist twisting or squeezing, and the pneumatic type, which employs the 'springiness' of air in compression. Both types provide soft suspension under low deflection but stiffen up rapidly under heavier loads.

INDEPENDENT FRONT SUSPENSION

On the majority of cars built before about 1948 the front wheels are mounted at the ends of a beam axle which couples them rigidly together, giving 'non-independent' suspension. This arrangement has several disadvantages including the high unsprung weight of the beam and a tendency for gyroscopic interaction between the wheels to set up wheel wobble or 'shimmy'. Also, the beam occupies valuable space and it acts as a lever tilting the whole car if one wheel is lifted by a bump (Fig. 86).

Much of the improvement in the ride of modern cars can be attributed to the almost universal adoption of independent front suspension (i.f.s.). This arrangement implies that each front wheel is separately hinged so that up or down movement of one does not directly affect the other (Fig. 86b). The manner in which this is

Fig. 86. Effect of bump on a vehicle with
a. Beam axle *b*. Independent front suspension

achieved varies widely amongst different makes, and some of the arrangements are shown in Fig. 87. The simplest method is to cut the normal beam axle at the centre and place the cut ends on a hinge, this being known as 'divided axle' suspension (or 'knock-kneed'). It has disadvantages which are discussed later, not the least of these being that the unsprung weight is not reduced significantly, although the independent effect is achieved.

A very common arrangement of i.f.s. is that known as 'unequal links', used with either coil or torsion-bar springs. When it was first generally employed in the late thirties, being then known as 'knee action' springing, or 'wishbone' suspension, the links were massive forgings and vaguely resembled wishbones in shape.

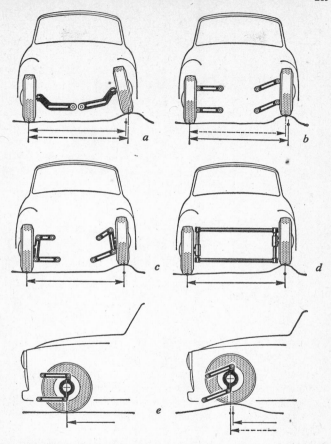

Fig. 87. Effect of bump on some types of independent front suspension.

a. Divided axle – change in track and wheel camber.

b. Equal upper and lower links – change in track, not wheel attitude.

c. Unequal upper and lower links – no change in track but slight change in wheel camber.

d. Vertical slide – no change in track, wheelbase, or wheel attitude.

e. Trailing Link – slight change in wheelbase, but track and wheel attitude unaffected.

Modern designers have found that lighter links are both desirable and satisfactory, so that in modern versions the upper links are often part of the shock-absorber arrangements and the lower links are often assembled from steel pressings. In some cases the upper link has been reduced to a single arm, with the lower 'wishbone' spread out to form a wide-base triangle, this arrangement being better able to resist braking and accelerating forces.

Another popular arrangement of i.f.s., used by Aston Martin and Volkswagen, amongst others, is the 'trailing-arm' suspension developed by the late Dr Porsche (Fig. 85). The reverse of this, but using only one 'leading-arm' and known as Dubonnet suspension, was used on certain Vauxhall cars and also as a means of converting existing beam axles to i.f.s.

Whatever i.f.s. arrangement is used it should be designed so that, as the wheels rise and fall, the distance between them, at the road surface, does not alter, i.e. constant 'track' must be maintained. If this is not so, a 'scuffing' action occurs which quickly wears the tyres, and some early i.f.s. systems were offenders in this respect.

It is impossible entirely to eliminate 'side-scrub' with split-axle suspension, but modern 'wishbone' systems nearly do so, using links of unequal length (Fig. 88). The perfect method of wheel suspension (from this point of view) is that employed by Morgan and Lancia, in which each wheel moves up and down on a vertical slide (Fig. 89).

In very high speed cars it is considered desirable that the wheels should always remain tilted to the same degree in order to avoid the peculiar gyroscopic effects which occur when a fast-rotating wheel is caused to alter its plane of rotation. In these cases equal length upper and lower suspension links are sometimes used, if the small amount of sideways scuffing which these entail can be tolerated.

The adoption of i.f.s. which permits greater up and down travel of the wheels has brought with it the use of softer springs and an increased tendency for the car to roll sideways on corners. Some early cars with i.f.s. exhibited a marked 'dipping' towards the outside of a corner. The rolling on modern cars is much reduced by the use of the *anti-roll bar* or *stabilizer*. This is a torsion bar placed

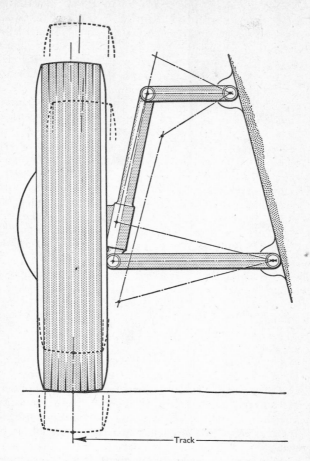

Track

Fig. 88. In the widely used system of front wheel suspension employing unequal length links, constant *track* is maintained (no side-scrub at the road surface) with only a small variation in wheel camber angle, as the wheel rises and falls.

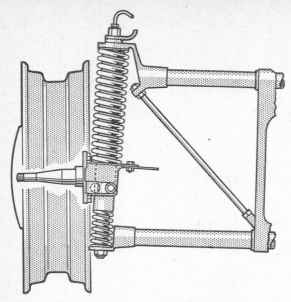

Fig. 89. In the Morgan vertical slide independent front suspension, the stub axle slides on a long swivel pin which also carries the main coil spring and a smaller rebound spring. The suspension is lubricated by oil supplied from the engine lubrication system and fed in at the top of the swivel pin when the driver presses a foot-plunger (about every 50 miles). (*Based on a drawing supplied by Trader Publishing Co.*)

across the front of the car and connected to the suspension links in such a way that it resists any tendency for the wheels to move up or down in opposite directions, relatively speaking. This, of course, is what happens when the car tilts bodily sideways relative to the road (Fig. 91). Note that the bar does not stiffen the springing if both wheels move up or down together, since it is not anchored rigidly to the chassis. Fig. 90 shows an unusual front suspension used on one version of the Vauxhall Viva, in which a transverse leaf spring is anchored in such a way that it acts both in the normal springing sense and also as an anti-roll device. If one wheel is lifted by a bump the adjacent end of the spring is deflected

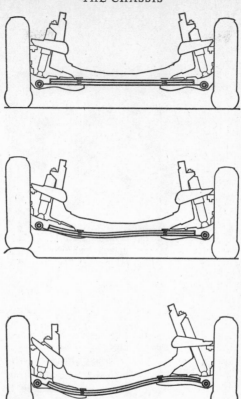

Fig. 90. In the front suspension of one version of the Vauxhall 'Viva' the transverse leaf spring is so anchored that it gives an anti-roll effect. (*By courtesy of Vauxhall Motors Ltd*)

in the usual way; however, if the car tends to roll sideways, the spring takes on a compound curve which has the effect of stiffening up the end of the spring coming under load and thus the roll is resisted.

A number of models in the British Ford range use spring strut suspension in which an anti-roll bar has its ends arranged to form

Anti-Roll Bar

Fig. 91. The tendency for the car to roll outwards, when traversing a curve is resisted by the twisting of a spring steel anti-roll bar attached to the suspension arms. A similar bar may be fitted to the rear suspension.

'wishbones' in conjunction with lateral links. Another interesting feature of this suspension is that the weight of the front of the car is supported, on coil spring units, high up under the bonnet structure; in this way the stresses are more evenly distributed throughout the integral bodywork. An extension of the latter principle is used in the Rover 2000 front suspension (Plate 2 and Fig. 6) where the vertical wheel movements are translated by a bell-crank system into horizontal deflections of coil springs which are supported against the exceedingly strong bulkhead.

On some cars using torsion bar springing provision is made for adjusting the springs to suit the loading, whilst the car is in motion, an electric motor being used to adjust the torsion-bar settings.

It should be mentioned that on modern cars particular attention is paid to 'phasing' the front and rear springing. This means that the 'period' or natural rate of vibration of the springs is chosen so that motion of one end of the car does not tend to promote similar motion of the other end. If this were so there would be a tendency for severe pitching to build up on certain types of road surface at

specific speeds. Usually the front springs are designed with a
natural frequency slightly higher than that of the rear springs.

SHOCK ABSORBERS

When a weight hung upon a coil spring is pulled down and
released it continues to bounce up and down for a considerable
time. If a car is mounted on coil or torsion-bar springs it, too, will
continue to bounce up and down after striking a bump, unless
some form of damping device is fitted.

On older cars with leaf spring suspension, the friction between
the spring-leaves was often sufficient to damp the bounce, but
usually an additional friction device, such as the Hartford shock-
absorber, was fitted. The latter name is rather misleading, since it
is the spring which actually absorbs the initial shock of a bump,
the 'shock-absorber' only serving to prevent any further oscilla-
tions, and it is better described as a spring-damper.

Since the friction between leaves in a leaf spring is a somewhat
variable quantity, modern designers elect to reduce friction to a
minimum by 'interleaving' with soft metal strip or 'buttons', or
by greasing the leaves and sealing them with 'gaiters'. The damping is then provided to a controlled extent by the spring-damper,
which in these days is usually hydraulic. This means that a
deflection of the suspension linkage causes a piston to move in an
oil-filled cylinder with a defined rate of 'leak'. The advantage of
this method is that the amount of damping for a heavy bump is
very much greater than that for a small one. In some damper designs the shape and action resembles that of a telescope, and such
dampers are known as *telescopic* or *direct-acting struts*. They can
be so placed in a rear suspension system that they confer a certain
degree of resistance to rolling of the body, and may also contribute
to some extent to sideways location of the axle. Popular also are
piston-type dampers in which movement of a piston, or pistons,
within the cylinder assembly, is brought about by a lever system
connected to the suspension links. These dampers are often used in
wishbone type front suspension systems, the damper lever being
utilized as a suspension link.

On some cars in the higher price range provision is made for adjusting the degree of damping while the car is in motion, giving a measure of 'ride control'.

The damper is one of the components of the modern car which has come in for a great deal of criticism. There is no doubt that the amount of work it has to do has been greatly increased with the advent of soft suspension systems which allow a long range of movement, and which possess no inherent damping properties. This means that considerable heat is generated within the damper, and it may be necessary to provide dissipating fins. Also, in hydraulic dampers the fluid must be chosen so that it remains sufficiently viscous at the higher temperatures and the design of the damper must be such that aeration (frothing) of the fluid is minimized.

HYDROLASTIC SUSPENSION

The original 'mini' in the B.M.C. transverse-engined range of cars used a novel suspension system in which all the wheels were individually suspended on rubber cone spring units; these units were developed by Alexander Moulton, and used rubber within a housing so shaped that the spring effect stiffened up under increasing load, thus providing a variable-rate spring. The spring units were damped by conventional hydraulic telescopic dampers. A further development of this system resulted in the Moulton *Hydrolastic* suspension system, used on a range of B.M.C. cars from the 'mini' upwards, which is a fundamentally simple arrangement designed to reduce fore-and-aft pitching of the car. Rubber spring units are again used but instead of wheel movements operating directly against the rubber, the wheel linkage deflects a flexible diaphragm which transfers the movement to the rubber by hydraulic effect via a fluid trapped within the system. The vital feature is that the Hydrolastic units, or *displacers*, on the front and rear wheels on each side of the car are connected together by a pipe so that fluid can flow between the displacers. The result is that if, for example, the front wheel on one side is deflected upwards, fluid is forced out of the front displacer along the pipe into the rear displacer and virtually 'pumps' the rear of the car upwards to maintain it on the level. In this way the car can be designed within a short wheel-base without the tendency to pitching which this normally entails.

The Hydrolastic units contain restrictor valves to give the system self-damping properties and no conventional spring dampers are used; the system is completely sealed, the fluid being water-based with anti-freeze additives. The complete Hydrolastic suspension system may be supplemented by anti-roll torsion bars.

Fig. 92 shows how Hydrolastic units are used in the front suspension of the Austin 1800, wheel movement being transferred by a bell-crank lever to the displacer unit which is neatly accommodated within a tubular cross-member; the illustration shows the fluid lines which would be connected to the corresponding rear units on each side of the car.

ROLLS-ROYCE SUSPENSION

A complex all-independent suspension system incorporating automatic height-correction is used on the Rolls-Royce 'Silver Shadow' and Bentley 'T' Series cars (see Fig 5). The wheels are mounted by basically conventional methods using double wishbones and anti-roll bar at the front and trailing arms at the rear, with coil springs and telescopic hydraulic dampers. However, the abutments of the springs at the top ends are taken on jacks or rams fed from a hydraulic system operating at 2,500 pounds per square inch; the supply of fluid to the rams is controlled by height-sensing valves, one on the front suspension and two on the rear suspension, such that the car is maintained at a constant riding height and attitude regardless of the load it is carrying. The system is so arranged that when the doors are open or when Neutral gear is selected (implying that the car is stationary) the response to load changes is rapid, but with the car running a restrictor valve is introduced so that the system responds only slowly and does not attempt to correct for transitory bump conditions.

Other notable features of the Rolls-Royce suspension are that the geometry is arranged so as virtually to eliminate any tendency for the car to 'nose-dive' under heavy braking, and that special measures are taken to prevent the transmission of suspension and road noises to the car body; this is liable to be a difficult problem when independent rear suspension is used, particularly in conjunction with a unit-construction body. The rear suspension trailing

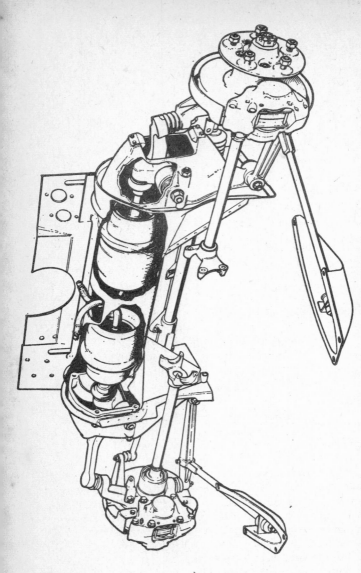

Fig. 92. The front suspension system of the Austin 1800 with Hydrolastic units housed in a cross-member and operated through bell-cranks. (*By courtesy of the Austin Motor Co. Ltd*)

links are pivoted on a massive cross-member which is itself attached to the body by *Vibrashock* flexible mountings, resembling cylindrical woven steel wire 'pan-scrubbers'; the fore-and-aft movement of this cross-member are positively controlled by tie-rods and a hydraulic damper, so as to eliminate rear wheel steering effects. The complete front suspension system, together with the engine and gearbox, is carried on a sub-frame which is again attached to the body by Vibrashock mountings, sideways movements of the sub-frame being controlled by a Panhard rod (similar to that in Fig. 76).

CITROEN HYDRO-PNEUMATIC SUSPENSION SYSTEM

A hydro-pneumatic suspension system is fitted to the Citroen D S front-wheel-drive saloon, a car of advanced design which incorporates hydraulic power operation of almost all controls. All wheels are independently suspended, each wheel being linked to a hydraulic cylinder, at the end of which is a sphere containing gas confined under pressure by a rubber diaphragm. Movement of the wheel causes further compression of the gas which acts as a springing medium. Damping and rebound control is due to a valve which controls the flow of hydraulic fluid. Height corrector valves at front and rear automatically adjust the amount of hydraulic fluid in the respective suspension units so that the car is maintained at constant height in relation to the road, despite variations in loading.

Rack-and-pinion steering with hydraulic power assistance is also fitted to the D S saloon.

CHASSIS LUBRICATION

Although many of the various joints in the suspension and steering are nowadays bushed with rubber so that they do not require lubrication, or are permanently sealed after initial lubrication, there are still certain points such as steering swivels which require regular greasing on many cars.

The problem has been reduced on certain cars by piping the lubricant to each of the required points from a common, easily-accessible position on the chassis. On some expensive cars servicing is reduced still further by arranging for oil to be fed automatically, in the required amounts, to the correct points, each time the engine warms up. In others the lubricant is supplied by the driver depressing a small pedal, either at his discretion or at the prompting of a light which appears every 100 miles or so. The system is known as 'one-shot' lubrication.

One some of the more recent cars, the necessity for routine chassis lubrication in the traditional sense has been completely eliminated by the use of rubber- or plastics-lined bushes and by pre-packing sealed pivot bearings with lubricant 'for life'.

STEERING

It is probably true to say that there have been no major changes in the methods used to steer a four-wheeled car for at least fifty years; attempts have been made to steer by the rear wheels, but the difficulties involved in this become very apparent to the learner-driver the first time he tries to manoeuvre a car in reverse.

Everyone appreciates that all vehicles which do not run on rails or tracks are steered by twisting the front wheels from their normal position. What we are concerned with is by how much each wheel has to be twisted, and how this is achieved.

Firstly, it must be understood that when a four-wheeled vehicle is travelling on a curve, the inner and outer wheels are travelling on circles of different radius and that, if none of the wheels are to skid, these circles should be based on the same centre. From Fig. 93 we see that this centre lies on the line of the rear axle and, most important, that the outer front wheel is turned to a lesser extent than the inner wheel. Furthermore, this state of affairs has to exist for all positions of the steering. In practice, this is only possible if we attach the front wheels to the ends of a beam, pivoted at the middle, as on a traction-engine, but childhood experience with soap-box trucks will have shown many of us how unstable this arrangement can be at speed. Therefore, we find on cars that each front wheel revolves on a short 'stub' axle which is pivoted on an approximately upright spindle known as the '*king-pin*' (Fig. 99). Connected to the stub axle is a short lever called a steering arm, the two steering arms being connected by a bar

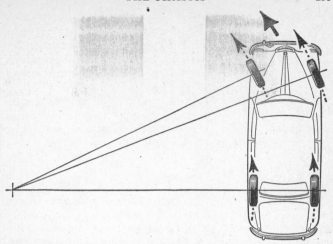

Fig. 93. All four wheels should travel about the same centre of turn.

passing across the car and termed the *track-rod*, so that the movement of one wheel is followed by the other (Fig. 94). If the car has non-independent suspension this rod will be in one piece, but in an i.f.s. system it is usually necessary to hinge the rod in two or three sections so as to allow for the relative movement of the wheels (Fig. 95).

In some suspension systems the orthodox kingpin arrangement is abandoned in favour of ball-joints at the ends of the suspension arms. These ball-joints then perform dual functions, as 'hinges' in the suspension linkage, and as steering swivels.

The important thing about the arrangement of the steering-arms, track-rod, etc., which comes under the general title of steering geometry, is that by pointing the steering arms towards the centre of the back axle when the wheels are set in the straight-ahead position (Fig. 96), a close approximation to the steering requirements, mentioned above, can be obtained. This is known as Jeantaud-Ackermann steering; in practice the idea is somewhat modified and on some very advanced high-speed cars the steering-arms are set almost parallel.

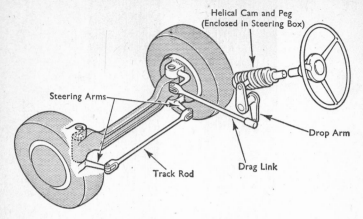

Fig. 94. Basis of steering gear used with beam axle.
Rotation of steering-wheel is converted into forward or backward
motion of the drop arm, causing the drag link to deflect the offside
wheel.

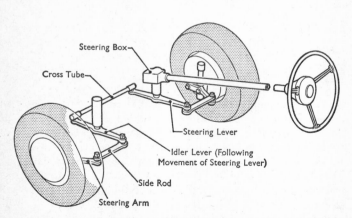

Fig. 95. A typical arrangement of steering gear used with independently
suspended wheels. The 'track rod' is in three parts – cross tube and two
side rods.

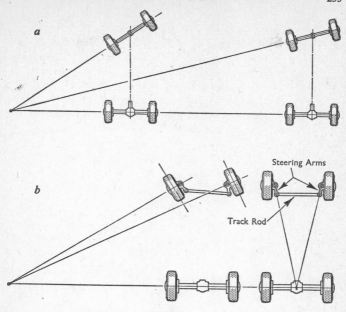

Fig. 96a. Pivoting the front axle at its centre would give the ideal conditions for all degrees of turn but is impracticable in a car.

b. Jeantaud-Ackermann steering linkage gives an approximately correct result. The outside front wheel runs on a greater radius than the inside wheel and therefore requires less deflection.

Next, we have to consider how turning the steering wheel is made to move the steering arms. Obviously, even the smallest car would be impossibly heavy to steer if the steering system was 'direct', as on a bicycle, but on the other hand, to separate the driver from the wheels by a complex linkage may inspire road-test reviewers to quote the well-worn phrase 'steered via rubber rods'. Also, the shocks received by the wheels ought not to be transmitted to the driver's hands, and yet at the same time he must not lose the 'feel' of the steering.

The majority of cars still use the well-established steering arrangement basically as shown in Fig. 94. Rotating the steering wheel causes a short *drop-arm* to be swung backwards or forwards by means of a mechanism contained in a *steering-box* at the bottom end of the steering column. One of the many types of this device is shown in Fig. 97. The steering-box has two jobs to do. One is to gear down the motion so that the driver has increased leverage over the steering, and the other is to ensure that, whilst the road-wheels cannot actually 'take charge' of affairs, the whole arrangement will act in the reverse sense. This means that is should be

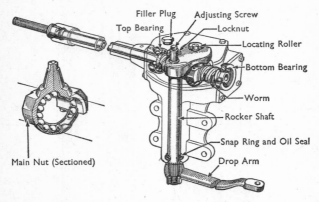

Fig. 97. In this worm-and-nut steering box, steel balls are used to reduce friction in the main nut (Sunbeam). (*By courtesy of Rootes Motors Ltd*)

possible to spin the steering wheel by pulling at the road-wheels. The reasons for this are mentioned later.

The free end of the drop-arm is connected indirectly to the off-side steering-arm by a *drag-link*. Thus one wheel only is positively steered, and its movement is transferred to the other wheel by the track-rod; an undesirable feature of this arrangement is that wear in the joints of the steering linkage may more seriously affect the steering of the near-side wheel.

A steering system which does not suffer from this disadvantage is that known as *rack and pinion*, which, formerly mostly confined to sports and racing cars, can now be found on a number of production cars. A row of teeth, or rack, is either connected to, or made part of, a divided track-rod. A small toothed wheel attached to the steering column is meshed directly with the rack and thus moves it from side to side when the steering wheel is rotated (Fig. 126). The normal steering box arrangement is done away with entirely. Rack and pinion steering produces a very direct 'feel' and is obviously perfectly reversible. The rack is usually enclosed in a grease-packed casing with rubber gaiters at the ends to accommodate its movement.

In some arrangements of rack and pinion steering-gear it happens that the pinion meshes with its rack at a point not far from the centre of the car. This would obviously bring the steering wheel to an inconvenient position, particularly in modern saloons with full-width bodywork and short bonnet length. In these cases, therefore, a slightly flexible joint is provided at the lower end of the steering column, which is set over to the off-side. Thus, the driver does not sit quite 'square to the wheel' normally, but the arrangement is particularly convenient when three people are riding on a bench-type front seat.

Whatever steering arrangement is adopted, allowance must be made for relative movement between the various links, and these are usually connected together by means of ball-joints. Such joints are made slightly non-rigid, either by the use of a sprung ball-and-socket device or rubber bushes, in order to allow for slight inaccuracies in the steering geometry and to take up wear. Flexible joints in the steering column, already mentioned, are sometimes used to enable the column to take a convenient path through the under-bonnet space.

TURNING CIRCLE AND STEERING RATIO

The diameter of the smallest circle which the car can traverse, obtained when its wheels are at their extreme deviation, is referred to as the *turning circle*, the steering being then at full left or right *lock*. The turning circle varies from about 32 feet, for a small saloon, to 45 feet for a large limousine. A particular case is the London taxi-cab, which is required by law to be capable of turning, without reversing, in a roadway 25 feet wide.

The amount of movement required at the steering wheel to obtain a given deflection of the wheels varies widely between cars of different types. On a racing car where 'quick' steering is essential and the necessary muscular effort is available, the wheels may be turned from full left to full right lock by less than two complete turns of the steering wheel, and such steering is said to be high-geared or to have a high ratio.

POWER ASSISTED STEERING

On a large vehicle, where great weight is borne by the front wheels and large section balloon tyres are used, heavy steering loads are imposed and demand a low-ratio gear involving up to five or more turns of the wheel, lock to lock. Obviously this renders manoeuvring difficult in confined spaces or in emergency and therefore many large cars are now equipped with power-assisted (servo) steering. Movement of the steering wheel operates valves or clutches which apply power from the engine to the steering linkage. The control is so arranged that the 'feel' of the steering is not lost to the driver, although the heaviest car may be steered by fingertip. On some systems the power assistance is not operative for small movements of the wheel so as to preserve direct feel in straight line guidance. In all cases the normal manual steering operates in the event of power failure.

WHEEL ATTITUDE

Factors are introduced in normal steering systems which reduce the effort required at the wheel. Firstly, the king-pins, upon which the wheels pivot, are leaned slightly backwards at the top (about 2° – 3° usually), this causing the wheels to 'trail' in much the same way as the casters used on furniture (Fig. 98). The result is that the wheels tend always to stay in the straight-ahead position, and this is particularly noticeable on leaving a corner, when the wheels will straighten-up of their own accord, by caster-action. Note that this is only possible because the steering gear is made reversible, as explained earlier.

Secondly, it will be seen that, viewed from above, each front

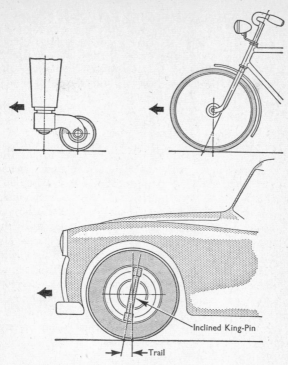

Inclined King-Pin

←Trail

Fig. 98. By arranging the steering axis so that it meets the ground ahead of the point of contact of the wheel, a self-aligning or *caster* action is obtained.

wheel is 'outside' its king-pin, and clearly the wheels tend to get 'left behind' or to 'splay', especially when the brakes are applied. Theoretically, the king-pin should be directly above the point at which the tyre is in contact with the road, thus giving what is known as true centre-point steering. It is achieved in some cases by placing the king-pin 'within' the wheel, but in the majority of cars an approach to centre-point steering is obtained by canting each wheel outwards at the top, this being known as positive camber, and by inclining the king-pin in the opposite sense. Seen from the front, the line of the king-pin then passes close to the centre of the tyre tread at the road surface (Fig. 99). Most authorities agree that true centre-point steering is undesirable, owing to its high sensitivity and lack of self-centring or caster action.

The remaining tendency for the wheels to splay is counteracted by adjusting the track-rod to give them a very small amount of

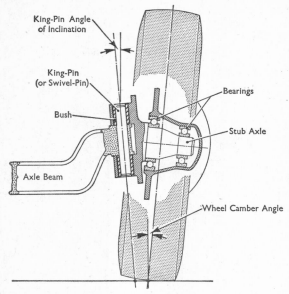

King-Pin Angle of Inclination

King-Pin (or Swivel-Pin)

Bush

Axle Beam

Bearings

Stub Axle

Wheel Camber Angle

Fig. 99. Simplified front wheel pivot system showing king-pin inclined and wheel cambered to give near centre point steering.

'toe-in', the front edges of the wheel rims being set closer together than the rear edges by anything up to $\frac{1}{8}$ inch, though often much less.

A subsidiary effect of inclining the king-pins is that when a wheel swings to the side it must also rise slightly (unless the steering is true centre-point) and tends to lift the front of the car. The weight of the car, resisting this, contributes to self-centring of the steering.

The slight changes in wheel attitude which occur with suspension movements can sometimes promote the onset of wheel 'shimmy' due to gyroscopic effects, as already mentioned in connexion with beam-type front axles, and some cars are fitted with *steering dampers*. The damper may be a friction or hydraulic type similar to that used in suspension systems and is connected between the car structure and some point in the steering linkage; besides serving to suppress any tendency to shimmy, it helps to cushion the steering system against shocks due to bad road surfaces and damps out any vibration caused by imperfect wheel balance.

OVERSTEER AND UNDERSTEER

Although for a given deflection of the front wheels the car should travel on a predictable curve, this path is rarely followed in practice owing to a variety of influences which may not necessarily include the obvious factor of side-slip.

Many saloon cars, especially when heavily loaded at the rear, exhibit a tendency to take a curve more sharply than was intended by the driver and in fact the steering may have to be 'unwound' to prevent the car from slewing round. This unstable characteristic, which becomes increasingly evident as speed rises, is known as *oversteer*. It may also manifest itself as instability when the car is travelling on a straight road but under the influence of side forces such as might be due to cross-winds or severe surface camber. Oversteer may often be attributed to the fact that the rear wheels for some reason have less 'cornering ability' than the front wheels; one cause of this is associated with the fact that side thrust on a tyre produces lateral distortion so that the wheel is enabled to follow a path which is at an angle to its true plane of rotation, this being known as the *slip angle*. If the rear end of the car is the more heavily loaded the slip angle of the back wheels may be greater than that of the front wheels. It follows that oversteer may be lessened if the resistance of the rear tyres to distortion can be increased, by raising the inflation pressure for instance.

Another factor which may contribute to oversteer is variation in the attitude of a rigid rear axle, due, for instance, to changes in the effective length of leaf springs when flexing under load (Fig. 74).

The opposite effect to oversteer, and usually more desirable, is that of *understeer*. An understeering car tends to follow a wider curve than that determined by the deflection of the front wheels so that the car has to be 'held' into the corner. Whilst this may call for additional muscular effort it also means that the car is inherently stable and not likely to leave the corner tail-first.

The cornering ability of a wheel also varies with alteration in its camber (angle to the road as seen from front to rear). Under- or oversteer effects may therefore be present where suspension arrangements permit variation in camber, as in 'wishbone' type front suspension and swing-axle rear suspension; since such effects are often predictable, a car may be designed in theory to possess any desired steering characteristic.

Handling behaviour is also influenced by whether drive is taken to the front or rear wheels. The slip angle of a wheel is increased whilst it is transmitting power, so that if a rear-drive car is understeering, i.e. tending to run out on a curve, it may be brought back by *increasing* the power; this may be visualized as thrust outwards on the rear of the car to keep it 'in balance'. Conversely, a front-drive car tends to run wide if power is applied on a curve, so that oversteer would be promoted by *reducing* power. The natural tendency of the average driver is to lift the foot if the car is tending to run out so in this respect front-wheel drive has an advantage, especially on twisting roads; no doubt this accounts for the excellent 'swerveability' reputation of the small front-wheel drive cars in particular.

Wheels

Early cars inherited the wood-spoked wheel of the carriage type, but with a steel hub and steel rim, later rubber-shod. Despite accidents caused by spoke breakage, this type of wheel was in use for many years until the introduction of the 'artillery' wheel using hollow steel spokes. On many cars the wheels were non-detachable and tyre replacement was effected *in situ*, aided by various arrangements using split detachable flanges. A special mention must be made of the Stepney rim, carried like a spare wheel with a tyre in position, ready to be secured to the rim of any wheel which suffered a punctured tyre; this concept is revived in the Firestone 'Space-Saver', a spare wheel carrying a narrow tyre which can be attached to the normal wheel and so allow a journey to be completed without necessitating a wheel-change and incidentally occupying the minimum space when not in use.

Also in early use were wheels of the wire spoke type, sometimes with a disc covering the spokes.

The departure from true spoked wheels came with the first pressed steel wheel, consisting of two discs welded to a separate rim, followed later by the 'Easiclean' type. Used on the majority of cars built immediately before and after World War II, the 'Easiclean' is made from a deeply dished single disc riveted to a steel rim; the disc has a series of swaged perforations which give the appearance of short spokes and also serve to stiffen the disc, besides assisting in brake ventilation. The wheel is attached to its hub by four or five studs, these being concealed under a decorative nave plate, 'sprung' over a series of projections.

This type of wheel was superseded in the late forties by a pattern in which the perforations are reduced to four narrow slots close to the rim. On cars where this arrangement would give inadequate brake cooling a series of circular perforations are provided closer to the hub.

There has been a tendency in recent years towards a reduction of wheel diameter, which, in consequence of the accompanying reduction in unsprung weight, gives improved suspension characteristics.

Despite recent assertions that a fifth wheel is superfluous in the modern car, motor manufacturers continue to provide a spare wheel, and comment on the location of this will be found in Chapter 9. An ingenious solution to the spare wheel problem which permits a reduction in the overall weight carried, may be seen on some Renault models, where the wheel hubs are enlarged to form fixed 'spiders' and only the rims are detachable (Fig. 100).

The wire-spoked wheel has been in use for many years on cars, motor-cycles, and pedal-cycles. It depends on the fact that a steel wire can support a great load when under tension. To appreciate the use of this property, one must imagine the weight of the vehicle supported by the wheel hubs, hanging by the vertical spokes from the upper part of the rims, the latter being held in shape by the other spokes. Besides carrying the weight of the car, the spokes are required to transmit the forces of acceleration and braking, and to resist side-to-side forces; wire wheels are, therefore, usually made to the *tangent spoke* pattern, the spokes being tangential to the central hub rather than truly radial. These wheels, which possess

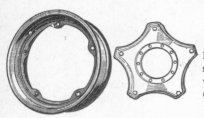

Fig. 100. Renault wheel consisting of fixed central spider with detachable rim.
(*By courtesy of Renault Ltd*)

great strength and relative lightness, are nowadays used only on high performance cars and are mounted on special splined *centre-lock* hubs (Fig. 101). Each wheel is held in position by a large wing-nut and can be removed very rapidly, this being a valuable feature in racing. It may be noted that in certain countries there is safety legislation relating to the use of wing-nuts on road vehicles.

The centre-lock hub has also been utilized in conjunction with pressed steel wheels of the ventilated disc type on some sports cars.

The use of light alloys to obtain wheels of low weight has received some attention; in particular, magnesium-alloy wheels have been used on certain racing cars.

WHEEL BALANCE

The rising speed of touring cars, combined with the adoption of smaller wheel diameters, has promoted increasing interest in the question of wheel balance, since wheels which are badly unbalanced can cause serious vibration when rotating rapidly, with adverse effect on steering and tyre wear. Out-of-balance may be due to slight irregularities in the construction of wheel and tyre and also to the presence of the tyre valve. Tyre manufacturers mark the lighter part of the outer cover and the heavier part of the inner

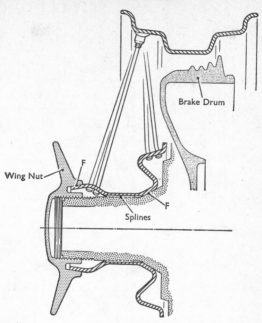

Fig. 101. Section through a wire wheel showing the wedging action which occurs at the faces F. This illustration also indicates the extent to which the rim overhangs (in order to bring the tyre tread close to the swivelling axis at the road surface), and shows the profile of the wellbase rim. (*Based on drawings supplied by the Dunlop Rubber Co. Ltd*)

tube so that these may be assembled next to each other and partly 'cancel out'. Most large service stations are equipped with an apparatus which tests the complete wheel for *dynamic* balance (i.e. with the wheel spinning) and which also indicates the amount of correction required, this being applied by attaching small lead weights to the wheel rim. On older sports cars it was the usual practice to balance wire wheels by wrapping lead wire around the spokes diametrically opposite the tyre valve. On certain expensive cars the wheels are accurately balanced during assembly, by means of adjustable weights concealed within the hub covers.

TYRES

Apart from some experiments with sprung wheel rims from time to time, including some recent development in this field, rubber tyres have always been standard equipment on cars. Early pneumatic tyres were unreliable, partly because of the poor state of road surfaces, and solid tyres were widely used but were later discarded on account of their weight and harsh, noisy running.

The early pneumatic tyre had an unribbed tread (sometimes augmented by a steel-studded leather band), canvas construction and beaded edges which had to be stretched over the shallow rim. This is in great contrast with the modern tyre and rim, where the tyre has inextensible beads formed from bunches of wire and the rim is of the *well-base* type which simplifies tyre fitting. The tyre is of *plied* construction, i.e. the carcase of the tyre is formed of a number of layers of rubberized rayon or nylon cords. The tread is applied to the carcase as a mix of raw rubber, sulphur, and carbon black, and the whole is vulcanized (i.e. heated and 'cured') in a steel mould which also impresses the tread pattern.

Early pneumatic tyres obtained the necessary load-carrying capacity by the use of high inflation pressures. The modern tyre achieves it by using relatively low pressure air (20–25 pounds per square inch) in a 'balloon' tyre of large cross-section. There has been a tendency lately towards an increase in the width of the wheel rim, in order to improve side-to-side stability, and also to make the tread 'flatter', thus increasing the area which is in contact with the road.

TYRE SIZES

Because a tyre is a flexible object it is difficult to specify its dimensions under all conditions, since the final size is determined in part by the type of rim to which the tyre is fitted. The size of the wheel rim is denoted by the width between its flanges, a code letter signifying the shape of the rim section, and the diameter at the seating of the tyre bead; for example, $5\frac{1}{2}K \times 16$ denotes an International Standard Wide-Base rim Style K, $5\frac{1}{2}$ inches between flanges and 16 inches seat diameter.

For each rim size a number of tyre sizes are recommended, but it is possible to fit other tyres which may be either under- or over-size in respect of width. The size of the tyre is given as the nominal overall width of the tyre and the diameter of the wheel rim for which the tyre is designed; for example, a 6·50–16 tyre ('six fifty by sixteen') denotes a tyre of nominal width 6·50 inches and suitable for a 16-inch rim. However, the actual width of the tyre in service depends upon the type of rim used, and this particular tyre could be fitted to any of the following rims: 5K × 16, 5½K × 16, 4·00D × 16, 4·50D × 16, or 5·00F × 16.

A very approximate estimation of the overall diameter of a tyre may be obtained by doubling the first part of the tyre size and adding the second part; for example, the diameter of a 6·50 – 16 tyre is roughly 29 inches ((2 × 6·5) + 16).

TREAD PATTERN

The actual pattern of the tread varies greatly according to the service for which the tyre is intended. In general, the tread designed for normal touring is patterned to produce the minimum of noise; it usually has continuous ribs around the circumference, with irregularly spaced serrations which reduce the tendency to generate any particular musical tone. Also, there are serrated edges to the tread, providing more resistance to side-slip, and slits known as *slicings* or *stop-notches*, for extra tractive grip.

'Knife cuts' or *sipes* are also used to provide a large number of wiping edges to squeegee surface water into the main tread pattern which channels it away from under the tyre, thus drying the road; according to information supplied by the Avon Rubber Company the effective contact area between the average car tyre and the road is no larger than a man's size nine shoe and at 50 m.p.h. in moderate rain the tyre clears water from the road at the rate of one gallon per second.

Some tyres are provided with specially contoured shoulders and anti-wander ribs to resist deflection of the car by raised white lines, road joints and similar surface irregularities.

Most tyre manufacturers offer special tyres for use on mud or snow, having much more pronounced tread patterns with deep shoulder 'lugs'; such tyres are popularly termed 'Town and Country' though this is actually a proprietary name used by the Firestone Tyre and Rubber Company for their tyre of this type. The deep tread on these bad-weather tyres allows 'squirming', producing additional running noise and heating of the tyre and they are not generally recommended for sustained high speeds on dry roads. Some types have sufficiently massive rubber areas to allow the fitting of *snow studs*; these are steel or tungsten-carbide pegs which are screwed or pressed into the tyre tread to provide extra grip on ice and are used in particular by rally drivers.

The average type of touring car tyre is not usually regarded as suitable for sustained speeds above 100 m.p.h. and special 'motorway' tyres are available for high-performance cars; these tyres can be run safely for long periods at speeds up to 125 m.p.h. and at even higher speeds for short periods.

If a tread pattern becomes worn away and if the carcase is sound, it may be possible to replace the tread by a remoulding process. The practice of retreading is dealt with in Chapter 10.

RADIAL TYRES

One problem which faces the tyre designer is that of achieving flexibility in the vertical plane, in order that a comfortable 'ride' is obtained, and at the same time to provide the tyre with sufficient lateral rigidity. If the latter characteristic is not provided there will be a tendency for the tyre to collapse under side loads or, in other words, the tyre will have an excessive slip angle. A solution to this problem is provided by treating the functions of casing and tread separately in the *radial* or *belted* tyre, a form of construction pioneered by the Michelin 'X' tyre. The cords which form the casing are laid across the tyre from bead to bead, as opposed to the more usual method of laying them 'criss-cross'. It is claimed that this provides maximum lateral stability and ensures a very supple casing. Because flexing is now confined to the casing it is possible to provide the tread with a high degree of resistance to sideways distortion, and this is achieved by placing three layers of steel cords at the base of the tread (Fig. 102). This 'stabilized tread' has a slip angle which is only about one half of that of ordinary tyres,

and the reduced flexing of the tread results in almost doubled mileage, and improved fuel consumption. Radial tyres have an 'under-
inflated' appearance when fitted, because the tread is flatter and
the side-walls more flexible. If a car is fitted with two radial tyres
only, they *must* be on the *rear wheels*. If they were fitted at the
front the conventional tyres at the rear would inevitably have
greater slip angle and excessive oversteer would result.

Fig. 102. In the Michelin 'X' tyre the casing cords are laid
from side to side and lateral stiffness is obtained by three layers
of steel cords at the base of the tread.

Almost all manufacturers now include radial tyres in their
range, although in some cases the 'belt' is composed of fabric
rather than steel cords. It is the common though not invariable
practice to use inner tubes with radial tyres, a special type of tube
being recommended to withstand the extra flexing.

CLING RUBBER TYRES

A comparatively recent development in tyre technology is the use of *high hysteresis* or *cling* rubber. Hysteresis is a measure of ability to absorb energy under deformation and in this context the term 'high hysteresis' implies a deadness or lack of bounciness inherent in certain special rubber compounds. This property is made use of in tyres in that it discourages the setting up of small local deformations in the rolling tread and ensures that the maximum area of tread remains in full contact with the road surface. This results in increased adhesion and superior road-holding and is especially valuable under wet conditions. However, the energy absorbed by high hysteresis rubber leads to internal heating, thus imposing limitations on its use for the entire tyre construction. An example of a 'cling' tyre is the Avon H.M. New Safety tyre, in which an exceptionally high hysteresis rubber is used for the patterned tread layer whilst conventional resilient rubber is used for the under-tread and side walls, which are subject to the major part of the tyre flexing movement. The combination of this construction with a special tread pattern is claimed to give an extra 38 per cent adhesion compared with a conventional tyre, with a marked absence of squeal during cornering.

As the name implies, 'cling radial' tyres are a type specially designed for high-performance cars and combine radial ply construction with the use of high hysteresis rubber for the outer tread.

TUBELESS TYRES

A great advance in pneumatic tyre design has been the introduction of tubeless tyres, which are standard original equipment on most new cars. As the name implies, no inner tube is used, the cover being designed to form an airtight seal at its seating on the wheel rim. Obviously the rim must be in perfect condition and these tyres cannot be used with wire-spoked wheels.

It has been shown that the tubeless tyre will hold its pressure longer than the conventional tyre and tube, and this is explained by the fact that the rubber is in an unstretched condition and is less porous, this property also assisting the tyre in sealing possible leaks around any object which penetrates the tyre. Tubeless tyres have to be fitted carefully to the rim, using a circumferential strap or 'tourniquet'.

TYRE VALVES

One of the most striking features of the pneumatic tyre is the universal standardization of the Schrader inflation valve. Fig. 103

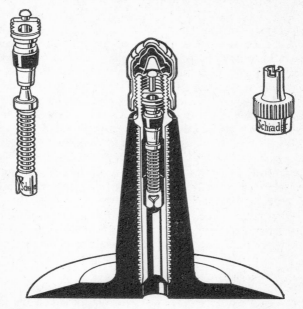

Fig. 103. Standard Schrader valve for tubed tyre showing valve core and cap designed as core removal tool. (*By courtesy of A. Schrader's Son, Division of Scovill Manufacturing Co. Ltd*)

shows the modern form of the valve in which the body is embedded in rubber which is bonded to the inner tube. Fig. 104 shows one version of the valve which is used in conjunction with the tubeless tyre, the valve being mounted directly in the wheel rim.

The cap of the Schrader valve is designed to provide a secondary air seal, and one design of cap can be used as a tool to unscrew

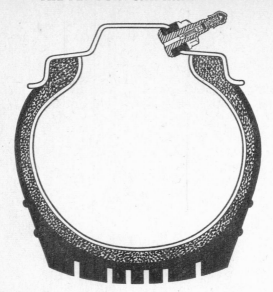

Fig. 104. One design of Schrader valve for use with tubeless tyre. (*By courtesy of A. Schrader's Son, Division of Scovill Manufacturing Co. Ltd*)

the valve core, the latter being interchangeable with that from any other valve.

WHITEWALL TYRES

A feature finding only limited popularity in Britain but widely used in the United States is the whitewall tyre (also now available in colours). The whitewall is obtained by bonding white rubber to the tyre carcase, and although it is primarily intended to enhance appearance, it is also said to be of value in reducing the running temperature of the tyre in hot countries, by reflecting the sunlight.

TYRE WEAR

The rate at which a tyre wears is subject to many influences, including, of course, the manner in which the car is driven, suitability of the tread pattern, road surface, wheel suspension, etc. It is important to remember that under-inflation and misalignment of the wheels are prime factors in causing tyre wear, besides adversely affecting the handling characteristics, and also that a tyre driven at 60 m.p.h. may wear twice as fast as the same tyre driven at 40 m.p.h.

In order to obtain even wear of the tyres, it is essential that they should be changed around on the car at intervals, and this subject is dealt with in Chapter 10.

CHAPTER EIGHT

BRAKING

WHILE cars capable of high speeds have been made for fifty years, it is only comparatively recently that the brakes fitted to production cars can truly be said to allow the full potentialities of engine and roadholding to be realized in safety. A great deal of the credit for the efficiency of modern brakes is due to experience obtained in motor racing and with aircraft brakes.

METHODS OF BRAKING

Almost all cars employ the same basic system of braking, namely, the application at each road wheel individually of some kind of friction pad to a surface which rotates with the wheel, although the method of applying this principle differs between various makes. The energy possessed by the car due to its motion, i.e. kinetic energy, is converted into heat which is dissipated into the surrounding air.

Other methods of braking have been used to a limited extent; of these, one of the most spectacular was the retractable flap air-brake fitted to certain Mercedes-Benz sports-racing cars and used to supplement the normal type of brake when slowing from speeds approaching 200 m.p.h. Another type of brake which is still fitted occasionally is the transmission brake; this is usually a contracting drum brake operating directly on some part of the transmission between gearbox and back axle. Whilst this provides braking effort perfectly balanced between the two rear wheels, the brake is difficult to cool in this position and is therefore normally intended as a parking brake only.

BRAKING EFFECT OF THE ENGINE

In some forms of power unit, e.g. the steam engine and the electric motor, it is possible to rearrange the sequence of events within the working cycle of the unit in such a way that the resulting torque is in opposition to that which is tending to keep the unit rotating in its original direction; in this way the power unit can be made to act as a brake. For example, in the electric motor the connexions can be so modified that the motor becomes a generator and absorbs the energy of the moving vehicle by converting it into electricity which is passed back into the supply system. This is termed *regenerative braking*. We have seen that the sequence in the cycle of the petrol engine is controlled by a mechanism which does not lend itself to instantaneous reversal. However, this type of engine does provide a valuable supplement to the wheel brakes, by virtue of its resistance to being rotated against a closed throttle. The braking effect of the engine, which becomes diminished in a worn engine with poor compression, can render the use of the brakes almost unnecessary if the gearbox is used skilfully. The effect is, of course, increased if a lower gear is engaged, as the road-wheels are then compelled to rotate the engine at a relatively higher speed. This is a particularly valuable feature when descending long hills, as prolonged application of the brakes may cause them to overheat and 'fade'.

A vehicle should never be allowed to coast down a hill in neutral (or with the clutch disengaged), this being an illegal practice in the case of public service vehicles. Apart from the possibility of brake failure or inadequacy there is also the danger that the engine may be damaged if the speed of the vehicle is misjudged when an intermediate gear is re-engaged. The ignition should not be switched off during a descent of a hill as this may lead to oiling-up of the sparking plugs and there is also a danger that an accumulation of unburnt gases will explode and split the silencer when the engine is re-started.

FOUR-WHEEL BRAKES

Before the 1920s it was unusual to find brakes fitted to front wheels, and, in fact, front wheel brakes were considered to be dangerous, possibly because up to then designers had not always fully appreciated the effects of movement of the wheels relative to the brake linkage. This problem was not always overcome in later designs; one very popular small car with cable-operated brakes was apt to apply one front brake, without any help from the driver, if the steering was turned to full lock.

It has, of course, for many years been normal practice for all four wheels to be braked simultaneously by the operation of one foot pedal. In addition, a hand lever is provided which may operate on the same linkage as the foot pedal or on a separate mechanism, usually coupled to the rear brakes only. In most cars the handbrake is only required for parking and the operating lever is automatically locked in the 'on' position by a ratchet device. In competition driving the 'fly-off' handbrake is more convenient and many sports cars are fitted with this type, in which the lever automatically returns to the 'off' position unless it is deliberately secured by operating the ratchet. Since the parking brake may take considerable effort to set it effectively in the 'on' position, on some larger cars it is applied by a separate foot pedal and released by a hand control.

It is generally held that the maximum braking effect which can be obtained by the method of retarding the rotation of the wheels is produced when the wheels are about to 'lock'; the braking force available in this condition is greater than that when the wheels are actually skidding. The point at which any wheel begins to skid is determined both by the weight carried by that wheel and by the condition of tyre and road surfaces. To obtain maximum retardation it is necessary to bring all wheels up to the locking point simultaneously, and whilst this is reasonably easy to bring about for each pair of wheels and thus avoid slewing due to unequal braking on each side, it is more difficult to achieve balance between front and rear wheels. This is because the action of braking causes the car to pitch forward so that weight is transferred from the rear wheels to the front wheels; besides affecting the handling of the car, particularly on bends, this allows the rear wheels to slide more easily than the front. Fortunately, skidding of the rear wheels is less serious than a front wheel slide, which also involves loss of steering ability. In modern systems the front brakes are made more powerful than the rear to cater for the transfer of weight and in some cases special provision is made for limiting rear wheel braking, as described later in this chapter.

It is, of course, dangerous practice to apply the brakes whilst traversing a bend, one of the Golden Rules of driving being 'use the brakes only when the front wheels are pointing straight ahead'. Driving schools advocate the engagement of second gear for corners, since the engine then provides an immediate balanced braking effect when the accelerator is released and also enables the driver to accelerate away from the corner without delay.

DRUM BRAKES

The vast majority of cars use drum brakes of the internally-expanding type; the principle of operation of these is shown in Fig. 105, where it may be seen that two curved shoes fitted with friction linings and carried on a *backplate*, mounted rigidly on the wheel suspension member, are caused to move outwards so that they bear on the inside of a drum which rotates with the road wheels. This system has the great advantage that the drum can be reasonably well sealed against the ingress of water and dirt.

The friction lining is made from a woven material containing a high proportion of asbestos, with other constituents to improve the conduction of heat away from the rubbing surface. The linings are shaped to fit the shoes and are usually attached to them with brass or copper rivets or with special adhesive.

The mechanism shown in Fig. 105 for expanding the shoes is a very simple type of cam operation; amongst several disadvantages associated with this sytem are the reduction in leverage as the brake linings wear, difficulty in adjustment and the sensitivity to wear in the cam spindle bearings, the latter allowing the spindle to rock rather than rotate. Linkage to the cam levers is by a system of cables or rods with compensating lever devices to balance the pull on each lever.

A considerable improvement in the method of expanding the shoes was the introduction of the Girling wedge-and-roller expander. Here the movement is applied as a pull at right angles to the brake drum. A special feature of the Girling brake is the conical adjuster; the correct clearance on each brake is obtained by tightening up a square projection on each backplate as far as it will go and then turning it back two 'clicks'. Girling adjusters have also been used in conjunction with cam operation.

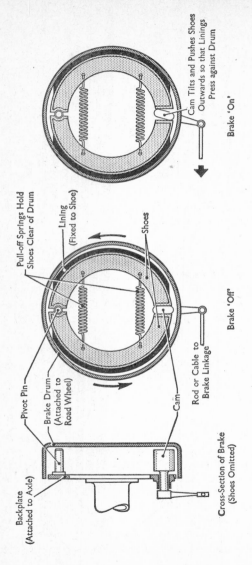

Fig. 105. Principle of internally-expanding drum brake.

HYDRAULIC OPERATION

The majority of brakes today are hydraulically operated, some-times on the front wheels only but more often on all four wheels (Fig. 106). Movement of the foot pedal causes a piston to move inside a main or *master cylinder* and to force fluid along a number of narrow bore pipes, one connected to each brake back plate; mounted on the back plate is a small cylinder with a piston which is forced outwards to expand the brake shoes. The proportions of the pistons are chosen to provide the necessary leverage. Hydraulic operation depends on the fact that the fluid is virtually incom-pressible and thus acts as a rigid connexion. If any air is permitted to enter the system, then movement of the brake pedal is taken up by compression of the air, and this may either produce 'sponginess' in brake operation or complete failure. For this reason hydraulic brake connexions must be bled of air when being charged with fluid. Here it must be emphasized that brake fluid, although resembling a light lubricating oil, has special properties, particularly in that it does not attack the seals used throughout the system. Hydraulic brakes should never be charged with fluid other than that recommended.

The advantages of hydraulic operation are the automatic equal-ization of the force applied to each brake, the ease with which movement of the drum can be accommodated by the use of flexible connexions, and the absence of cables and rods with their prone-ness to rattling. In addition, the mechanism is self-lubricating, and straight runs for the pipes are not essential.

Individual screw adjusters are fitted to each brake drum for the maintenance of correct clearance.

The correct amount of fluid is maintained by a reservoir; it is common practice to mount the brake master cylinder in unit with a similar cylinder used for hydraulic clutch operation, both cylinders sharing a common reservoir (Fig. 20).

Since fracture of one pipe could lead to loss of fluid and total absence of braking, the master cylinder is sometimes arranged to operate the front brake independently if there is failure in the rear brake connexions and vice versa. However, it is obligatory to pro-vide an alternative method of operation, and this usually takes the

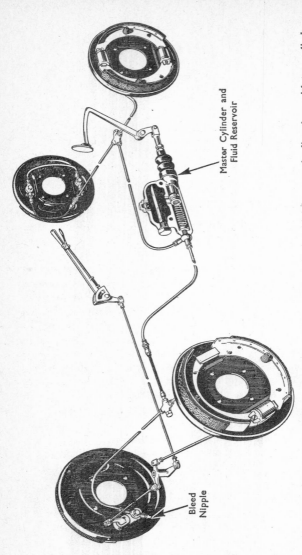

Master Cylinder and
Fluid Reservoir

Bleed
Nipple

Fig. 106. Lockheed four-wheel hydraulic brake system. Front brakes (right) are two leading shoe, with two cylinders per wheel. Rear brakes have one leading and one trailing shoe, with alternative mechanical actuation by hand-lever. (*By courtesy of Automotive Products Co. Ltd*)

form of a mechanical linkage to the rear brakes, operated by the hand lever.

TWO LEADING SHOE BRAKES

The flexibility of hydraulic operation has fostered the development of the so-called *self-energizing* or *self-wrapping* brake; study of Fig. 105 shows that the left-hand shoe is tending to 'trail' behind the rotating drum, whilst the other shoe is inclined to 'wedge' into the drum, thereby increasing its own braking effect. The result of this is to cause unequal wear of the linings. Use was made of the effect by detaching the anchorage of the shoes from the back plate and hinging them on a common 'floating' pin (Fig. 107a), so that the self-energizing tendency of the wedging or 'leading' shoe to rotate bodily was transmitted to the trailing shoe, thus increasing the force of this shoe. Although this method provides improved braking it also produces a tendency to 'grab'. A further step was to operate each shoe independently and to arrange the pivots so that both shoes were 'leading'; this system thus became known as 'two leading shoe' or '2.L.S.' (Fig. 107b). The independent operation can easily be obtained by providing each back plate with two cylinders, and has been achieved, with added complication, in mechanical brake systems. It is clear that leading and trailing shoes exchange functions if the direction of rotation of the drum is reversed so that two leading shoe brakes would be relatively ineffective if used when reversing. For this reason the system is usually confined to front brakes where, as stated earlier, the additional braking power can more usefully be employed.

A more recent development is that of the two trailing shoe brake (2 T.S.). This arrangement has been shown to be less sensitive to high temperature effects (fading) than the two leading shoe system, and also provides more consistent and progressive braking. ('Progressive' implies that braking effect is proportional to pedal pressure.) However, since the tendency is for the brake shoes to 'unwrap', higher operating pressures are required, and in order to reduce the force required at the foot pedal it is usual to provide *servo* assistance. Briefly, this means that the pedal controls the application of a reinforcing pressure supplied by the engine, in a

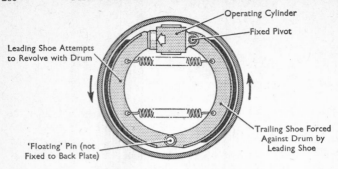

Fig. 107*a*. Self-energizing brake.

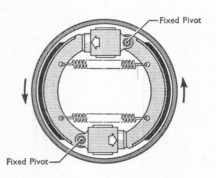

Fig. 107*b*. Two leading shoe (2.L.S.) brake.

similar manner to that described earlier in connexion with power steering. In most brake servo systems the assistance is obtained from the partial vacuum existing in the engine induction manifold; this is applied, by way of a valve controlled by the foot pedal, to a large cylinder in which is a piston connected to the brake mechanism either by a mechanical linkage or by a hydraulic system. The unbalance of pressure on this piston provides the assisting force.

Use has also been made of an engine-driven pump to provide the necessary pressure for a hydraulic brake system.

In all brake servo systems, failure of the servo mechanism leaves the directly-operated linkage unaffected, though, of course increased pedal pressures are then required.

A slight delay in response is a characteristic of servo systems in general, though in modern brake systems this has now been made negligible.

It is a relatively simple matter to fit a power assistance unit to an existing hydraulic braking system and several makes of modification kit are on the market. The unit is self-contained, without any independent controls, and is fitted in any convenient position in the engine compartment; it is connected by flexible pipes so that it is directly in the hydraulic circuit between the existing master cylinder and the lines to the wheel cylinders. The unit detects the hydraulic pressure produced throughout the system when the foot pedal is depressed; it then automatically reinforces this pressure in proportion by regulating the thrust produced by a large vacuum piston actuating a hydraulic boost cylinder. The vacuum is derived from the engine manifold depression. There is no direct mechanical connexion between the power-assistance unit and the foot pedal. The degree of reinforcement produced by units of this type is such that the hydraulic pressure is approximately doubled; if the vacuum system should fail to function the hydraulic system can be operated in the usual way, without power assistance.

HEAT DISSIPATION

Whatever method of operation is adopted, the limiting factor in all friction brakes is the rate at which the heat generated can be dissipated. If the brake lining is permitted to attain an excessively high temperature the phenomenon of *fade* may occur. This is said to be due to the bonding material being driven to the surface of the lining and reducing the frictional properties. Another effect of high temperatures is to cause the drums to expand away from the shoes until the brakes cannot be applied fully. The problem of cooling brakes is aggravated by the modern tendency towards all-enveloping bodies, small disc wheels, and a general desire to minimize the weight of the wheel assembly, and various alleviating measures have been taken. Ducting may be provided to direct an air stream on to the brakes (in one extreme case an electric blower was used for this purpose); vents may be formed in the drum to draw air through it by turbine effect, aided possibly by perforations in the wheel disc; the brakes may be entirely removed from the wheels and situated near the centre of the car, i.e. on the ends of the differential casing at the rear, or driven by universally-jointed shafts at the front. In this way they can be cooled by a direct air flow, besides reducing the unsprung weight of the wheels. Also, the large amount of space available for the inboard mounting of the brakes means that much wider drums can be accommodated, with a corresponding increase in lining area and therefore a reduced tendency to overheat.

From the heat dissipation point of view, the brake drum must perform two functions. It must be able to absorb the large amount of heat generated in a short time when the brakes are applied hard, and it must be able to dispose of this heat before the next brake application. Therefore, the drum must be reasonably massive, so as to form a 'heat sink', and must possess adequate cooling surface. The first requirement may involve excessive weight, since the drum is usually made from cast iron in order to obtain good wearing qualities, whilst the second can be catered for by providing the drum with fins. A method of obtaining the necessary heat capacity and dissipating surface, together with light weight and resistance to wear, is by the use of the *Al-Fin* process, operated in Britain by Messrs Wellworthy Ltd. The brake drum, complete with finning, is made as a light alloy die-casting molecularly bonded around a thin cast-iron liner. This arrangement enables the weight of the drum to be reduced by up to 40 per cent, whilst the high heat conductivity and dissipation result in lower operating temperatures, giving uniform braking and absence of brake 'fade'.

New trends in Automobile Brakes

AUTOMATIC CLEARANCE ADJUSTMENT

Mention has been made of the necessity of maintaining the correct clearance between brake lining and drum; owing to the 'multiplying' effect of the brake operating mechanism, necessary to obtain sufficient leverage, a small movement of the brake shoes appears as a large movement of the foot pedal, and if the lining clearance is allowed to become excessive then the pedal may move through its full travel without fully applying the brakes.

One method of preventing pedal travel from becoming excessive is the use of automatic clearance adjusters, which restore the correct clearance after each brake application. There are various ways of achieving this, a typical method being to allow the shoes to retract by only a fixed amount each time the brakes are released after a full application by using a friction or ratchet device to advance the position of the back 'stop' progressively, thus maintaining a constant clearance between linings and drum. In some cases the increase of clearance as the linings wear may be detected automatically by the increasing travel of the hand brake linkage, which is so arranged that it makes the necessary adjustment; in others the clearance is automatically reset on each occasion when the brakes are applied with the car moving backwards.

DISC BRAKES

A radically different type of brake, which, although by no means new in principle, has only been rendered a practicable proposition within recent years by the development of new friction materials, is the *disc brake*. This had been used in the past mainly on aircraft and fighting vehicles, but after being applied successfully to racing and sports cars, it is now beginning to oust the drum brake as standard equipment on production cars. The true disc brake resembles a type of flat clutch fitted to each wheel, but the version that has now been adopted generally is that originally known as the 'spot' brake. On each wheel is rigidly mounted a thin plate, made either from steel faced with chromium or from cast iron, and this plate can be gripped by a device resembling the caliper used on bicycle brakes, but hydraulically operated. There may be several calipers to each disc, all operated simultaneously.

A typical example of the disc brake is that produced by Girling (Fig. 108). It will be seen that one caliper per disc is used, with specially shaped pads to ensure even wear of the disc. The operating mechanism is balanced so that there is no tendency to push the disc sideways. It is claimed that the life of the pads is comparable with that of drum brake linings, and the open construction of the caliper permits the state of wear of the pads to be seen at a

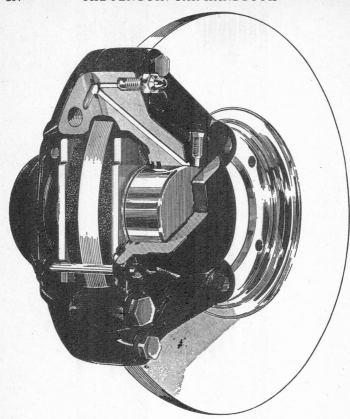

Fig. 108. Girling disc brake showing how the pads are retained by pins to allow quick replacement. (*By courtesy of Girling Ltd*)

glance. The pads are retained by a simple pin arrangement and can be replaced rapidly.

The advantages of disc brakes are manifold; they are less bulky than drum brakes, present few cooling problems, and are self-cleaning of water and dirt. Braking effect is consistent and not affected by high disc temperatures.

The legal requirement of an alternative method of actuation can be met by providing an additional small caliper on the rear discs only, operated by a mechanical linkage; however, since an efficient hand brake system is rather more easily achieved with drum brakes and since the superior braking of disc brakes is best utilized at the front wheels, it is quite usual to find disc brakes used only at the front and drum brakes at the rear.

Owing to the absence of any self-energizing action, the retardation produced by disc brakes may be regarded as proportional to pedal pressure, i.e. braking is progressive; to reduce the high pedal pressures required for peak braking, servo assistance is often provided.

ROLLS-ROYCE BRAKING SYSTEM

Rolls-Royce and Bentley cars are fitted with a unique and highly efficient braking system, incorporating mechanical servo assistance, which is illustrated in Fig. 109. A duplicated hydraulic system is provided, with two trailing shoes at the front and single cylinder operation at the rear. A cable-operated hand brake also actuates the rear brakes and can be augmented by a parking lock which operates on the automatic transmission system (see page 180). The servo mechanism consists of a plate clutch which is driven from the gearbox output shaft. Depression of the footbrake, besides operating the hydraulic system, causes this clutch to engage, and the clutch-plate, in attempting to rotate, applies an assisting force to the brake mechanism.

The braking system of the Rolls-Royce 'Silver Shadow' and Bentley 'T' Series models is, however, quite different from the earlier mechanical-servo system described above. These cars have triplicated braking arrangements, using Girling disc brakes on all four wheels, with partial hydraulic servo operation. The brakes are fed by two independent hydraulic systems, each supplied at 2,500 pounds per square inch by one or other of two engine-driven pumps. One hydraulic system feeds one caliper on each front wheel disc (and also supplies the automatic height control rams in the suspension system), providing 31 per cent of the total braking effort. The second system feeds a second caliper on each front disc

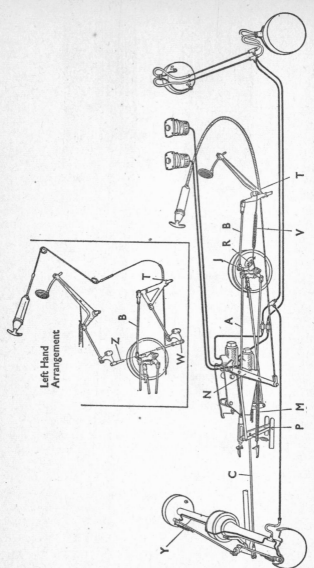

Left Hand
Arrangement

Fig. 109. Rolls-Royce braking system using mechanical servo. (*By courtesy of Rolls-Royce Ltd*)

and a caliper on each rear disc, to give 46 per cent of the braking. The brake pedal, in addition to actuating the valves which control these two servo systems, also operates directly on a normal hydraulic system in the rear brakes to give the remaining 23 per cent of the braking; this last system incorporates a 'g-sensitive' valve, as described later in this chapter, to prevent premature locking of the rear wheel brakes.

An interesting safety feature is incorporated in the handbrake in this system. The brake is actually a positive transmission lock within the automatic gearbox, and is engaged by selecting 'Reverse' with the car stationary and with the ignition switched off; however, the brake cannot be released even if the gear selector lever is subsequently moved accidentally (the lever being a light finger-tip control with this gearbox), since the ignition must be deliberately switched on again to unlock the transmission.

CITROEN DS BRAKING SYSTEM

The brakes on the Citroen DS front-wheel-drive saloon are servo-operated by hydraulic pressure derived from an engine-driven seven-piston pump which also serves a number of other power-operated controls. Disc brakes are used inboard at the front, i.e. immediately adjacent to the final-drive unit, and conventional drum brakes at the rear. Front and rear brakes are fed by entirely separate pipe systems and the distribution of braking force between front and rear is automatically adjusted according to variations in load on the rear axle. A mechanical system is also fitted, for operation of the front brakes only, and is controlled by a separate foot-pedal which can be locked in the 'on' position.

REAR WHEEL BRAKING CONTROL

The increased effectiveness of modern braking systems and the forward positioning of the mass of the engine and transmission has aggravated the problem of weight transfer from rear to front wheels during braking, which tends to promote rear wheel skidding. Various means have been introduced to limit the braking effort available at the rear wheels. A simple relief valve may be fitted in the hydraulic system of the rear brakes to set a fixed limit on braking pressure, and this may be so arranged that the pressure setting is automatically increased if the vehicle is heavily laden. Also used is an *inertia valve*, incorporating a large steel ball which rolls up an incline according to the rate at which the vehicle is decelerating and ultimately shuts off the hydraulic pressure to the rear brakes. In the Girling Skid Control Valve (Figs. 110 and 111) a ball-valve of this type is used in conjunction with a *pressure transducer*, a differential valve which proportions the pressures applied to the front and rear brakes so as to obtain the optimum ratio of braking effort between front and rear wheels.

ANTI-SKID DEVICES

Further developments in braking are aimed at eliminating locking of wheels and thus preventing skids. The Dunlop 'Maxaret' unit has been used on aircraft undercarriage brakes for some years and is under further development for commercial vehicle and car applications. Individual Maxaret units are fitted at each road-wheel, each unit containing a small flywheel driven by direct gearing from the adjacent wheel. When the brake is applied, the road-wheel and flywheel both decelerate but if the road-wheel tends to lock, the flywheel 'over-runs' against a spring and causes a valve to open, relieving hydraulic pressure until the brake unlocks and allows the road-wheel to rotate. In this way the brakes are held just below the wheel-locking point, which gives maximum braking effect; this results in balanced non-skid braking and gives the minimum stopping distance, even when the driver applies the brakes heavily on a slippery surface.

Also under development is the Lockheed 'Antilok' braking device, an example installation of which uses a single sensing-unit driven from the propeller shaft; this unit again incorporates a flywheel, which over-runs a clutch drive if locking of either or both rear wheels occurs, and operates an air valve controlling a servo unit to relieve hydraulic pressure in the rear brakes.

BRAKE WARNING LAMPS

The legal aspect regarding brake warning or stop lamps is mentioned in Chapter 12.

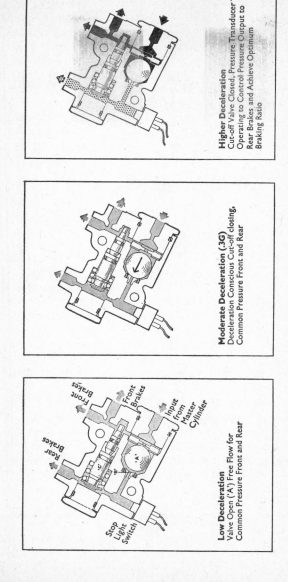

Low Deceleration
Valve Open ('A') Free Flow for
Common Pressure Front and Rear

Moderate Deceleration (.3G)
Deceleration Conscious Cut-off closing,
Common Pressure Front and Rear

Higher Deceleration
Cut-off Valve Closed, Pressure Transducer
Operating to Control Pressure Output to
Rear Brakes and Achieve Optimum
Braking Ratio

Stop Light Switch

Rear Brakes

Front Brakes

Front Brakes

Input from Master Cylinder

Fig. 110. In the Girling Skid Control Valve deceleration causes a ball to climb an incline to block pressure applied to the rear brakes. (*By courtesy of Girling Ltd*)

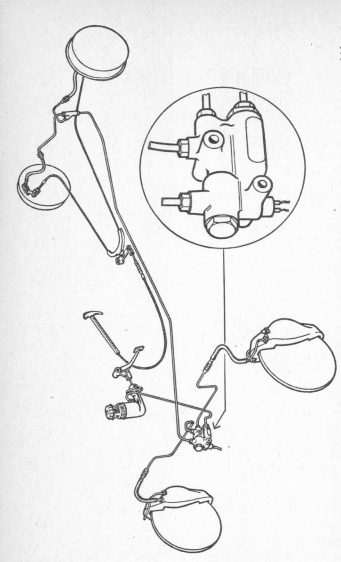

Fig. 111. Complete braking system with disc front brakes and drum rear brakes and incorporating a skid control valve. (*By courtesy of Girling Ltd*)

Modern cars are usually provided with two stop lamps, which take the form of additional filaments in the tail lamps.

Operation of the stop lamps is automatically performed by depression of the brake pedal. This is achieved either by a microbreak switch coupled to the brake operating rod by a tension spring, or by a switch incorporated in the hydraulic system. In the latter case, the increased pressure in the brake line forces a spring-loaded disc on to two contacts, thus completing the stop lamp circuit.

BRAKE LININGS

Each brake shoe is faced with a lining of special friction material, which may be attached to it by means of copper or brass rivets, though cementing is also used. The linings can be renewed when worn, and, while this work can be done by a local garage, it is common practice for the entire shoe to be replaced, the old shoe being returned to the manufacturer for relining, on an exchange basis.

The lining is invariably composed basically of asbestos, which used at one time to be in the form of woven cloth impregnated with resin. Other constituents, such as zinc or brass wire which could be woven into the cloth, were included for heavy-duty applications. However, the problem of 'fade' intensified research into the development of linings which retained their frictional properties at high temperatures and this led to the introduction of *moulded* linings using asbestos fibres rather than woven cloth as the basic material, with the inclusion of various new ingredients. Moulded linings are now almost universal and they have an incidental advantage in that they recover more rapidly from water immersion than do the woven type.

DISC BRAKE FRICTION PADS

The development of disc brake pads is more difficult than that of drum brake linings because the smaller area of the pads means that both operating pressures and temperatures are much higher. These problems are aggravated by the fact that disc brakes tend to be used particularly on cars of higher-than-average performance, although their use has also extended to small family saloons. Brake pad surface temperatures of 600°C. are not uncommon, and materials which will give satisfactory service under these conditions are expensive to produce.

In addition to possessing high frictional properties and low rates of wear at elevated temperatures, disc brake pads must have low heat conductivity so that heat is not transmitted to the brake fluid, causing it to boil. Some designs of brake also require the pads to have a low coefficient of thermal expansion to avoid jamming of the pads within the brake housing.

CHAPTER NINE

COACHWORK

THE changing outward appearance of the car has been influenced both by changes in the disposition of the various components and by the new approach to its construction.

Early cars inherited the skills in body building which had been developed over many years of carriage work, and the traditional method of construction was established as the attachment of hand beaten steel panels to a timber framework. However, panel-beating by hand is a tedious business and long experience is required to produce a first-class finish. The power press replaced the craftsman in the production of relatively simple steel panels, and during the 1930s most car bodies were built from pressed-steel panels on a timber framework.

Further advances in steel-pressing and in welding made it possible to unite more elaborate pressings so as to form a self-supporting body structure with no underlying framework. The next step was to replace the traditional girder chassis by a steel underpan which, when welded to the body, formed an exceedingly rigid 'box'. The first British car made on this principle, known variously as *unit*, *monocoque* (i.e. 'single shell'), *integral*, or *chassis-less* construction, was the Vauxhall 10 Saloon introduced in 1937. Today the majority of cars are constructed in this way including some in the highest price bracket.

Unit construction gives great strength in comparison with weight, and the car is designed so that stresses are distributed evenly throughout the structure. An important feature is that the roof contributes a great deal towards the torsional strength, i.e. the resistance to twisting. It is significant that it is comparatively rare to find a unit construction car offered in the drophead style. When this is done, the cost is invariably higher than the saloon version, partly because additional strengthening members have to be incorporated in order to compensate for the absence of the roof structure.

The adoption of unit construction has had considerable effect on the number of models which are available from any one manufacturer. The introduction of a new unit-construction car involves vast expenditure on press tools and on jigs (i.e. accurate aligning structures upon which the pressings are assembled and welded). In order to make the best possible use of this capital outlay, it is customary for one body style to be adopted, either totally or in part, for several models. This may mean that the same basic body style will be offered with a choice of two or three engines, or certain basic pressings may be utilized, with variations in bonnet or wing treatment.

Although the use of steel pressings has been associated with the mass-produced car, they are now used in top quality cars though the inspection standards are, of course, exceptionally rigid.

ROVER 2000 CONSTRUCTION

The unorthodox construction of the Rover 2000 saloon and its test procedure are worthy of special mention. Despite the fact that this is fundamentally a unit-construction or chassis-less car, its design allows it to be taken to a fully mobile and driveable state whilst still in 'skeleton' form. The final panelling, which is non-load-bearing, is not added until almost the end of the production sequence. The object is to maintain maximum accessibility during fitting and testing of the running gear (engine, transmission, suspension, steering and so on) and the electrical equipment, and to eliminate any possibility of damage to finished painted surfaces during these stages of manufacture. It also makes it possible for dealers to stock replacement panels in the finished state, other than top-coat painting, for quick repairs to the outer skin.

This form of construction demands extreme accuracy to ensure precise location and fit of the panels. In principle this is achieved by first constructing the *base unit* (shown at an intermediate state in Plate 2) which is inspected to a meticulous standard befitting this quality of car; the 62 holes needed for the attachment of the running gear, panelling, etc., are then made in bosses welded into the base unit which is mounted for this purpose in very large jig fixtures acting as giant multiple drilling machines.

After assembly of the running gear and electrical equipment the skeleton car is driven over a 'cattle grid' to settle the suspension and then mounted on rollers in an enclosed booth where it is 'driven' at speeds up to 75 m.p.h. to check for engine and transmission noises and to test the brakes. The building of the car is then completed by the addition of the seating, upholstery, trim, doors, outer panels, etc., after which it is tested for several minutes in a 'shaker' booth; here the road-wheels are supported on cradles which are vibrated to simulate very severe road conditions and this enables any potential rattles to be located and rectified. The car is then tested in a 'storm' booth in which it is subjected to 70 m.p.h. water sprays to reveal any leaks, and finally each car is checked out whilst being driven around a test track.

SOUND-PROOFING

A problem which arises from unit construction is that of 'drumming'. This is the rumbling noise which is generated initially by the road wheels and then accentuated by the 'hollow box' effect of the car structure.

Two remedies are in use, one being the provision of insulation between the wheels and the body by the incorporation of rubber bushes and pads in the suspension system, and the other being the treatment of large panels with sound-deadening material either by a type of flock-spraying or by the attachment with adhesive of rubberized-felt.

Similar precautions are taken with cars employing conventional chassis frames and the extent of the sound-proofing treatment is, of course, partly determined by cost considerations; in some Rolls-Royce and Bentley cars it extends to the virtual elimination of all metal-to-metal contacts between chassis and body.

BODY STYLING

In general it may be said that most changes in body styling constitute improvements, although, as with all fashions, some features have been subject to exaggeration; for example, the sloping of the windscreen for its streamlining effect has been overdone in some cases so that the driver is at an excessive distance from the screen and undesirable optical effects are produced.

The development of certain mechanical features which are common to many cars has resulted in a general conformity in styling. These include the forward mounting of the engine, resulting in a short bonnet length with pronounced slope to improve visibility, and the adoption of the full width body which affords maximum seating space.

Another feature which is common to most cars is the provision of wide doors all hung at their forward edges. In many cases the edge of the rear door is arranged to overlap the front of the rear wing so that the surface of the latter is kept clean where it is liable to come into contact with clothes. One marked improvement in the modern small four-door saloon is the provision of rear doors of satisfactory width, made possible by the general 'forward move' mentioned above.

A further practical design point is the use of a pronounced turned-out 'lip' to the edges of the wheel openings which assists in limiting damage in the event of a sidescrape. Sometimes, a chromium plated rubbing-strip is fitted to the waistline of a slab-sided model to provide a similar protection. On some unit-construction cars the outer portions of the wings are made detachable so that repair to these vulnerable parts does not involve cutting of the load-bearing portions of the body structure.

The use of smaller road wheels means that in some cases the spare wheel can be mounted vertically at the side of the luggage boot where it is readily accessible.

The inner panels of the wings (*flitch plates*) usually form an integral part of the body structure and the bonnet must be of the one-piece type. It is usually hinged on either front or rear edge, though it is generally considered that the accessibility provided by this arrangement is inferior to that afforded by the traditional side opening bonnet. In the Triumph Herald, which has a separate chassis frame, the front portion of the bodywork is unstressed and is made to hinge forward in one piece.

LAYOUT OF CONTROLS

Some recent control arrangements have shown exceptional standards in design, in contrast with the unfortunate layouts prevalent in the immediately post-war years. A particular improvement is the asymmetrical positioning of knobs which enables them to be readily identified by feel, as opposed to the frequent 'six knobs in a row' approach. More attention is also paid to the grouping of essential instruments so that the deflection of the driver's line of sight is kept to the minimum. The degree of instrumentation varies according to the type of car with a trend towards the replacement of dials by lamps, in the touring car.

Gear levers appear in a variety of arrangements, and handbrakes likewise. Lever type handbrakes give a more positive feel than the 'umbrella handle' or pull-out type, but many manufacturers persist in so placing the lever that it cannot be operated by the same hand as is used for gear changing.

It is gradually being appreciated that the proper design of the control system is in itself an aid to safety, and the subject is receiving a full *ergonomic* study, the object being to give each control an ideal position, mode of operation and identifying shape of knob or lever; examples of this may be seen in the facia layout of the Rover 2000.

PEDAL ARRANGEMENTS

Foot pedal arrangement has become virtually standardized, with clutch or gear-change pedal on the left, brake pedal in the centre, and accelerator to the right, except that in a few cases the accelerator is found in the central position.

The development of hydraulic control for the clutch as well as the brakes has made possible the use of *pendant* or top-suspended foot pedals; these obviate the necessity for holes in the footboard, with their attendant potential draughts.

Spacing of pedals is still open to criticism in some cases, particularly with regard to the provision of adequate resting space for the left foot, to the left of the clutch pedal. However, in some cases a rest is provided for the left foot, and it may also be utilized to operate the dip switch in the form of an 'organ' type pedal, of the shape often used for the accelerator.

With a carefully designed pedal arrangement it is possible to employ the 'heel-and-toe' technique practised by racing drivers. This is used when making downward gear changes prior to the negotiation of a corner, and entails braking with the sole of the right foot whilst the heel or edge of the foot operates the accelerator; the engine can thus be speeded up to match the gear change, with the left foot operating the clutch, and braking maintained all the while. It may be argued that this practice is unnecessary with the modern synchromesh gearbox and that it makes more work for the clutch mechanism but enthusiastic motorists welcome the encouragement to skilful driving afforded by correct pedal placing and the heel-and-toe technique certainly contributes to safety, at the same time relieving the synchromesh mechanism of considerable strain if double declutching is also practised.

In those cars where the clutch pedal has been eliminated by the provision of an automatic or semi-automatic transmission the brake pedal is often enlarged to a size where it may be operated by either the right or left foot or by both feet together.

SEATING

Close attention is being given to the design of seats, in order to obtain a satisfactory 'anatomical' shape. In the majority of cases the seat filling is a spring interior with foam rubber overlay, but tubular frame seats of the 'hammock' type are also in use.

Modern body design has influenced seating capacity in two ways. The use of steering column gear controls, or the total abolition of the manual gear shift, has left the floor of the driving compartment almost completely unobstructed, permitting the use of a full width bench type seat, capable of accommodating three people. It is significant that in the smaller cars individual front seats and floor-mounted gear controls have been retained, the width being insufficient to justify a bench-type seat. Forward engine mounting also allows all seating to be moved forward so that the rear wheel arches do not cause significant obstruction of the rear seat (Fig. 113).

It is usual to provide backward and forward adjustment of the front seats, both for the benefit of the driver and of the occupants of the rear seats. Unfortunately, it is rare nowadays to find that the steering column is also adjustable in length to match the seat movement. An increasing number of cars are being equipped with front seats in which the squabs (backs) are instantly adjustable for rake, or angle of slope; in some cases they can be laid flat to form beds in conjunction with the rear seats.

INTERIOR TRIM AND UPHOLSTERY

Synthetic materials of various types have almost entirely supplanted the traditional materials for interior trimming, other than for seat upholstery, although woven cloth is still used for head-linings. A particularly well-known plastics material is *Vynide*, produced by I.C.I. Ltd., which is basically a woven or knitted fabric backing coated with p.v.c., and which is widely used as an alternative to leather for seat upholstery. On the Continent, materials woven directly from synthetic fibres are also used for upholstery though in Britain they are more usually found in the protective seat covers fitted as 'extras' by some motorists.

Vynide material specially proofed against 'wicking', or sucking-up of moisture, is also used for collapsible hoods in place of rubberized fabric, the joints being either welded or stitched; transparent rear-view panels of flexible plastics material are incorporated into the hood by welding.

In some cars a porous or 'breathable' type of p.v.c., known as 'Vynair', laminated with polyurethane foam, is attached with adhesive directly to the inside of the roof instead of the more usual detachable head-lining; this gives an increase in headroom and also contributes to sound damping. Foam-backed plastics materials are commonly used for many other trim details, including facia panel coverings and mirror-surrounds where they afford a degree of crash protection. Unsupported plastic sheet is used for door trim panels, the styling features being produced by radio-frequency welding techniques; hardboard backings are used, with inner packing of weldable plastic foam or cellulose acetate wadding.

Another I.C.I. material is *Vulkide*, which retains embossed patterns well and can be vacuum-formed and foam filled to make such features as crash-protection rolls and arm-rest coverings. It is also available as a rigid material which can be vacuum-shaped, complete with decorative effects, to make facia panels, gearbox covers and the like.

The traditional leather, in which the firm of Connolly Bros. are specialists, is still very widely used for upholstery and trim panels, particularly of course in high-quality cars, and is very often offered as an alternative to plastics seat materials at some small extra cost on de-luxe models in the lower price brackets. Top-quality tanned natural cowhide is used and modern developments in dyeing and finishing have made leathers available in a wide range of colours, including light pastel shades, and with a variety of surface textures. Despite the excellence of modern plastics materials, real leather is still regarded as an ideal upholstery material of unquestionable durability in its resistance to wear and the effects of age and exposure; it has a pleasant feel without clinging to the clothes and imparts a sense of luxury with the special satisfaction of its association with craftsmanship and good taste. In some cars leather is used for those parts of the upholstery which receive direct wear, whilst the less prominent surfaces, such as the backs of the seats, are covered with plastics material of the 'Vynide' type.

WINDOWS

Modern body designs feature larger windows, or *lights* as they are correctly termed, and in particular deep curved windscreens and rear lights with pronounced 'wrap-round'. Curved glass may also be used in side windows to provide additional passenger space at shoulder level without increasing the overall vehicle width (Fig. 112); further scope in this field lies in the development of *flexible* glass.

Although the law requires only forward-facing glass to be of the safety type, 'safety glass all round' is the rule for most cars. In Britain a particularly well-known safety glass is manufactured by the firm of Triplex, and in many cars the variety known as *Triplex Toughened* is used. This is a single thickness of plate glass which has been heated to softening temperature and then rapidly cooled on the outside faces. (The pattern of the cooling air jets can be observed on some windscreens when viewed obliquely.) This process leaves the glass in a state of internal stress so that immediately the skin is broken the whole sheet disintegrates into small non-injurious fragments. (From this is follows that a toughened sheet

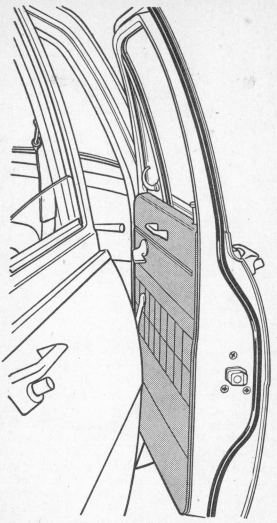

Fig. 112. The use of curved window glass to increase passenger space at shoulder level. (*By courtesy of Vauxhall Motors Ltd*)

Fig. 113. Side elevations of comparable cars of 1937 (Morris 12–4), 1958 (Morris Cowley) and 1967 (Austin 1800), showing the movement of the seating forward of the rear wheels. (Based on drawings supplied by the British Motor Corporation.)

of glass must be manufactured to the required shape and cannot be altered by cutting.)

A fractured toughened screen may present a hazard because the glass takes on a 'frosted' appearance and can become almost opaque. For this reason there have been developments in *zone-toughened* windscreens, in which particular areas of the glass are so treated that they disintegrate into larger fragment patterns and so yield improved visibility. The first zone-toughened screens incorporated a single zone in front of the driver but later editions of the relevant British Standard B.S.857 allow for a larger zone, extending almost the full width of the screen; in a further development the craze pattern appears as vertical bands alternating in coarse and fine particle sizes and this type of screen is known by Triplex as 'Zebrazone'.

In all toughened screens the border region of the glass is tempered so that it disintegrates into small particles, to ensure that no large pieces of glass remain in the screen surround when the screen is smashed out of its frame.

In some countries toughened glass is not permitted in windscreens and *laminated* glass is used. Triplex Laminated consists of two thin sheets of conventional glass between which is sandwiched a clear plastic film of polyvinyl butyral; if the glass is broken the pieces do not scatter since they are bonded to the film.

Laminated glass can be cut to shape, the plastic film being severed by a hot wire or a razor blade. With 'vinyl' interlayer, edge sealing is no longer necessary as was the case with previous materials. This was to prevent the yellow discoloration which was at one time a characteristic of this type of glass after it had aged.

Triplex 'Sundym' is a glass made to absorb a substantial amount of the sun's heat. It also slightly reduces the glare, although this is not its primary function. In Laminated Sundym the interlayer can be dyed, either all over or graduated from dark at the top to nothing at eye level, to reduce glare.

Triplex also manufacture electrically heated laminated rear windows, or backlights, in which an almost invisible fine wire element is embedded in the glass; these windows have an electricity consumption of 30 watts per square foot and will remain free from ice and mist, both inside and out, giving clear visibility under all conditions.

Window Regulators. Side windows are almost always arranged to drop down into the doors, although sliding divided windows have been used in some small cars. In some forms of the winding type of window regulator a clutch is provided which prevents the window from being forced down from outside the car. On some of the more expensive cars the *quick-lift* regulator with a long lever is used; it may be so arranged that the window can be locked either fully closed or slightly open, to allow for ventilation. Electric window-lifts which enable the driver to operate all windows remotely are also used and units for conversion of manual window regulators to power operation are available.

WINDSCREEN EQUIPMENT

Wipers. The majority of windscreen wipers are electrically operated, but some car manufacturers have fitted pneumatically actuated wipers. The driving mechanism of the latter type is a cylinder and double piston device which makes use of the partial vacuum existing in the engine induction manifold. A vacuum reservoir is provided to compensate for the collapse in vacuum which occurs under certain engine conditions.

In an electric wiper a small motor is geared down to a crank mechanism and causes a slow oscillation of the output shaft. The wiper arm may be mounted directly upon this shaft or coupled to it by a flexible connexion.

Many modern cars are fitted with Lucas 'reciprocating rack' wipers. The motor and crank mechanism (Fig. 114*a*) is mounted at any convenient point remote from the windscreen and the motor can therefore be made large enough to drive the long, curved wipers required on modern screens, without its overheating. A simple crank and connecting rod causes a cable 'rack' to move backwards and forwards inside a flexible casing, the 'teeth' of the rack being formed by a wire, wound helically around a central core. Each wiper arm is actuated by a *wheelbox* (Fig. 114*b*) containing a toothed wheel which meshes with the rack.

Wiper mechanisms are usually arranged so that the arms are

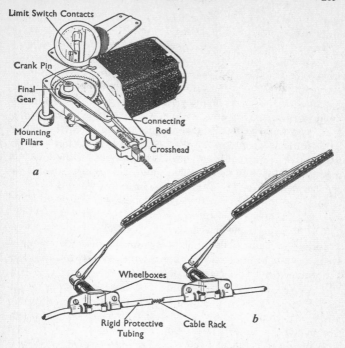

Fig. 114. Lucas reciprocating-rack screen-wipers.
a. Motor and crank mechanism. *b.* Wheelboxes and wipers.
(*By courtesy of Joseph Lucas Ltd*)

'self-parking' and in some cases a two-speed control is provided, giving an increased rate of wiping for abnormally heavy rain.

Sometimes a thermostat device is fitted which automatically cuts off the current if the motor overheats from overload, such as might be caused by clogged snow.

Messrs A C-Delco produce a windscreen wiper which is independent of electrical or pneumatic systems, in that it is driven directly from the engine by means of a flexible cable. It thus has the special feature that the rate of wiping increases with engine speed.

Further developments in wipers include aerodynamic design of the blade itself to obviate 'lifting-off' at high speed, retracting the wipers completely into slots when not in use, and providing an intermittent control which operates the wipers automatically every few seconds; the latter is to cope with spray conditions when the road is wet but rain is not actually falling.

Windscreen Washers are now fitted as standard equipment on a number of cars. They are particularly valuable when used in conjunction with curved screens, which are especially prone to peculiar optical effects when coated with dust. Two adjustable jets are installed just forward of the screen and are supplied with fluid from a reservoir; the fluid may be plain water, but is more effective if a wetting agent is added. The simplest form of washer is operated merely by squeezing a polythene reservoir, but others function automatically by push-button and give a controlled duration of spray. The operating pressure may be derived from induction manifold vacuum, whilst in the Lucas washer a small electrically driven pump, submerged in the reservoir, delivers a definite quantity of liquid at each operation.

AIR-CONDITIONING

Air-conditioning in its most complete form is found only on a very few British cars, and these are intended for export. A full air-conditioning system supplies warmed or refrigerated air at the correct humidity. However, almost all modern cars are fitted with some means for admitting fresh air to the car interior and for heating the air. Often, the air intake is situated on the bonnet of the car just forward of the windscreen, where the air is less liable to contain fumes and dust than at radiator grille level.

For heating the air, most systems utilize waste heat from the engine, though in some cases an electric heater is used. The heater may either constantly re-circulate the air contained within the car body, or it may provide a continuous stream of air drawn from outside. In the latter case a slight pressure is built up inside the car and prevents draughts from entering.

The Smith's heater, shown in Fig. 115, takes hot water from the cooling system and passes it through a small heat exchanger, the

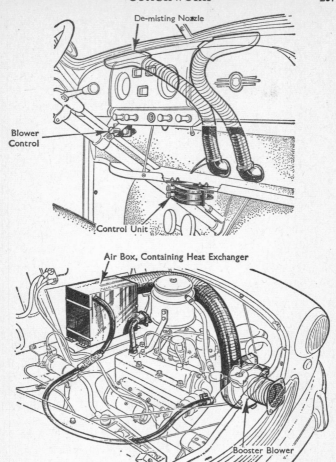

Fig. 115. In the Smith's 3½ kilowatt heating and ventilating unit an electric blower is used to boost the intake of fresh air, which may be heated by passing it through a heat-exchanger supplied with hot water from the engine cooling system. (*By courtesy of Smith's Motor Accessories Ltd*)

heat being transferred to air supplied by an electric blower. Most of the heaters fitted to modern cars operate on this basis.

A simple form of heater consists of a trunk connected to a funnel which collects warm air from immediately behind the radiator block and leads it directly into the car interior.

In a car which has an air-cooled engine, a convenient supply of warm air is available, and provision can be made for diverting some of this air into the car interior.

The problem of face-level ventilation has received a good deal of attention. Although many cars have hinged 'quarter-lights' for this purpose, these need considerable ingenuity in their design to avoid the creation of wind-noise, even when closed, and also to make them leak-tight when closed and not prone to drip water inside the car when open. Some cars have dispensed with quarter-lights in favour of face-level ventilators on the facia, with individual controls for air volume and direction.

A further recent improvement in ventilation is the provision of ducts towards the rear of the car, specifically designed to extract stale air from the car interior.

PAINTWORK AND OTHER FINISHES

Cellulose is frequently mentioned in connexion with car finishes but in fact cellulose paint is nowadays used only for re-finishing ('re-spraying') after repairs. It is convenient to apply, for this type of work, and although the older types of cellulose required both burnishing and polishing to produce a high gloss finish, modern cellulose enamels which dry quickly without stoving (i.e. are *air-drying*) can give a good gloss direct from the spray-gun.

The average mass-produced car is finished originally in stoved synthetic enamel, usually an alkyd/melamine mixture, which gives a high gloss without polishing; the enamel film is hard and tough and is better able to retain its gloss under exposure to weather than is cellulose paint. The typical painting sequence is as follows:

One coat of body primer, applied by dipping, and stoved.

Two coats of primer filler, applied by spraying, and stoved.

Wet rubbing down.

Two coats of synthetic enamel, applied by spraying, and stoved.

The sprayed coats may be applied in a tunnel through which the entire car body passes on a conveyor. The paint is sprayed from nozzles which are charged to a very high voltage, this technique being known as electrostatic painting; the object is to cause the paint particles to be repelled from each other so that they are deposited evenly without forming 'tears'. Also, since the paint is attracted only to the 'earthed' body-work the wasteful deposition of paint where it is not required (*over-painting*) is very much reduced.

The painted body then passes between banks of infra-red lamps which stove the paint rapidly to a dry, hard finish and allow a number of coats of paint to be applied in relatively quick succession. The stoving temperature for alkyd/melamine enamel is 260°F. approximately.

Other types of production finish are also used, including *acrylic* paints which may be of the thermosetting type requiring high temperature stoving, or thermoplastic, which can be stoved at low temperature. Acrylic finishes are extremely tough and have the property of not retaining dirt; they give a permanent high gloss finish, with good colour retention, the appearance of which can be restored by simple washing without the need for polishing. Low-temperature enamels can be stoved at temperatures to which a fully-trimmed car can be subjected without damage to its upholstery, etc., or danger from petrol in its fuel tank. These enamels are making a notable impact in the re-finishing trade since they allow the car to be re-surfaced rapidly in a material equivalent to the manufacturer's original finish.

A comparatively new production finishing process, which is particularly valuable for depositing uniform paint films in difficult locations such as the interior of the fuel tank, is known as *electro-painting*. As the name implies, this is very similar in principle to electro-plating. The article to be painted is immersed in a vat containing a special resin-type paint dissolved in a water base, and is connected to one terminal of a supply of direct-current electricity at about 120 volts. Also immersed in the vat are electrodes, connected to the other supply terminal, and these may be passed into the interior of the article if necessary. The effect of the electric field set up in the vat is to cause the paint to be deposited evenly on to the article, whilst the water base is liberated at the electrodes. Means are needed to prevent the paint solution being steadily diluted as the water base is released; in the electro-painting process developed by Pinchin Johnson & Associates Ltd., this is achieved by enclosing the electrodes in a membrane which allows electric current to pass but which virtually traps the liberated water base.

The theory of deposition in electro-painting is very complex and involves a combination of various phenomena known as electrolysis, electro-endosmosis and electrophoresis; the process is sometimes described more generally as *electrophoretic* painting.

Chromium is a very hard metal and well suited to resist abrasion, besides taking a permanent high polish when buffed. However, it is porous in the electro-deposited state and is therefore unsuitable as a protection for steel if used alone. Chromium plating is usually applied over a nickel layer which is itself deposited on a copper coating on the steel. The quality of the underlying metals greatly influences the effectiveness of chromium plating; the brown stains which appeared on the brightwork of some cars built in the early post-war years are attributable in particular to deficiencies in the underlying nickel plating.

Chromium plating is also conveniently applied to such articles as door handles which are manufactured as die-castings in zinc-base alloy. The continental practice of using polished aluminium fittings instead of plated finishes is rarely applied in British cars, though extruded aluminium alloy sections have been used in place of steel for fenders (bumpers); these may have rubber inserts in the impact faces to cushion minor collisions.

On many cars some parts of the bright-work such as windscreen surrounds are now made from solid stainless steel in place of chromium plated finish; stainless steel has, of course, a bright self-finish and, being non-corrodible, has a life outlasting that of the car. Also used ingeniously for such fittings as rear lamp housings is moulded clear plastic material with an internal metallized coating, giving the impression of solid metal with a permanent bright finish.

RUST PREVENTION

The problem of rust prevention in steel structures is always a serious one, and particularly so in the case of the modern unit-construction car, where corrosion of the relatively thin pressed-steel bodywork could cause irreparable damage. As is well known, it is now common practice to rust-proof car bodies by the process known as '*Bonderizing*', which is operated under licence from The Pyrene Co. Ltd. Usually, the bodies are treated immediately after assembly from individual pressings, being conveyed through a series of sprays which first clean the metal and then produce a phosphate coating on the steel. The bodies are then dried and primed. Larger installations exist in which the bodies are cleaned and 'Bonderized' by a combination of dip and spray techniques and subsequently dip-primed before leaving the plant.

The coating produced by 'Bonderizing' performs several functions. It is itself firmly attached to the perfectly clean steel surface; it forms a highly receptive bond for the paint primer, and in particular the coating prevents the paint 'running away' from exposed edges. It greatly increases the adhesion of the paint finish. Most important, it ensures that, should the finished surface be damaged, rusting is confined to the exposed metal and is prevented from spreading outwards underneath the paint.

DESIGN FOR SAFETY

Although modern developments in steering and suspension systems contribute towards safety in the controllability of the car, the accompanying increases in performance tend to worsen the effects of accidents, particularly in the head-on collisions which are inevitable whilst we have so many roads with bi-lateral vehicle movement.

Whilst so many car users decline to use safety belts, it is necessary for the car designer to regard the passenger compartment as a package for fragile objects; in addition to the obvious precautions such as the padding of sharp edges, some measures already taken include:

Recessing of door handles and window winders into the doors or arm-rests.

Provision of soft surrounds to the rear-view mirror and sun visors.

Collapsible construction for facia panels and glove boxes, to absorb the impact of a passenger when thrown forward.

Various methods to reduce the effects of the driver being thrown against the steering wheel or of the steering column being driven backwards; these include the use of deeply dished steering wheels by B.M.C. and the provision in the Triumph Herald of a steering column deliberately designed to 'telescope' under end-impact. Modern steering layouts lessen the risk from the steering column since the steering-box, being set farther back, does not directly receive the initial impact as in some early layouts with the box forward of the front axle (in which the steering linkage was particularly vulnerable to damage in quite minor accidents). In the Rover 2000 the steering linkage is placed high up to the rear of the engine compartment and the steering-box is located immediately ahead of the bulkhead, the short connexion to the steering wheel being taken via a universal joint which allows the angle of the wheel to be adjusted (see Fig. 6).

Many injuries are caused when persons are flung out of the car due to the doors bursting open in a crash. Door latches have received much development and many vehicles use the Wilmot Breeden 'Zerotorque' rotary-cam latch which enables the door to be closed without slamming but to be opened by only a light pressure on the release catch; no amount of force applied to the door will rotate the cam to release the door and there is no dependence on springs, which might release under impact. The most recent door latches are provided with an 'anti-burst' feature, the two parts of the latch being made to overlap in the fore-and-aft sense so that severe distortion of the door aperture cannot separate the latching elements.

Further safety construction developments may be aimed at deliberately designing the ends of the car to collapse under impact to absorb collision energy whilst preserving the integrity of the central passenger 'box', and the provision of a deflector plate to direct the engine downwards and away from the passengers if it is rammed out of position.

For many years automobile marketing men opposed, for psychological reasons, the advertising of safety features of the kind described above, but of late there has been a total reversal of attitude; the beginnings of this were seen in safety regulations laid down for cars to be bought for use by the U.S. government, which were naturally reflected in standard production vehicles both in the U.S.A. and elsewhere. Features which have been or may be expected to be incorporated include:

The provision of seat-belt anchorages of specified strength for all occupants, both front and rear.

Essential controls to be within reach of the driver when wearing a shoulder harness.

Instrument panel to be padded to a specified standard and control knobs to present adequate impact area; other projections to bend or break off under impact.

Steering column to be collapsible under impact, with a specified collapsing force.

Door latches to withstand specified loads without bursting.

Dual braking system to be fitted (i.e. front and rear) such that adequate braking is achieved without swerving when part of the system has failed; visual indication of partial failure to be provided. Hydraulic systems to be fully sealed against ingress of water.

Automatic transmission to have a standard sequence of selection.

Windscreen wipers to have at least two speeds and to sweep a minimum defined area of screen; windscreen washers of minimum specified capacity to be fitted.

Glare reduction treatment to be applied to objects within the driver's field of view.

Exhaust system to emit no more than specified amounts of hydro-carbons and carbon monoxide.

Fuel tank to withstand specified impact conditions without rupturing.

Flashing indicators to be capable of being switched to all

four flashing simultaneously; flashers to be fitted with automatic cancellation after operation for overtaking (i.e. by time-switch) in addition to the normal cancellation after turning a corner.

Folding seats to be capable of being locked; all seat mountings to be of specified minimum strength.

Tyres to be suitable for carrying specified loads and wheel rims to be designed to retain deflated tyres.

Reversing lights and outside mirrors to be fitted.

Although not included in regulations, there is evidence that a light-coloured car is preferable from the point of view of visibility and collision avoidance.

SAFETY BELTS

There has been much argument for and against the use of safety belts in cars, despite the fact that they have been accepted in aircraft for many years. In view of the large number of facial injuries due to persons being thrown forward in relatively minor accidents and more serious injuries when passengers are thrown from cars, the case for the use of belts is very strong indeed. Regulations requiring the fitting of seat-belts to the front seats of all new cars came into force in Britain from April 1967.

There are several types of belt, ranging from simple lap types which are of limited value, through the diagonal-strap and lap belts which are quite adequate if correctly adjusted, to the complete shoulder harness which is obviously the most effective. Most of the objections to the use of belts, other than apathy, stem from the nuisance of fastening them, the feeling of constriction and fear of being trapped in a crash; these factors are largely overcome by belts of the *inertia reel* type, which allow the wearer freedom of movement under normal conditions. Typical of these is the Britax 'Auto-lok' diagonal-strap and lap belt, which unwinds from a reel mounted on the floor behind the seat and is secured by a simple quick-release buckle. The wearer feels only light pressure from the belt and can move freely, including leaning forward, when the car is being driven normally. However, if the car is accelerated or decelerated violently in any direction, due to braking, collision, fast cornering or overturning, the reel is automatically locked so that the belt holds the wearer securely. The locking mechanism is basically very simple and comprises a steel saucer inside the reel housing, with a steel ball resting in its centre; acceleration in any direction causes the ball to roll up the saucer and to tilt a plate which brings a toothed segment into mesh with a pinion on the end of the reel spindle, a small movement of the belt then causing the segment to rotate against a fixed stop and so lock the belt. An additional feature of the 'Auto-lok' is that the spring loaded reel automatically retracts the belt neatly against the door pillar when not in use.

COACHBUILDING

Coachbuilding in the traditional style is confined to high-quality cars, where the cost permits individual attention and exclusive design.

The well-established method of construction, using panels attached to a framework of ash, is still used, but with the application of modern techniques. The frame components are shaped by machinery and pressings may be used in place of hand-beaten panels. Extensive use is made of jigs to ensure accurate alignment.

The saloon and limousine bodies fitted to the Austin 'Princess' L.W.B. chassis by Messrs Vanden Plas are examples of the modern approach to coachbuilding. A relatively large number of these cars are produced, to a standardized design, as opposed to the 'one-off' treatment which is traditionally associated with coachbuilt cars.

The ash frame components are machine-cut and assembled on jigs; they are then mounted on a pressed-steel floor which is subsequently attached to the chassis. The bodywork proper is built up as a unit by welding together pressed-aluminium panels (Plate 4a).

Much use is made of sound-proofing materials, while great care is taken with the paint finish. The body, including the interior of the luggage boot, receives fourteen or more coats of paint.

The equipment of the 'Princess' limousine is typical of that found on this class of car and includes such items as noiseless door locks, glass division behind chauffeur's seat, flush-fitting folding

occasional seats, walnut veneer interior woodwork, and illuminated step boards.

TYPES OF COACHWORK

The development of the motor car has been accompanied by a
gradual change in its outward appearance, from the entirely open
and unprotected 'dog cart' to the fully enclosed saloon. In British
cars particularly, there are indications that the traditional love of
the open air was only reluctantly abandoned. The inadequate
'Cape cart' hood was succeeded, in turn, by the full length fabric
cover and the cabriolet and landaulette styles, until the sunshine
roof became the only remaining vestige of fresh-air motoring. Today open cars are very much in the minority and invariably are in
the sporting class, except for a limited number of drop-head touring coupés; even the sunshine roof is normally only available as a
special fitment. As explained earlier, mass production methods are
more suited to unit construction, in which a strong roof structure
plays a vital part. Opening-roof conversions are, however, available for a wide range of cars, the firm of Weathershields being well
known for this type of work. Besides the original sliding-panel
sunshine roof there are also folding fabric types which slide back
to form multiple pleats, and Weathershields incorporate a perspex
deflector which automatically lifts up at the front edge of the
aperture to minimize draughts. Some sliding roofs can be fitted
with electric operating mechanism. The modifications to the roof
structure to install a sliding roof are designed to avoid any loss of
strength.

Some manufacturers are now producing only saloon cars,
though in many cases the design is modified at the rear end to
produce estate car styling. The latter arrangement is becoming increasingly popular with domestic users, especially now that estate
cars are available with the four normal side doors, thus providing
the benefits of a saloon but with greatly increased luggage capacity.

Given below is a summary of the various styles in which cars
are, or have been, available. It must be emphasized that some of
the names are liable to change with fashion and, occasionally,
similar body styles are described differently by individual manufacturers; for instance, the fixed head coupé is sometimes referred

to as a sports saloon, whilst the terms station wagon, estate car, and traveller's car are practically synonymous.

CLOSED CARS

Saloon (Plate 8*a*). Roof is part of the body structure, has two or four doors, permanent seats for four, five, or more persons in a single open compartment.

Limousine (Plate 6*a*). Has occasional folding seats in the rear compartment, which is separated from the driving compartment by a sliding glass division.

Landaulette. A rather rare type of limousine in which the entire section of roof over the rear seats can be folded back.

Coupé (Plates 5*a* and 8*a*). Has seats for two or three people, but sometimes rudimentary seats are provided in the rear, in which case the term *two-plus-two* is occasionally used. Usually, but not necessarily, implies a car of above-average performance, especially if *G.T.* (*Grand Touring*) is included in the name. The term coupé has also been used for an otherwise normal saloon with lowered roof-line.

Hard-top (Plate 6*b*).

(*a*) Closed car with two doors; the roof sometimes gives the impression of having been added afterwards, owing to its being finished in a contrasting colour and also, occasionally, in a different texture from the main body structure.

(*b*) A detachable roof structure of metal or glass-fibre which replaces the hood on a sports car and thus converts it to a closed coupé.

OPEN CARS

Sports. Invariably two doors, or less, used normally as an open car, possibly with a fold-flat windscreen, and provided with a collapsible hood and detachable side-screens. The hood covering may be completely detachable.

Drop-head Coupé or Convertible (Plate 5*b*). The hood is of more elaborate construction than that fitted to a sports car, and may have an inner lining. The side windows are usually of glass, of the type associated with a closed car; manufacturers of this type of coachwork claim that, when closed, the drop-head coupé provides comfort comparable to that of a saloon car. The hood, which may be power-operated, can often be secured at an intermediate point between open and closed, this being known as the *de-ville* position.

OTHER STYLES

Estate Car. Bodywork similar to that of a van in that doors are fitted at the rear, but provided with windows all round. Seats normally provided for four or more persons, the rear seats folding to give a flat floor.

Shooting Brake. A style, falling out of fashion, utilizing a capacious wood-panelled body with ash framing, rear doors and seating as Estate Car.

Station Wagon or Traveller's Car (Plate 4*b*). The modern form of the Shooting Brake. Some British versions still employ timber 'framing' but only as a finish applied over the load-bearing steel structure.

Cabriolet. A comparatively rare type, best visualized as a saloon with a fabric roof panel arranged so that it can slide back leaving the top of the car open.

FIBREGLASS

The term 'Fibreglass' is heard with increasing frequency with regard to its use in constructing car bodies. It should be understood that the term is a loose one, the correct description being *Fibreglass Reinforced Plastics* (*FRP*). These materials have unique properties of high strength, low weight, good weather- and chemical-resistance, and, perhaps most important of all, they can easily be formed into shells of complex shape. They have been made possible by the development of glass fibres in various forms, and of synthetic resins which can be 'cured' (i.e. set hard) without applying heat and pressure. Glass fibres are stronger in tension, weight for weight, than any other structural material; when the fibres are bonded together by resin the resulting material has greater strength, in relation to its weight, than mild steel and has particularly high resistance to impact.

The process usually employed in the manufacture of articles

such as motor bodies is known as *wet lay-up*, and consists basically of applying to a mould a layer of glass fibre mat which is then impregnated with resin, usually of the polyester type though epoxy resins are also used, together with chemicals necessary to bring about curing of the resin. The shell can be removed from the mould after 1–2 hours at room temperature, although it continues to cure for several days.

To produce an FRP panel, a model is made from low cost materials such as wood and plaster of paris. Using this as a pattern a mould is made in FRP and in this mould the finished FRP panel is produced. An existing metal panel can also be used as a pattern to produce an FRP mould, or the mould can be a specially formed metal unit.

To obtain stiffness equivalent to that of metal panels, FRP is used in greater thickness, but even so a saving in weight is obtained, depending to a degree on the amount of double curvature incorporated in the panel. The weight of an FRP sheet is roughly half that of a similar unit in aluminium and one fifth that of steel. The cost of glass fibre and resin is rather more than the equivalent in steel, although close to that of aluminium, but this is soon recovered if the expense of producing compound curves in beaten sheet metal is considered. FRP is particularly suited to the deep flowing curves which characterize modern body styling, and the wet lay-up process is thus especially applicable to the manufacture of specialized bodies in limited production, where the high costs of press tools for metal cannot be spread over a large number of vehicles. It is estimated that the maximum economic rate for producing FRP bodies by wet lay-up is around 200 units per week.

The more recent introduction of pre-impregnated glass fibre materials, in which the glass reinforcement is already impregnated with a thermo-setting resin, makes the manufacture of vehicle bodies in FRP at high production rates increasingly feasible. In this case the materials require the application of heat and pressure to effect a rapid cure but much larger panels can be produced in a single press operation than is usual with metal, at a much lower tool cost.

FRP is now used in a large number of delivery truck cabs and for the front and rear panelling of luxury coaches, where the ease of forming complicated shapes has had a·marked effect on recent styling improvements. FRP is also used for certain panels on omnibus bodies; it is particularly valuable at such points as the vulnerable rear corners, as it is easy to repair and the vehicle thus spends minimum time out of service. Garages also use FRP for repairs to metal bodywork and 'do-it-yourself' kits are also available for this purpose.

CHAPTER TEN

RUNNING THE CAR

THIS chapter is not intended to be a guide to home maintenance, as it is felt that the motorist who is prepared to undertake such work will either already be informed, beyond the scope of this book, or will refer to one of the many books especially devoted to car maintenance.

However, there are a number of ways in which the motorist who is not particularly interested in technicalities can contribute to the smooth running of the car, without necessarily performing any maintenance work himself. In addition, the ability to recognize and diagnose faults may save costly repair bills (see Chapter 11).

FUEL AND LUBRICATION

The premium grade petrols are worth the extra pence, especially if your engine has a moderately high compression ratio, and it may be advantageous to have the carburetter adjusted to suit a particular brand and to stick to that brand thereafter. It is not worth the extra expense of using the new 100 octane 'super' petrols if your engine is not designed with a suitably high compression ratio.

Lubrication, from the engine point of view, entails changing the oil at the intervals recommended on the lubrication chart. Starting in winter will be greatly eased and rate of wear reduced in summer if the appropriate grades of oil are used, but if the engine is in good condition it is recommended that a 'multigrade' oil should be used throughout the year. Incidentally, there is no need to be alarmed by the apparently abnormal thinness of this type of oil. In any case, the behaviour of an oil at the temperature at which it leaves the can is not a reliable indication of its viscosity at engine temperature. However, the new oil will tend to find leaks more readily, and attention should be paid to sump and rocker-cover joints. The use of low-viscosity oil in a badly-worn engine is not recommended, as oil consumption is then likely to be heavy; there is also a chance that the detergent effect of the oil may dislodge dirt deposits in an old engine and eventually cause blocking of the oil ways. Multigrade oil should not be mixed with the ordinary type.

Also recommended is the regular use of an *upper cylinder lubricant*, a special oil added in small quantities to the petrol in the tank, usually during refuelling; as the name implies, the purpose of this is to provide a lubricating film in the upper part of the engine to reduce starting wear and to give protection against corrosion from combustion products remaining when the engine is stationary. In addition, the lubricant encourages any carbon deposits to take on a 'fluffy' form so that they are more easily dispersed.

Another point to be remembered is the replacement of the oil filter element when it becomes clogged. Although a dirty filter does not impede the circulation of the oil, it does mean that impurities are no longer being extracted from the oil and will therefore involve replacement of both filter element and oil. Regular replacement of the oil filter element is particularly important on certain cars with automatic transmission.

Chassis lubrication is best performed at a service station, where high pressure greasing equipment is available. If greasing is carried out at home a hand gun of the side lever type is preferable.

The correct lubricant *must* be used in a hypoid axle; different brands must not be mixed.

A lubricant-additive which has received considerable publicity is *molybdenum disulphide*, a substance capable of adhering to metallic surfaces to provide an anti-friction finish. It is widely used throughout industry as an 'anti-scuffing' compound to prevent seizure between parts working under severe conditions of loading and friction. Molybdenum disulphide additives for cars are on the market, usually as a suspension in oil of the finely-divided material (capable of passing through a normal oil filter), which can be added to the usual lubricants in the engine, transmission and steering gear, to minimize friction and wear and to reduce the noise from gears. 'Moly' is so effective as an anti-friction material that it is claimed that an engine in which it has been used can be driven a considerable distance without damage even if all the normal oil has been lost from the crankcase. It must be remembered, however, that some car manufacturers may consider their guarantees invalidated if any type of additive which they have not specifically recommended has been used in the lubricants.

Remember that electrical equipment does not react kindly to over-lubrication and the oilcan should be used sparingly in the vicinity of an item such as the distributor.

When starting the engine the excessive use of the choke is to be avoided. Besides the possibility of wetting the sparking plugs, it is possible that neat petrol may enter the cylinders, washing oil from the cylinder walls and thus promoting rapid wear. For the same reason the practice of giving the engine a burst of throttle prior to switching off should be avoided.

'RUNNING-IN'

When a new or reconditioned engine is first installed its moving parts inevitably have a certain degree of surface roughness which must be smoothed down before the engine can safely be placed on full load. In order to ensure a perfect fit when the smoothing down is complete, bearing surfaces are necessarily assembled on the tight side, and if the engine is overstressed early in its life there is a danger that seizure may occur and cause permanent damage.

With a new engine, the first stage of the bedding down or 'running-in' process is carried out by the manufacturer. For instance, the engine may be rotated 'dead' by an electric motor and then be made to run against a light load. A similar effect may be achieved by using a sequence system in which a newly assembled engine is motored round by a partially run-in engine from a previous batch and is then itself used to rotate an engine from the following batch. The engine is flushed with oil from an outside source during this period to ensure that all manufacturing swarf is washed away. In very high quality cars the running-in process is virtually completed by the manufacturer and includes a period on the road.

With the mass-produced car it is incumbent upon the driver to complete the running-in, and there is a great deal of controversy as to how this should be done. At one time it was customary for the manufacturers to specify maximum speeds which should not be exceeded in each gear, and although this is still done a rather more liberal interpretation is permissible. This is because in general the engine stroke is becoming shorter and permits the engine to be run faster without incurring excessive piston speed. Also, the bearing surfaces are given special finishes which assist running-in. These include graphite coating of pistons and micro-groove finishing of the cylinder bores to ensure the retention of an oil film.

The up-to-date recommendation in running-in concerns not so much the adherence to a rigid speed schedule as the need to prevent the engine 'slogging'. This is simply achieved by maintaining a light touch on the accelerator (no more than half-way depressed), the avoidance of fierce acceleration, and changing to a lower gear immediately it is felt that the engine is about to flag. Driving at 15 m.p.h. in top gear can do more harm than 20 m.p.h. in third.

The period of restraint usually extends over about 1,000 miles, after which normal driving techniques may be used, but it is important that the manufacturers' recommendations regarding the changing of engine oil should be strictly adhered to, as well as any other instructions, such as those relating to chassis lubrication and brake adjustment.

Special attention to driving during the critical running-in phase contributes materially to long engine life, and the following points are worth observing:

(1) Have the carburetter set to give an idling speed higher than normal; this will ensure a copious flow of oil at all times.

(2) Give the engine a few minutes' warming-up period before driving off.

(3) Even when cruising easily on the level, lift the foot off the accelerator occasionally so as to relieve the load on the bearings and allow free passage of oil.

(4) Allow the engine to idle for a few minutes before putting the car away.

Running-in a reconditioned or re-bored engine can be just as essential as with a brand-new engine, if not more so, since there will not normally be any running-in on the bench in this case.

FUEL ECONOMY

Most 'family' motorists are interested in the matter of fuel economy, and it is generally known that the most significant factor in determining petrol consumption is *speed*. A series of figures for the consumption measured at various road speeds will show that fuel is consumed at a minimum rate when the speed is around 30 to 35 m.p.h. or at slightly higher speeds in the case of modern high compression engines. This means that consumption is *increased* if the car is driven exceptionally slowly and, of course, the rate of consumption rises very steeply as speed is increased above about 40 m.p.h. This is because wind resistance then becomes more and more significant and increases in much greater ratio than the increase in speed. In addition, the mixture supplied by the carburetter increases in richness as the throttle is opened beyond the half-way point.

For the everyday motorist, economy can be achieved by driving in a mild manner; this includes, besides restricting speed generally to the range mentioned, the avoidance of fierce acceleration and the maximum use of top gear. By looking well ahead the throttle foot can be lifted earlier than usual, so avoiding the need to dissipate power unnecessarily in braking. The most favourable settings of carburetter and ignition are best determined at a well-equipped service station, which will have apparatus especially for this job.

Many service stations are equipped with electronic testing gear, with which the performance of the engine can be checked visually from indications on an oscilloscope display. A well-known range of such testers are those made by Crypton Equipment Ltd, which include, in one portable unit, means for checking electrical system voltages, precise measurement of engine speed, condition of the distributor, contact-breaker and plugs, and overall ignition efficiency; the equipment also provides for accurate adjustment of the ignition timing and for checking centrifugal and vacuum advance, and for testing engine vacuum and fuel pump pressure. Some testers also include exhaust gas analysing equipment for accurate checking of mixture strength.

The use of winter grade or multigrade oil will reduce engine drag and also shorten the time during which the choke need be used;

the choke should, of course, be used as sparingly as possible. The warming-up period can be much reduced by use of a radiator muff or blind, especially on short journeys, and this, in addition, will make the car heater more effective.

To minimize rolling drag, tyre pressures can be raised by two or three pounds, though the exceptionally high pressures used by economy trials experts are not recommended for everyday running. Wheel alignment should be checked and brakes adjusted to ensure that no rubbing occurs in the 'off' position.

BRAKE ADJUSTMENT

Brake adjustment on most modern cars can be carried out quite easily by the car owner, though it may be a tedious job on some of the older models with entirely mechanical brake systems. The adjustment, which is the setting of the correct clearance between brake shoes and drum, is nearly always by means of 'click' adjusters, access to which is via the back plate of each brake. If this does not involve removal of the wheels it may be possible to carry out the adjustment without even jacking-up the car, though it is preferable to do this if practicable. This is because the drum may be slightly eccentric and cause rubbing in some places, even though the adjuster is operated correctly, and it is easier to check this point if the wheel can be spun freely.

It is a good habit to give the brakes a test every time the car is taken on the road. Do not delay in servicing the brakes if the pedal travel becomes excessive or if 'pumping' the pedal is necessary. The latter fault indicates that there is insufficient fluid in the hydraulic system, which may imply the presence of a leak, whilst an indefinite or 'spongy' brake action means that air is trapped in the system. This entails bleeding the system and can be a fairly involved procedure.

'COCKPIT DRILL'

It is worth while, and may save expensive repairs later on, to develop a habitual routine before driving the car away, even after a short stop. The regrettable modern trend towards the elimination of instruments is to be deplored on this score. However, the following procedure is suggested:

(1) Check that the handbrake is on and gear lever in neutral.

(2) Switch on ignition – the red ignition warning light should glow showing that the battery is not then receiving charge. If an ammeter is fitted this will show a small negative or discharge reading. Also, if an electric fuel pump is fitted this may be heard to tick a few times and stop. The oil pressure gauge, if fitted, will be indicating zero, or a green or amber light may glow to indicate zero pressure; however, on some cars this light appears when oil pressure is satisfactory and disappears at zero or low pressure. This point should be carefully checked. The fuel gauge should now be indicating the contents of the tank.

(3) Start the engine – the red light should disappear and the ammeter reading swing to a slight charge reading. This reading may increase if the engine is speeded up, but a low reading is no cause for alarm, as it shows that the battery is in a good state of charge.

The pressure gauge should now be indicating a reading of the order of 25 lb. or higher, though the actual reading depends upon the engine type, grade of oil, engine temperature, state of wear, and also varies to some extent with engine speed. The oil pressure warning light will disappear, or glow, according to which system is used.

Of all the instruments, the oil pressure gauge is most significant from the engine-care point of view, and should be under constant attention from the driver not only when starting the engine but during the subsequent journeying. If the reading vanishes altogether, stop at once. If the reading fluctuates on fast bends the oil level is low and requires topping-up. If no gauge is fitted, watch continually for the warning light.

ENGINE TEMPERATURE

The temperature gauge is a fitting which, unfortunately, is not found on all cars but which is of good value, especially to the motorist who runs his car for the most part over short distances. Under these conditions the engine rarely has time to become really warm and therefore does not work at its highest efficiency. In addition cool running tends to encourage the formation of acids with accompanying corrosion and wear. If it is evident, from the time taken to warm up (requiring protracted use of the choke) that the engine is running cool, an adjustable radiator blind can be fitted, and in some cases the fan belt may be removed with advantage, though this is not advisable where a great deal of running in traffic is involved, and is, of course, impracticable if the same belt also drives dynamo and water pump. In any case a temperature gauge is informative and can be fitted quite easily. The element should be positioned as near to the engine water outlet as possible, and in this location it should read about 80°C (180°F) when the engine is fully warmed-up. However, even with the water at boiling point the engine is not necessarily 'overheated', i.e., it is not at a temperature where damage will inevitably result. An engine will run quite happily at 200°F, though excessive thinning of the oil may occur

ELECTRICAL EQUIPMENT

There is little home maintenance which can be carried out on the electrical system, apart from occasional attention to the battery. This entails cleaning the terminals if they become corroded, and smearing them liberally with petroleum jelly, and topping-up the battery with distilled water if it becomes possible to see the top edges of the plates inside. A special filler bottle can be obtained which automatically tops-up to the correct level. The ice from the *outside* of a refrigerator freezer unit (i.e. the accumulated frost) is a stand-by source of distilled water.

IGNITION EQUIPMENT

Inspect the sparking plug leads from time to time to check that they are not perished, as this may lead to a subtle form of trouble, especially under damp conditions.

Have the sparking plugs cleaned and tested periodically at the service station. If it becomes necessary to replace the plugs, make sure a recommended type is used, as plugs are many and varied.

Check the tightness of the sparking plugs from time to time, but do not overtighten. A loose plug may overheat, because the plug depends upon good contact at the copper seating washer to conduct away the heat; if the washers are excessively flattened they should be renewed.

As a general rule it is a good practice to fit a new set of sparking plugs after 10,000 miles, especially on a modern high compression engine.

The appearance of the interior of the plug is a good indication of the running condition of the engine and can reveal faults in ignition, lubrication, carburation, or the plug itself, including wrong choice of plug grade.

If a plug is wet with fuel it is clear that the cylinder in question has not been firing, whilst persistent fouling with oil is indicative of worn cylinder bore or piston rings.

A correctly running plug will carry a light grey, flaky deposit on the outer rim and earthed electrode, and the base of the insulator will be light brown in colour. A plug which has been running too hot will have a bleached appearance, with a deposit resembling cigarette ash, and requires replacing by a harder grade of plug. If the plug has oil on the base of the insulator and electrodes it requires replacing by a softer plug which will burn off the oil (but see previous paragraph). Heavy soot deposits indicate that mixture has been too rich and that carburation requires adjustment. If the centre electrode is eroded away and the earthed electrode wafer-thin the plug is worn out and should be replaced.

INTERFERENCE SUPPRESSION

If the car was built later than 1953 it will already be fitted with interference suppression equipment, but owners of older cars may find the following of interest:

There is at present no legislation requiring old vehicles to be suppressed, but no new vehicles may cause interference above a certain level. All Service vehicles comply with the legal requirement. There is ample evidence to show that not only does the fitting of suppressors have negligible effect on engine performance, but easier starting can result therefrom.

In an unsuppressed engine the discharge of the spark at the sparking plug electrodes is of an oscillatory nature and brings about the radiation of wireless waves which produce television interference. Each spark begins as a very high flow of electric current, which falls rapidly away in a series of fluctuations. It is thought that the violence of this discharge may actually blow the fuel mixture away from the spark, so that firing does not occur. This effect would be most severe at starting, with the engine cold and the fuel only partially vaporized. The fitting of an interference suppressor merely introduces an electrical resistance into the high tension circuit. This has the effect, not only of removing the oscillatory effect which contributes to the interference, but also reduces the very high current peak to about one three-hundredth of its former value. The current flow is smooth and extended over a much longer period, which, nevertheless, is still measured in micro-seconds.

The resistance itself has a value of about 10,000 ohms and is very easily fitted at the distributor end of the high-tension cable leading from the ignition coil. Even more effective suppression is achieved if each sparking plug is fitted with an individual resistor. Aircraft sparking plugs and some types of motor car plugs are fitted with built-in resistors with the object of reducing electrode wear. The use of 'resistor plugs' reduces the rate of wear by about forty per cent, and, incidentally, permits smoother slow running of high-compression engines.

The cost of fitting suppressors is only a few shillings, and, apart from the general benefit to the television-viewing public, can positively enhance the performance of the vehicle, particularly with regard to starting.

It is also possible to obtain special ignition-lead cable in which the high resistance is included in the core material.

TYRES

The maintenance of recommended tyre pressures is most important, and it is as well to develop a routine for checking the pressures regularly at a filling station, not forgetting the spare wheel. With modern extra low pressure tyres the loss of a few pounds per square inch pressure can adversely affect not only the handling qualities of the car but also the wearing life of the tyre. The increased flexing of the tyre casing may result in damage which will make the tyre unsuitable for re-conditioning (see later in this chapter). Excessive over-inflation should also be avoided, since apart from giving an uncomfortable ride it may cause undue slipping and wearing of the treads.

It may be found that the car is easier to handle and tyre wear reduced if the near-side tyres are inflated 2–3 lb. per square inch harder than those on the off-side, especially when the car is driven on winding or heavily cambered roads. Also, if a full load of passengers is carried regularly, the rear tyre pressure should be increased by two pounds per square inch.

Driving habits also affect tyre wear, especially such crimes as scuffing the tyres against kerbs and cornering at high speed.

Tyres will wear at different rates according to their location on the car; in particular, wear patterns will appear on those at the front, especially if there is any misalignment of the wheels. The remedy here is to change the wheels around, about every 3,000 miles, the usual procedure being to change 'corner to corner'.

A regular search should be made for stones and glass embedded in the tread, and any gashes should be filled with rubber stopping sold for the purpose.

If heavy loads are to be carried, raise the tyre pressures and drive more slowly. If possible, place the load in the rear passenger compartment rather than in the luggage boot, so as to divide the extra weight between front and rear tyres.

A general rule is that the better tyres of a set should be on the front wheels, with the best tyre on the offside, as a blow-out here can cause the car to swing across the road. It is important that the front tyres should possess a good resistance to skidding, not only because the steering is dependent upon this but also because the greater part of braking effect is concentrated on the front wheels.

It is considered a wise precaution to replace the inflation valve cores and valve caps from time to time.

The tyres should not be allowed to wear beyond the point at which the tread pattern is about to disappear, for it is at this stage that the tyre is suitable for reconditioning.

TYRE RECONDITIONING

It has already been pointed out in Chapter 7 that the tread rubber on a new tyre, although bonded to the casing, may be regarded as a separately applied layer. When this layer becomes worn away it is possible to renew it, provided that the casing itself is safe and otherwise suitable. The modern tyre casing is, in fact, designed to this end, and is capable of outliving two, three, or more treads.

A well-known tyre reconditioning process is that operated by Tyresoles Ltd, and entails buffing the worn tyre to a suitable profile, depending upon the extent of the wear, and restoring the tread life by vulcanizing new rubber to it. This may involve entirely Re-Treading, which includes renewal of the shoulders and sidewalls; Re-Capping, which extends to partial renewal of the shoulders; or Top-Capping, in which only the tread crown is replaced. Care has to be taken to ensure that the existing rubber is not over-cured during the process.

In the Tyresoles Plus process new rubber is applied to the complete exterior of the tyre, which then has an 'as new' appearance and which, by virtue of the care taken in using a tread rubber compound, has a mileage equal to that of a new tyre.

A further Tyresoles process, known as 'Wyresoles', provides the tyre with increased resistance to skidding, especially on wet or icy surfaces. This is achieved by embedding coils of steel wire in the tread. After the initial tread wear has taken place, the coils wear through to form thousands of claws which are 'unsheathed' as the rubber compresses under load and which provide improved grip, besides protecting the tyre against penetration by stones, etc.

It may be noted that the practice of 're-cutting' tyres, i.e. restoring a tread pattern by grooving the worn surface, is no longer permitted for car tyres; it is, however, allowed on omnibus tyres which are specifically designed with a tread thickness to accept re-cutting.

COACHWORK

Modern welded construction does not lend itself easily to home repairs and even apparently straightforward replacement jobs, such as insertion of new windows, require special techniques. However, a great deal of good may be done by a general check on the tightness of screws, especially on such items as door striker plates, rear lamp bezels, and so on. Incidentally, many of these screws will be found to be of the Phillips cross-recessed head type, which require a special screwdriver. If this check is extended to include nuts and hexagon-headed screws, take care not to over-stress these, a great temptation with modern slender spanners. It is probable that many 'flat nuts' will have been used for the lighter duties and these will not normally need any attention. Push-on 'fixes' may have been used for such purposes as attachment of radiator grilles and should not be interfered with.

It is recommended that paintwork should be cleaned with sponge and water once a fortnight, or more often. Working up-wards initially will prevent grit washed from the upper sides accu-multating lower down, and a small amount of detergent in the water is beneficial. The use of a liquid polish about every two months will help to seal and preserve the finish. Eucalyptus oil is effective in removing tar. Some types of pastel finish tend to lose their gloss and may require more vigorous attention with an abrasive polish followed by liquid polish.

Water-repellent silicone polishes are available; a special point in connexion with these is that particular care has to be taken in removing the polish if the car needs repainting.

If the paintwork has been slightly chipped it may be touched up with one of the useful retouching pencils which are available in manufacturers' original colour tints. Take care that the exact colour is used – there are sixteen grades of black from which to choose.

Do not be tempted to paint over rust, however; remove the worst with emery cloth and then treat with de-rusting fluid.

Chromium plate should not normally require special treatment but chromium cleaners are available. Chromium plate is porous and its resistance to attack beneath the surface can be increased by the application of a sealer. Metal polish should not be used on chromium plate, but steel wool will not harm the plating if used gently.

Modern headlamp reflectors are sealed to the front glass, but on older models the reflector can be detached quite easily. Tarnished reflectors should not be treated with metal polish, but the applica-tion of one of the liquids sold for the dipping of silver cutlery can be very effective.

UPHOLSTERY AND HOODS

There are a number of proprietary cleaners on the market, intended specifically for the treatment of car upholstery. These should be used with some circumspection since the producers of plastics upholstery materials warn that chemical cleaners and polishes may damage the surface of the material. Both genuine leather and plastics upholstery can be cleaned with a cloth or sponge damped in warm soapy water, care being taken to use a neutral soap; deeply grained surfaces can be scrubbed gently with a soft brush.

In addition to occasional cleaning, stitched hoods should be inspected periodically and if necessary the seams should be re-treated with stitch-sealing solution.

UNDERSEALING

A treatment which is particularly valuable on a new car, though not normally provided as standard finish, is that of having the underside of the car sprayed with a rubber compound. This forms a protective barrier against the water and stones thrown up by the wheels and also against the salt which is sometimes put down on streets in icy weather. The acoustic 'deadness' of the rubber layer also reduces the drumming which is inherent in some cars of unit construction. Precautions have to be taken, during the spraying, to 'mask' certain components; in particular, no compound must be deposited on the propeller shaft, since any out-of-balance loading could cause serious vibration.

TRICKLE CHARGER

For the motorist whose journeys are short and numerous, or whose car remains in the garage for long periods, some independent means of charging the battery is very desirable. In winter, especially, a number of engine-starts may drain the battery beyond the stage at which the car dynamo can re-charge it in the subsequent running time. A simple way of overcoming this is by the use of a *trickle charger*; as its name implies, this is a device for feeding current to the battery at a low rate, or 'trickle', and it almost always utilizes a transformer and metal rectifier to convert the alternating mains voltage to a direct voltage suitable to the battery. A typical charger includes an ammeter to indicate the charging current and a switch to select the appropriate output voltage to feed either a 6-volt or a 12-volt battery at a charging current of about 2 amperes, which is automatically reduced as the battery regains its charge. If the battery is working under particularly arduous conditions a low-rate trickle charger may be inadequate and a more elaborate charger capable of giving up to 5 amperes is advised. A home charger is intended for mounting on the garage wall and is normally connected to the battery terminals by a pair of leads with crocodile-type clips. On some cars a twin socket is permanently fitted to the facia panel to take either a charging plug or inspection lamp.

The charger is left in circuit overnight, so that not only is the battery re-charged but the electrolyte is kept warm and the effective capacity increased. If necessary the charger can be left connected whilst the engine is being started, ensuring that voltage across the ignition coil terminals is maintained when the heavy starting-current surge passes through the battery.

If the car spends much time away from its home garage it is worth while carrying a trickle charger in the car, with a suitable adaptor for plugging into any convenient mains supply. The charger may be permanently wired up to the battery.

HEADLAMP ADJUSTMENT

Modern headlamps have no provision for adjustment of focus since pre-focused bulbs are used. However, screws are fitted for adjusting in the directional sense, and these are exposed when the front rim and rubber gasket is removed (Fig. 116). Adjustment should be made with the car standing on level ground 25 feet from a blank wall, the lamps being switched to main beam (i.e. undipped). The beams should then be parallel to the ground and to each other, and shining straight ahead. The distance between the centres of the bright spots on the wall, and their height from the ground, should be the same as the equivalent measurements on the car. This point is more easily checked if one lamp is covered while the other is adjusted.

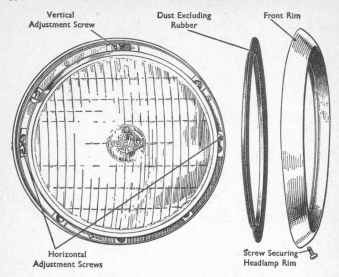

Fig. 116. Adjustment of headlamp beam alignment. (*By courtesy of Joseph Lucas Ltd*)

ENGINE RECONDITIONING

When an engine has been in service for a considerable mileage, carbon deposits begin to build up inside the cylinder head, and if allowed to accumulate they may cause serious obstructions to gas flow. Carbonizing becomes evident when the engine shows a tendency to 'pink' without much provocation and also loses pulling power. The remedy, of course, is *decarbonizing* or 'de-coking', which is usually reckoned to be a service station job. Basically, it involves removing the cylinder head and scraping and brushing away the carbon, but since removal of the head entails a fair amount of work it is usual simultaneously to carry out other routine maintenance, such as regrinding the valve seats. It is possible, however, to decarbonize by other methods, including that of blasting a suitable granular material through the sparking-plug holes and removing the debris by suction.

Decarbonizing can be carried out at home, though few motorists possess all the equipment necessary for a really thorough job.

After about 30,000 miles the average engine may begin to show signs of cylinder bore wear. The engine is noisy, especially when cold, and may be reluctant to start, because of poor compression, whilst oil consumption becomes excessive. All this is due to the cylinder bores having become worn very slightly oval because of the sideways thrust of the pistons. Gases can then 'blow-by' the pistons, resulting in loss of power, and oil escapes into the cylinder head to be burnt away. There are two possible treatments for this condition. One is to fit special piston rings, which will adapt to the ovality of the cylinders, and the other is to *rebore* the cylinders. In reboring, a revolving cutter is passed along the cylinder until the bore is perfectly circular and of the correct diameter to accept standard oversize pistons. Subsequent reborings can be carried out until the remaining cylinder wall thickness is considered inadequate. At this stage it is possible to renew the life of the cylinder block by inserting sleeves which restore the bores to their original diameter.

Other components in which serious wear can be expected eventually include the main and big-end bearings. These gradually enlarge until the clearances are such that hammering occurs; this tends to break up the white metal lining of the bearing shell, and if allowed to continue the lining will disintegrate. At best, scoring of the crankshaft journals will result, and there is a chance that the crankshaft or connecting-rod may break. When engine wear is approaching this stage it is worth considering having a reconditioned replacement engine, rather than repairing obvious faults. The existing engine is sent to a properly equipped factory where it is completely stripped, along with many other worn engines and the parts restored to as-new condition. The engines are then reassembled, but not necessarily, of course, using their own original parts. The scale on which this scheme is operated means that a dealer will always have a replacement engine available for fitting without delay and at less than half the cost of an entirely new engine.

It is also possible to obtain an Intermediate Engine Overhaul (I.E.O.) kit, comprising special pistons, and rings, big-end bearings, valves and springs, etc., which enable an engine to be given a new lease of life when it has reached a state of wear which does not yet justify a complete re-condition.

FITTING NEW RINGS

The loss of compression and increased oil consumption which occur when cylinder bores have worn so that they are no longer perfectly circular does not necessarily entail reboring the cylinders and fitting new pistons. It is now common practice to defer this expensive procedure by the fitting of special piston-rings which are able to accommodate the ovality, and other irregularities, of the worn bore. Two well-known examples of rings used for this purpose are described below:

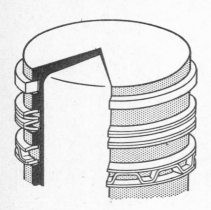

Fig. 117. Cords piston rings, 'Oilguard' oil control ring in bottom groove. (*By courtesy of Cords Piston Ring Co. Ltd*)

Cords Rings. These make use of a laminated construction in which each groove in the piston accommodates pairs of cupped rings, which are extremely flexible steel ribbons resembling sections cut from the rim of a saucer (Fig. 117). The flexibility of the rings ensures that a close fit to the worn cylinder is maintained, whilst the sealing of the groove prevents oil from being carried upwards by 'pumping' action. At the same time, the cavity between the rings acts as a reservoir to ensure that oil is present at the cylinder wall at the critical moment of starting.

The Cords 'Oilguard' shown fitted in the lower groove (Fig. 117) is also of laminated construction, and consists of one or more flat segments in the bottom of the groove, a cupped segment in the top, and a spacing segment between them to afford oil drainage. This arrangement provides highly efficient oil-control in worn bores.

Duaflex' Rings. 'Duaflex' oil-control rings are manufactured by Messrs Wellworthy Ltd, and are usually fitted in the scraper-ring groove of each piston on engines which are using excessive oil.

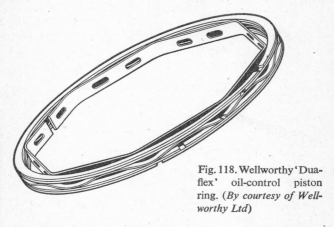

Fig. 118. Wellworthy 'Dua-flex' oil-control piston ring. (*By courtesy of Well-worthy Ltd*)

The ring is of multiple construction, the wiping parts being built up from 'rails', which have rounded, hard chromium plated edges (Fig. 118). Two such rails fit into the top of the groove and one into the bottom, and they are held against the sides of the groove by a waved spring placed between them. A spring steel expander fitted into the groove, behind the rails, presses them into intimate contact with the cylinder wall and ensures centralization of the piston in the bore. The expander is slotted to allow the wiped-off oil to drain through the holes in the piston, in the normal way.

CAR FIRES

Surprisingly few motorists take the precaution of carrying a fire extinguisher in the car. The two most likely causes of car fires are the short-circuiting of electric cables, especially the heavy cable to the starter motor (which is not protected by a fuse), and 'blow-back' in the carburetter. However, such fires usually have small beginnings, and can quickly be quenched with an efficient extinguisher, typical examples of which are found in the range manufactured by the Pyrene Co. Ltd. These extinguishers produce a jet of liquid based on carbon tetrachloride or chlorobromomethane, which blankets the fire in heavy vapour and suffocates the flames. This is particularly effective against petrol fires and, being electrically non-conducting, can be used in the presence of high voltages. Pump-type extinguishers are, perhaps, the most suitable for the motorist, since they can be refilled after being partially or completely emptied. Pressure-operated extinguishers (in which the liquid is expelled by gas pressure), can be used one-handed, but once the knob is struck the entire contents are released. Aerosol-type extinguishers are also available.

The extinguisher should preferably be mounted inside the car, as protection against weather and pilfering, but in a readily accessible position.

A further wise precaution is the mounting of an additional extinguisher on the wall of the garage. It is obligatory to provide means of combating fire in any place where petrol is stored, even if it is confined in the car fuel tank, and the usual bucket of sand cannot be considered an ideal means of fighting a car fire, especially if the engine is involved. Water is, of course, worse than useless for dealing with petrol fires, and foam-type extinguishers are probably the most effective. There are available extinguishers which eject dry powder instead of liquid, an example being the Pyrene P.D. 2·2 which is effective against all classes of fire outbreak, which includes freely-burning materials such as wood, paper and fabrics, flammable liquids, and electrical fires.

ELECTROSTATIC CHARGE

Considerable attention has been paid recently to the matter of the electrostatic charge which may accumulate on a car during a journey. This charge, which can be sufficient to give a sharp but harmless electric shock to anyone alighting from the car, is thought to be due to the action of the rolling tyres which, under certain circumstances, cause a constant transfer of static electricity between the road and the car body. When the car body is 'earthed', as by a passenger alighting whilst holding on to the door handle, an electric discharge occurs and sometimes sparks are produced. The electrostatic charge can be prevented from accumulating if an earthing chain is suspended beneath the car in such a way that it makes intermittent contact with the ground; more elaborate earthing devices are on the market.

It has been shown fairly conclusively that there is some relationship between static electricity and some kinds of carsickness, and the fitting of an earthing chain may effect a cure in these cases.

LAYING-UP

Many motorists keep their cars off the road during winter, and the following points should be observed:

Place the car on blocks with the tyres clear of the ground.

Drain the radiator and cylinder block. (See Chapter 11.)

Remove the sparking plugs, pour a little engine oil into the holes and turn the engine over a few times; plug the holes with non-linting rag, or corks.

Drain the petrol tank.

Treat all brightwork with the chromium plate sealing lacquer sold for this purpose.

Treat leather upholstery with preservative and spray interior with moth-proofing liquid, the aerosol type being very convenient.

Remove battery from car and arrange for it to be charged and discharged periodically to discourage sulphating.

Make regular checks on all tyre pressures, including spare, especially if tubeless tyres are fitted.

Remove the plugging from the sparking plug holes and turn the engine over occasionally with the starting handle.

Do not forget to reclaim any unexpired Road Fund Licence or Insurance charges.

CHAPTER ELEVEN

BREAKDOWNS

CARS are subject to a number of faults which can cause complete immobilization and yet can be rectified by the least technically-minded amongst us. A guide to the location of such faults is included in this chapter, while, for those who shy from even lifting the bonnet, a description of the activities of the Motoring Organizations is also given.

STARTING DIFFICULTIES

A remarkably high proportion of starting difficulties can be attributed directly to the battery being in poor condition. It must be remembered that even if the starter motor appears to be turning the engine over reasonably well, it is virtually short-circuiting the battery; if the battery has developed high internal resistance through age or neglect the voltage available at its terminals during starting may be inadequate to allow the ignition coil to provide sufficiently powerful sparking at the plugs. This is why it is essential to test a battery under load using a proper 'tong' tester. However, assuming that the battery is not suspect and that the starter motor is turning the engine quite freely, failure to start is almost always due to faults in the carburetter or ignition system. If the car has a mechanical fuel pump and has been standing unused for some days, there is a chance that fuel will have evaporated from the pump, which will require priming before an attempt to start is made. This is done by operating the hand lever several times until the pumping action ceases; if no pumping can be felt, the engine should be given one full turn of the starting handle, when it should be possible to operate the lever. Make sure that the starting procedure proper to the car in question is being closely followed, especially with regard to use of the choke. On some cars with automatic choke the accelerator pedal must be fully depressed to 'set' the choke before starting. No choke is required when re-starting a hot engine, but it is sometimes helpful to press the accelerator slightly whilst operating the starter. Trouble in the carburetter itself is fairly rare, but may result from a blocked slow-running jet or obstructions in the fuel line (or, of course, lack of petrol). Excessive wear in the throttle butterfly spindle can make starting difficult by admitting excess air. Dismantling of the carburetter is most decidedly not recommended, except that the float chamber may be removed to check that it does not contain sediment. If the carburetter is of the type in which the jets are readily removable these may be checked for blockages, but on no account should anything be poked through the jets. They should be blown clear and washed with petrol. On a variable-choke carburetter, trouble in the form of lack of response may be caused by sticking of the piston, due to lack of lubrication. The air-cleaner having been removed, the cylindrical slide just inside the carburetter mouth should be lifted gently to check that it has not stuck. On some carburetters a lifting-pin is provided for this purpose.

Ignition trouble is more common, and is usually traceable to either worn contact breaker points or sparking plug electrodes, or to damp and leaky ignition leads. Wiping over the leads may help to reduce the latter trouble, but perished leads need replacement.

In certain humid weather conditions a baffling refusal to start may often be traced to condensation on the *inside* of the distributor cap, which merely requires wiping dry. Contact breaker points will require attention by the Service Station, but sparking plug electrodes can be reset at home, provided that they are not badly burned; this is usually a matter of bending in the *outer* electrode(s) to restore to the recommended figure the distance from the central electrode (this measurement can be found on the charts displayed in Service Stations). A handy tool can be purchased which facilitates the bending and which incorporates feeler gauges for checking the gap.

If the engine is known to be in order and yet refuses to fire, there is a chance that the sparking plugs have been wetted with neat petrol. In this case release the choke, switch off the ignition, and operate the starter for a few seconds with the accelerator fully depressed. If the starter is normally operated by the ignition key it will be necessary to lift the bonnet and manipulate the starter relay and throttle linkage manually. Alternatively, remove the plugs and allow them to dry off.

If the ignition leads are detached from the plugs for any purpose *be sure to restore each lead to its respective plug afterwards*.

When the engine will not start, do not persist in using the starter, especially if the motor begins to 'flag', as this is an indication that the battery is approaching the discharged state. If the battery is run very 'low' it will be unable to operate the ignition coil, even if hand starting is resorted to. Therefore, as soon as the starter motor shows signs of tiring, try an alternative method of starting. If a starting handle is used, remember that the safe method is to pull up on the handle, holding the fingers almost flat underneath. Under no circumstances grip the handle firmly, as this may result in a broken wrist if the engine should 'kick back'. Remember, also, that with coil ignition, even a gentle movement of the handle may cause the engine to fire, so take care when returning the handle to the 'pulling up' position, preferably doing this by withdrawing and replacing the handle.

If no starting handle is provided, then towing or pushing must be employed, unless a convenient downward slope is available. Select top gear, depress the clutch, and switch on the ignition. When the car is moving at about five m.p.h. release the clutch gently and depress it again immediately the engine fires.

ELECTRIC STARTER TROUBLES

A potential source of trouble with the electric starter, especially in cold weather, is premature disengagement of the Bendix pinion, which occurs as soon as the engine has fired once although the engine does not continue to run. It is often due to a worn starter ring (see Chapter 4), and sometimes the following temporary expedient may prove effective. Before operating the starter and without depressing the clutch, push the gear lever into any of the intermediate positions which can be engaged fully, *and then return the lever to neutral*. This stationary engagement of the gears may cause the engine to be rotated slightly and so bring relatively unworn teeth into line with the starter pinion.

Occasionally, the starter pinion may fail to disengage, this being identifiable by a high-pitched whine when the engine starts. Switch off the ignition immediately. The starter motor will usually be found to have a protruding spindle with a 'squared' end, and it should be possible to free the starter pinion by applying a spanner to this spindle. If not, the alternative is to engage one of the gears and with the ignition switched off and the handbrake off, but without depressing the clutch, to attempt to rock the car backwards and forwards.

SNOW AND ICE

At home. In frosty weather troubles may arise from freezing of the cooling water, thickening of engine oil, and the low temperature of the battery. If anti-freeze is not being used, the water should be drained every night from the radiator, and from the cylinder block if a separate drain-cock is fitted. This will be found about half-way down the engine and usually resembles a miniature domestic tap. The drain cocks may be blocked by sediment, so it is as well to push a piece of stiff wire up through the opened cock at intervals during the draining to ensure that there is a clear passage. When the flow has ceased, run the engine for *exactly* one minute to dry it out. Leave the radiator cap on the driver's seat as a reminder that the system has been drained. (If a heater operating off the cooling system is fitted to the car, draining is no protection against frost, since the heater unit cannot be emptied through the drain cocks. In this case anti-freeze *must* be used.) Re-fill the radiator before starting, preferably with hot water, not forgetting to close the drain cocks. The use of a glycol-based anti-freeze is the most convenient safeguard, and it is recommended that the radiator drain should be wired up to discourage accidental draining-off. If any fluid is lost from the radiator the safest plan is to top up with anti-freeze/water mixture in the same proportion as originally used.

The standard defence against thickening of engine oil is the use of a suitable winter-grade or multigrade oil, together with paraffin or electric sump heater. Also available is a small mains-electric immersion heater, which is installed permanently in one of the radiator hose connexions and maintains the warmth of the entire engine overnight.

If the battery is allowed to become very cold its output is greatly reduced and the regular use of an overnight trickle charger is of value here because it keeps up the temperature of the electrolyte.

Any means of maintaining engine temperature is worth considering, because it ensures minimum use of the choke, thus not only improving fuel consumption but also reducing engine wear caused by neat petrol entering the cylinders. As stated previously, the fitting of a radiator blind or muff, and thermometer, is recommended, or at the very least a rug should be thrown over the bonnet if the car is parked out of doors.

On the Road. It goes without saying that driving slowly is the only possible practice for the average motorist on snow and ice. Chains are advisable, but speed must still be restricted to about 25 m.p.h. A reduction in tyre pressures may also be of assistance. For those who must drive extensively in snow and ice, special snow-tread tyres are available. Driving technique must be modified, use of the brakes being avoided as much as possible, especially on hill descents; the gears should be freely used to take maximum advantage of the braking effect of the engine. Care is needed when changing down, since the reduced friction will allow the rear wheels to spin if the engine speed is not properly matched when the clutch is re-engaged. It is preferable to make a change-down at the foot of a hill rather than while climbing. Do not stray too near the verges of steeply cambered roads.

Trouble in 'getting away' is usually due to excessive torque at the rear wheels. Sometimes it is preferable to use second gear, and in any case the engine should be run as slowly as practicable.

Fog freezing on the windscreen may sometimes be cleared by propping the rear edge of the bonnet on a matchbox or similar object, if the bonnet construction permits this.

When parking the car during extreme frosts, it is advisable to chock the wheels, rather than leave the brakes applied, since it is possible for the mechanical linkage to become frozen in the 'on' position. A useful trick when parking out-of-doors is to place sheets of newspaper against the windscreen, holding them in place with the screen wiper blades. This will prevent excessive frosting of the screen and simplify removal of caked snow.

If the car has been run on roads which have been cleared of snow by the laying of salt it is very desirable that it should be hosed down underneath as soon as possible afterwards, since the salt deposit is very corrosive. Washing down is not, of course, so necessary if the underside of the car has been treated with undersealing compound.

FAULTS ON THE ROAD

Some common troubles met with on the road are:

> Punctures
> Electrical faults
> Carburetter and fuel supply faults
> Fanbelt breakage
> Shattered windscreen
> Overheating

These are all troubles which can often be dealt with on the spot. Most other faults, especially those accompanied by 'expensive sounding' noises, are beyond the scope of the ordinary motorist.

Punctures are at once evident from peculiarities in the handling of the car, and no one should need to be told that a flat tyre means 'stop at once'. Actual repair of a puncture at the roadside is normally out of the question, so that the problem merely resolves itself into that of changing the wheel. The spare wheel should, of course, have received the same routine attention to tyre pressure as the other wheels. Most modern cars have special arrangements for jacking-up, but if the old type of jack is used first run the punctured wheel *only* on to a block about four inches thick (or on to the kerb) and apply the handbrake. The weight of the car will then have compressed the road spring and the minimum amount of labour with the jack is needed to lift the wheel clear. Ease the wheel-nuts slightly *before* jacking up.

Complete failure of electrical components is fairly rare, except for the burning-out of lamp bulbs. Occasionally a fuse may blow, solely on account of ageing or because of a temporary short-circuit such as might be caused by a bulb failure. The blowing of a fuse is readily diagnosed because more than one electrical item will be affected; for instance, one fuse may protect the equipment which is usable with the ignition switched off – horn, radio, etc. – and another fuse those items which only function with the ignition switched on – petrol gauge, trafficators, screen wipers, etc. The main lighting system has no fuses. Spare fuses are held loosely in sockets in the fuse-box. The blown fuse can be identified by scorching of the coloured paper slip inside the tube. It should be replaced by a fuse having a similar coloured slip. Most electrical faults are concerned with ignition equipment and manifest themselves as complete engine failure or chronic misfiring. Intermittent 'surging' of power but without total failure often indicates one faulty sparking plug. If the engine ceases completely, examine for detached or broken wires on ignition coil and distributor. Unclip the distributor cap, check that the contact breaker is in order, and examine the cap itself for cracks. Replace the cap, remove the central high tension lead from the distributor, and hold it, by the insulation, with the end about ¼ inch away from the engine. Turning the engine over should then produce a regular stream of sparks. Weak sparking may indicate failure of the condenser (the cylindrical object mounted alongside the contact breaker), and this will have to be replaced, since it is not repairable.

Checking that there is a sparking at the plugs themselves is difficult to carry out single-handed, but if help is available unscrew one of the plugs and turn the engine over with the ignition switched on. (The ignition lead should still be attached to the plug, which should be laid down with its body in contact with the engine, but with its terminal clear of any metal.)

If the spark is normal, complete engine failure is almost certainly due to absence of fuel. If an electric pump is fitted, lack of fuel will be indicated by an unceasing clicking from the pump when the ignition is switched on. If the pump is of the mechanical type, with hand priming lever, a lack of resistance to movement of the lever indicates absence of petrol. It is a fairly simple matter to remove the carburetter bowl to check whether or not fuel is present. Assuming that there is petrol in the tank, a dry carburetter can only be due to a blocked fuel line or complete pump failure. It may be possible to clear the line by removing the connexion from the pump and blowing down the pipe, preferably with a handkerchief over the end. It is helpful to have an assistant listening at the filler cap for the sound of bubbles in the tank.

Petrol cannot leave the tank unless air can enter, so if petrol flow ceases check that the air vent in the filler cap is not blocked. This will be evident if the engine will only run with the cap removed.

It is unwise to allow the fuel level to fall very low in the tank since this may mean that sediment is disturbed when fresh fuel is added and so encourage blocking of carburetter jets.

If the engine is subject to misfiring the most obvious faults are a fouled sparking plug (or plugs) or dirt or water in the carburetter, though misfiring may also be caused by more serious troubles such as a stuck or bent valve. In the latter case, however, there will probably also be spitting-back, and reports from the silencer. A faulty plug is located with the engine running, by rendering each plug inoperative in turn and noting in which case the sound of the engine is unaltered, this being the offender. The usual method is to hold a screwdriver by its insulated handle in such a way that the blade bridges from the brass terminal of the plug to the cylinder head. If the plug terminals are of the rubber-shrouded type, simply pull off each connector in turn. A fouled plug is at once obvious from its internal appearance, being covered with oil and soot. Plugs can only be cleaned satisfactorily at a service station, and it is best to carry out replacement plugs on the car. However, repeated oiling of plugs indicates that either the plugs are of an unsuitable grade or that the engine is passing excessive oil and is due for re-boring or fitting of new piston-rings.

Dirt or water in the carburetter is usually indicated by refusal to run slowly (tick-over) *or* to run fast, but not often both. In the first instance, the idling jet is affected, and in the second the main jet; an indication of main jet blockage is that the engine will regain some power if the choke control is fully extended. In any case the remedy is to remove and clean the jets, and if water is the cause of the trouble, to drain the fuel tank at the earliest opportunity.

Fan belt breakage is usually evident from the clatter under the bonnet and in most cases will also be indicated by illumination of the ignition warning lamp since the belt also drives the dynamo; in many cars the belt drives the water pump as well. Belt breakage need not immobilize the car which, once all loose pieces of belt have been removed to avoid causing jams, may be driven a short distance to a service station provided this is done very gently, to avoid overheating, and without using any non-vital electrical accessories.

Toughened glass screens are prone to shattering, usually when struck by stones thrown up by other vehicles. The nature of the glass causes it to craze all over and become almost opaque, so that usually the only possible action is to push a hand through the screen to clear the view and stop as quickly as possible, having regard to following traffic. No damage to the hand should result since the screen is made in such a way that it disintegrates into blunt crystals. If the car is to be driven any distance the remainder of the glass should be removed, since the police have been known to take the view that a small hole knocked through an otherwise crazed screen does not give adequate visibility within the law. It is possible to obtain a flexible-plastics temporary screen which can be clipped over the screen aperture and so allow a journey to be continued.

Overheating is an uncommon occurrence in the modern car, and can usually be attributed to slipping fan belt, choked radiator, binding brakes, 'tight' engine, or, of course, lack of coolant. If boiling does occur, the only thing to do is to stop and allow things to cool off, but great care should be taken in removing the radiator cap, since the water will almost always issue forth as a scalding geyser. Do not pour cold water into a very hot engine.

A rather different manifestation of overheating, fairly rare in Britain, is vapour-lock. This occurs in exceptionally hot weather, when the petrol vaporizes in the fuel line so that the pump is unable to function. Here again the only remedy is to wait, preferably under shade and with the bonnet raised, though it is beneficial to apply wet clothes to the fuel line and pump.

FLOODS

A flooded patch of road can be negotiated provided the depth is not sufficient to allow water to enter the exhaust pipe. Drive on the highest point of the road, using bottom gear, and keeping speed down to walking pace. Once out of the water drive slowly for several hundred yards to allow water to disperse and to give the brakes a chance to dry out. If water is picked up by the fan and thrown on to the ignition leads the engine may stall. In this case there are two choices. One is to remove the sparking plugs, engage a suitable gear, and wind the car along with the starting handle. If no handle is provided, or if this method does not appeal, it is possible to use the starter motor as an 'auxiliary engine', though it is definitely not recommended. Select first gear, depress the clutch, keep your finger on the starter, and release the clutch. This method must only be used for the shortest distances, since it imposes a heavy strain on the starter mechanism and will quickly drain the battery. Once on dry land give the ignition leads time to dry out before trying to restart the engine.

BOGGING DOWN

Obviously every care should be taken to avoid driving on soft ground, and in this connexion the law forbids driving farther than 15 yards from the road, and then only for the purpose of parking the car, saving life, or extinguishing fires. The most common cases of 'bogging down' occur when ordinary fields are used as temporary car parks. The obvious precautions here are to seek the firmest and highest ground and park as close to the exit as permissible. If there must be a choice, park with the driving wheels on the firmer ground. Should the wheels begin to spin they must be bolstered with brushwood or any other available material, and it is essential to treat both wheels, since slipping of *one* wheel means complete loss of traction at the other. The clutch and throttle must be operated gently so as to minimize wheel spin. Deflating the tyres to some extent may provide a little more grip.

TOWING

Certain regulations apply to towing a car, which is regarded as a four-wheeled trailer. There must be an attendant riding in the towed vehicle, unless the towing arrangements provide automatic braking on over-run, which is most unlikely. The registration number of the towing vehicle must appear on the tail of the towed car, which must also carry tail lights. Both vehicles must show full statutory lighting if the distance between vehicles exceeds five feet. The technique of towing consists mainly of ensuring that the towrope is kept taught, and this depends largely upon smooth driving of the towing vehicle combined with judicious brake application on the towed car. A clear system of signals is desirable, and all manoeuvres should be undertaken very slowly with the maximum time for anticipation on the part of the towed driver. In particular the latter should watch the towing vehicle for gear changes, for it is then that the danger of over-running the towrope is greatest. In attaching the towrope ensure that a safe anchorage is chosen. Bumpers are the obvious choice, but are often incapable of withstanding towing stresses.

Note that special precautions may be necessary in towing a car fitted with an automatic gearbox, otherwise its transmission may be damaged.

LIST OF ITEMS WORTH CARRYING

In addition to the standard tool kit, tyre pump, and jack, it is suggested that the following items be carried on the car:

Spare sparking plug
Replacement bulbs
Insulating tape
Coil of soft copper wire, for temporary binding of loose parts
Fire extinguisher
Spare cores for tyre valves
Small can of petrol, useful for cleaning as well as reserve supply
Torch, handlamp to clip on to car battery
Cleaning rags
Assorted small change for telephone – pennies, sixpences, and shillings
First-aid kit
Length of insulated wire for temporary low voltage connexions
Chamois leather, kept in a screw-top jar to retain its moistness, and dry duster, for cleaning windscreen.
Spare ignition key, concealed in some position where it is accessible when the car (and bonnet) are locked.

MOTORING ORGANIZATIONS

Every year many thousands of motorists are given assistance by the patrols of the motoring organizations, and a reference to the work of these valuable institutions is not out of place in a chapter on breakdowns.

There are three leading motoring organizations in Great Britain:

> The Royal Automobile Club
> The Automobile Association
> The Royal Scottish Automobile Club.

The organizations operate independently from a membership point of view, but representatives from all three form the Standing Joint Committee of the R.A.C., the A.A., and the R.S.A.C. This Committee was formed in 1944 'to secure unity of voice and action on all questions of importance to the motoring community'. All new legislation is scrutinized to ensure that proposals which are contrary to the interest of the motorist may be strongly opposed. The Committee takes action by placing its advice at the disposal of the authorities concerned, and in matters of national importance it may use its influence to have questions asked in Parliament, to lodge petitions, and to secure amendments to Bills, when necessary.

Amongst subjects with which the Committee has been concerned are Road Traffic Bills, parking restrictions, ferry charges, tolls, rights of way, speed limits, petrol rationing, motor taxation, road development and reconstruction, road safety, compulsory vehicle inspection, the law relating to lighting of parked vehicles, sign-posting of main traffic routes in London, qualification of driving instructors, headlight dazzle, and foreign travel formalities and currency allowances.

The three organizations also cooperate in the appointment of hotels in Britain, so that any hotel displaying the sign of one organization may be assumed to be recognized by the other two.

A further joint facility is in the matter of the roadside telephone boxes. The keys supplied to members of the A.A. and the R.A.C. give access to the call boxes of both organizations.

The motoring organizations offer to the motorist a comprehensive list of facilities, amongst which are:

Road Patrols.
Telephone Boxes.
Road Signs.

'Get-You-Home' and Breakdown Services, comprising extensive radio control systems operated between national and local headquarters and breakdown vehicles, and 24-hour emergency rescue services covering the whole of England, Scotland and Wales, operated in conjunction with local garages.

Legal Representation.

Home and Foreign Travel facilities, including itineraries, maps, documentation, shipping and air reservations for passengers and vehicles.

Road and weather reports, which include those broadcast in the television services and based on information supplied by the A.A. and the R.A.C.

Special insurance arrangements.

Technical advice on the purchasing and maintenance of cars, including car examinations.

In connexion with foreign touring, it may be mentioned that for the motorist travelling abroad, the services of a motoring organization are invaluable in that not only are all the necessary formalities connected with the transport of the vehicle arranged, but a comprehensive range of safeguards against trouble in foreign countries is provided; representatives are in attendance at home and overseas ports, and on some ferries, to assist the motorist.

The Road Patrols and certain of the Touring Services, including the assistance of Port Officers, which are available to members of the Royal Scottish Automobile Club, are provided on behalf of that Club by the Automobile Association.

A particular function of the Royal Automobile Club is that it represents Great Britain as a founder member of the Fédération Internationale de l'Automobile (F.I.A.). This is a world-wide organization which is concerned with motoring matters at an international level. In particular it is the world governing body of motoring sport, and its authority is delegated to the R.A.C. in respect of motoring sport in Great Britain and the British Commonwealth. Any motoring club which wishes to promote a competition on British territory must be approved as suitable for this purpose by the Motor Sports Division of the R.A.C. Permits must be obtained for the organization of all motoring competitions, except those confined to members of the promoting club and certain meetings which are mainly social, and the course for every speed event or race meeting must be approved by the R.A.C. Under Regulations effective from 1 March 1966, the R.A.C. acts as the agent of the Minister of Transport to licence motor rallies and other competitions involving the use of motor vehicles on the public highway in England and Wales.

The Automobile Association is a founder member of the Alliance International de Tourisme, or A.I.T., which embraces motoring organizations in many countries throughout the world. Its aims are to encourage the development of international touring and to coordinate the work of improving travel and traffic facilities for tourists. The A.I.T. and F.I.A. have formed jointly the Organization Mondiale du Tourisme et de l'Automobile (O.T.A.) through which representations on behalf of their members are made to the United Nations Organization and other official international bodies.

CHAPTER TWELVE

LEGAL AND INSURANCE*

LEGISLATION relating to motoring in all its aspects is continually being revised and extended and the reader in doubt on any specific point is advised to consult a solicitor or the Legal Service of a motoring organization.

The following section is divided into three parts, dealing with:
(a) Licensing Procedure
(b) Regulations regarding vehicles
(c) Motoring Offences.

Licensing Procedure

There are three requirements relating to a vehicle and its driver, namely, Road Fund Licence, Driving Licence, and Insurance, and in some cases a fourth, namely the vehicle Test Certificate. Insurance is dealt with in some detail later in this chapter, but it must be stated here that it is obligatory for every car to be insured in respect of Third Party Risk. A person driving a car which does not belong to him should make quite sure that the policy relating to the car covers an additional driver even though he himself is not a car owner. However, it is incumbent upon the driver to establish that he is covered, and it is therefore necessary to determine that there are no restricting clauses in the policy.

The Insurance Company will give warning that the policy is due to expire, by submitting a Renewal Notice, and this matter should be attended to promptly as insurance cover is effective only over a closely defined period, with no 'days of grace'.

ROAD FUND LICENCE

This is the licence which, in effect, grants permission for a vehicle to be run on public highways, and it is important to note that

* The author and publishers accept no responsibility in respect of any errors or omissions in this chapter.

the licence applies to the vehicle chassis (or frame in the case of a motor-cycle). The licence is closely linked with the Registration Book R.F.60A which is also related to the vehicle chassis, and which contains, amongst other details, particulars of the R.F. licences issued. It is a good practice to keep the Registration Book safely at home, and not to carry it in the car.

REGISTRATION OF A NEW VEHICLE

The registration of new vehicles is performed by the local authorities, to each of which are allocated code letters forming part of the registration mark; for example, the letters MO indicate that the vehicle is registered by the Berkshire County Council, as do the letters AMO, BMO, etc. Since 1963 the addition of a letter at the end of the registration mark signifies the year of first registration (A for 1963, B for 1964, and so on).

Usually, the car dealer will offer to handle the registering of a new vehicle, in which case his name will appear as agent in the Registration Book. Some owners prefer to handle the business themselves so that as few names as possible are entered in the Book. The application form for initial registration of a new car is R.F.1/1, R.F.1/2 for a motor-cycle, R.F.1/3 for an Invalid Vehicle, and so on. The form is sent to the relevant Local Authority, the address of which can be obtained from the Post Office or local constabulary.

The authority should be that for the area in which the owner normally resides; this is especially applicable to Service personnel and others who have temporary addresses. A current Insurance Certificate must be submitted with the application.

RENEWAL OF R.F. LICENCE

A R.F. Licence can be renewed at any Post Office which issues Money Orders, provided it is within the area of the registering authority and subject to provisions which are detailed on the application form R.F.1A. Otherwise the form must be submitted to the licensing authority. In either case the Registration Book and Insurance Certificate are required and a current Test Certificate where applicable. Fourteen 'days of grace' are allowed between expiry of the old licence and obtaining the new one, but only if the vehicle is to be re-licensed.

A R.F. Licence can be obtained for periods of 4 months, 8 months, or 1 year, commencing from the 1st of the current month. If the car is taken off the road the value of unexpired licence can be reclaimed by the submission of form R.F.47L.

The licence itself, which is circular in shape, must be displayed on the vehicle in a clearly visible position, and usually this is facing forwards on the nearside of the windscreen or facing sideways on the nearside of the scuttle. The registration number (or 'index mark') must also be displayed front and rear, and must conform to the regulation pattern. The figures may not be painted directly on the bodywork unless it is perfectly flat.

The Registration Book must be forwarded to the licensing authorities to notify change of owner's address and change in particulars such as colour, engine number, etc.

CHANGE OF OWNERSHIP

Vendor. The vendor must inform the licensing authority immediately the vehicle has been transferred to a new owner, and this can be done on a card (R.F.70), obtainable from any Post Office transacting Money Order business. However, notification by ordinary letter is quite satisfactory.

Purchaser. The purchaser must forward the Registration Book to the appropriate authority with his own name entered in the next vacant space in the book. No other form is involved in transfer of the registration and no fee is payable, though the purchaser may, of course, reimburse the vendor with part-cost of the licence by private arrangement.

TRADE PLATES

In order to avoid the short-term licensing of vehicles which pass through the hands of a dealer, it is customary for the dealer to make use of Trade Plates obtained under a General or Limited Trade Licence.

Trade Plates, which are distinguishable by their red and white

colouring, may only be used by a manufacturer or repairer of, or
dealer in, mechanically-propelled road vehicles, or by his representatives.

SCRAPPING A VEHICLE

If a vehicle is to be scrapped, the Registration Book must be
returned to the licensing Council, who will return it to the original
registration authority.

COMMERCIAL LICENCES

Commercial vehicles require Traffic Licences of Class A, B, or C
and these are issued by the Ministry of Transport Traffic Com-
missioners. Special regulations are applicable to these licences, including speed limits.

If a van is modified by the fitting of side windows to the rear of
the driver's seat it may then become liable to purchase tax as a
passenger car.

DRIVING LICENCE

Every driver must possess a driving licence *which he must sign in
ink*, and it is important to remember that the more recently issued
licences restrict the driver to vehicle groups for which a test has
been passed (older licences covered 'all groups').

Application for a driving licence is made on Form D.L.1, which
is submitted to the appropriate Council (relating to the area in
which the applicant permanently resides) with the fee. If no
substantive licence for the vehicle group has been held previously,
then the licence will be provisional and is valid for six months.
During this period a driving test should be taken, the application
for the test being made on Form D.L.26 and the fee being £1. If
the test is passed successfully a Certificate of Competence to Drive
is issued and enables the provisional licence to be endorsed as substantive by the licensing authority. A full licence can then be applied for, when the remainder of the six months has passed. In
the event of a failure, a further test can be applied for, though there

must be a period of one month between tests. (In point of fact, the waiting period is often longer than this, owing to shortage of test examiners.) The provisional licence must also be renewed every six months (at a cost of 10/- on each occasion) and the licensing authority can refuse to renew the licence if the learner has not applied for a driving test during the preceding twelve months, after a certain number of provisional licences have been taken out.

It must be emphasized that a holder of a motor-car licence (i.e. Group 1) must nowadays also have passed a Group 7 Test in order to ride a motor-cycle, or motor-assisted pedal cycle with engine capacity exceeding 50 c.c., without displaying L-plates.

A holder of a provisional licence must display the regulation pattern L-plates on the front and rear of the vehicle and must be accompanied on public roads by a person who holds a substantive licence. In the case of a motor-cycle, a learner may not carry a pillion passenger who does not hold a substantive licence. Learners may not drive on motorways.

The lower age limits for licence holders are, broadly, 16 years for Group 1 (i.e. motor-cycles) only and 17 years for Group 7. Persons under 21 years may not drive 'heavy motor-cars', i.e. vehicles exceeding 3 tons weight unladen.

A special licence is required for the driver of Public Service Vehicles, who must pass the P.S.V. Driving Test.

RENEWING A LICENCE WHICH HAS LAPSED

When a licence previously held has not been renewed for some years, it can be renewed in the usual way. Most authorities hold records dating back to 1903. However, a person whose licence has lapsed for ten years or more is required to pass the test as a learner-driver.

Regulations

The following regulations apply generally to the construction of a motor vehicle.

COMPULSORY EQUIPMENT (excluding lighting)

The vehicle must comply with the following:

Brakes must be maintained in efficient order; there must be two braking systems arranged independently so that failure of one system does not prevent effective braking of two wheels.

Wheels must be shod with pneumatic tyres, maintained in good order and not excessively worn.

An audible warning instrument, i.e. horn, must be fitted (certain types of signal are restricted to particular classes of vehicles, e.g. alternating two-note 'hee-haw' horns are only permitted on emergency-service vehicles). The horn must not be sounded in a built-up area between the hours of 11.30 p.m. and 7.00 a.m.

A driving mirror must be fitted to give warning of any over-taking vehicle. If an interior mirror only is fitted, the rear window must not be obscured (by 'stickers', for example).

The vehicle must not emit 'avoidable smoke, visible vapour or oily substances' and the exhaust gases must pass through a silencer which must prevent the emission of excessive noise. The vehicle must not be driven in such a way that excessive noise is caused.

Mudguards must be so fitted that annoyance is not caused to other road-users (and must be free from dangerous tears).

The windscreen and other forward-facing external windows must be of non-splintering glass. The windscreen, if fixed, must be equipped with a wiper or wipers.

A speed-indicating device must be fitted to every vehicle registered for the first time since 1 October 1937 and must be maintained in working order.

If a mascot is fitted it must be so designed that it cannot cause injury to any person in the event of a collision. (Nevertheless, manufacturers continue to fit emblems of most lethal appearance; in Switzerland new legislation has caused some well-known emblems to become illegal, and consideration is also being given to forbidding certain types of headlamp vizor which form dangerous projections.)

All new cars first registered on or after 1 April 1967 must have safety belts, conforming to the relevant British Standard, fitted to the front seats.

LIGHTING

The following lights must be shown on a motor vehicle during the hours of darkness, i.e. between half-an-hour after sunset and half-an-hour before sunrise in winter-time or between one hour after sunset and one hour before sunrise in summer-time:

Two front lamps showing white lights visible from a reasonable distance, and situated with centres not more than 5 ft from the ground and not less than 12 inches from the extremities of the width of the vehicle (excluding driving mirror and direction indicators). The power of each of these lamps must not exceed 7 watts.

Two lamps showing red lights to the rear of the vehicle.

A lamp illuminating the rear number plate so that it is readable from 60 ft to the rear.

Two red reflectors must also be fitted to the rear of the vehicle, though they may be incorporated in the rear lamp lenses.

Besides the obligatory front lamps, other forward facing white lights may be fitted provided that they comply with the following:

Any lamp exceeding 7 watts in power must be mounted so as not to dazzle a person standing 25 ft or more away, or must be capable of being deflected (i.e. 'dipped') so as not to dazzle; on vehicles first registered on or since 1 June 1952 such lamps must not be mounted with their centres more than 3 ft 6 ins. from the ground.

Any lamp having its centre less than 2 ft from the ground may only be used in fog or falling snow.

Apart from dipping headlamps no other lamp may be moved while the vehicle is in motion; this applies, for example, to a swivelling lamp used for reading signposts, etc.

When a vehicle is parked on the public highway at night, the side lights and rear red lights must be illuminated, except under certain conditions; for example, in some localities no lights need be shown if the vehicle is parked beneath a lighted street lamp, and the use of a single light, mounted on the offside and showing white to front and red to rear, is sometimes permitted.

It is illegal to park a vehicle so that it faces the traffic stream on the public highway at night.

It is possible that it will become compulsory to use dipped headlamps when driving in certain built-up areas, rather than sidelamps alone.

'Reversing' lamps may only be used when the vehicle is reversing; the switch must either be linked automatically to the reverse gear control or be provided with a warning lamp.

COMPULSORY VEHICLE TESTING

Vehicles over a certain age from date of first registration are required to be tested annually for specified minimum standards of efficiency of the braking systems, steering gear, lighting equipment and reflectors. Testing is carried out by garages specifically approved by the Ministry of Transport as Testing Stations and displaying a blue and white triangled sign. A vehicle eligible for compulsory testing cannot be re-licensed unless a current Test Certificate VT.20 is produced. The 'age limit' for cars required to be tested is liable to be reduced from time to time and is shown on public posters.

Motoring Offences

Under the present Road Traffic Act, the maximum penalty for offences, excepting those for which there are special penalties, is a £50 fine for the first conviction, sometimes with the alternative or addition of imprisonment. In addition many offences entail endorsement of the driving licence. Certain offences, such as driving under the influence of drink, may entail disqualification from driving.

Under the 1962 Road Traffic Act a motorist receiving three endorsements on separate occasions within three years can be disqualified from driving for six months.

It is worth remembering that for a prosecution for speeding, or dangerous or careless driving, to be successful, the driver must be warned at the time of the alleged offence that prosecution will be considered, or he must be served with a summons or a notice of intended prosecution within 14 days of the offence. It is also important to note that a charge relates to the committing of an offence at a particular place and time. For instance, a motorist who, having been charged with failing to display adequate rear lighting, continues to drive the car without rectifying the fault, is liable to be charged with committing a similar offence as little as, say, 100 yards away from the place at which the first offence was committed.

From the layman's point of view, motoring offences may be divided into two classes; those relating to the vehicle itself, and those concerning the manner in which the vehicle is used.

Most obvious of the many offences which may be committed are those which concern such matters as licensing and the maintenance of the vehicle in roadworthy conditions. Most of the legal requirements have already been stated, but a point worth mentioning is that in the event of a prosecution for an offence such as defective speedometer or faulty silencer it is a good defence to prove that the fault had occurred just previously or that arrangements to correct the fault had been made.

It is an offence to offer for sale any vehicle in an unroadworthy condition, unless it is established that any faults will be rectified before the vehicle is used on roads in this country.

ACCIDENTS

In the event of an accident involving injury or damage to any person, animal (including dogs but not cats), or vehicle, the driver must stop and give particulars on demand to any person who has reasonable grounds for doing so. If it is not practicable to do this at the time the driver must report the accident to the police within 24 hours.

If the accident involves injury to persons, the Insurance Certificate must be produced on demand or presented at a Police Station within 24 hours.

An accident involving damage to property only does not have to be reported.

If an unattended vehicle is damaged it is recommended that a card should be left to inform the owner, and, in any case, the accident must be reported.

DANGEROUS AND CARELESS DRIVING

Dangerous driving and careless driving constitute two alternative offences, that is, a driver acquitted of dangerous driving may subsequently be charged with careless driving. Dangerous driving is regarded as a very serious offence and carries the penalty on summary conviction (trial before Magistrates) of up to £100 fine or 4 months imprisonment, or both, for the first offence and up to £100 fine or 6 months' imprisonment, or both, for the second conviction. Conviction as a result of trial on indictment (before a jury) carries heavier penalties.

DRIVING UNDER THE INFLUENCE OF DRINK OR DRUGS

This is a serious offence and carries similar penalties to those for dangerous driving. Also, it is usual for the offender to be automatically disqualified from driving for 12 months.

Some of the ambiguity relating to the offence of 'being in charge' of a motor vehicle whilst under the influence has been cleared up but it still appears that if, for example, a drunken driver parks his car and 'sleeps it off' in the back he is liable to be charged.

New legislation is in hand covering on-the-spot checks for alcohol intake by means of 'breathalyser' tests.

SPEED LIMITS

Private cars are subject to a speed restriction of 30 m.p.h. within 'built up' areas, which are generally defined as those places in which street lamps are spaced at intervals not exceeding 200 yds. The entry to a restricted zone is indicated by the familiar '30' sign placed on both sides of the road, with the diagonal bar on the reverse of the sign showing the end of the restricted length. In places where the street lamp definition is obviously inapplicable, derestriction signs are posted, being miniature replicas of the diagonal bar device. These signs often appear on roads which are especially well lit and which pass through populated areas, but which are unrestricted. Special restrictions (e.g. 40 m.p.h.) are applied on some roads.

At the time of writing an overall speed limit of 70 m.p.h. applies to all roads, including motorways.

A car towing a two-wheeled trailer (e.g. a caravan) is restricted to 40 m.p.h. on all roads, including motorways.

RACING

It is an offence to take part in, or promote, a race or speed trial between motor vehicles on public roads. Incidentally, the use of a vehicle for such purposes usually excludes it from insurance cover.

PARKING

There are endless local restrictions on parking, but it should be remembered that no one has the right to leave a car on the highway, even before his own house. It is an offence to make repairs to a vehicle which is so placed as to cause obstruction, and a disabled vehicle must be removed from the road without delay.

There are specified situations in which a car may not be parked, including the approaches to a pedestrian crossing, and these are all detailed in the Highway Code.

PEDESTRIAN CROSSINGS

Apart from the parking aspect, two particular points arise in connexion with 'zebra 'crossings.

(1) A crossing which is divided by an island with a beacon is treated as two separate crossings.

(2) A pedestrian who has one foot on the road at the crossing has right of way, unless the crossing is being controlled by a police officer.

PETROL IN THE GARAGE

Since a home garage is a place where petrol is stored (even if only in the tank of the car) it is obligatory to provide means for extinguishing a petrol fire.

Fire extinguishers are dealt with in some detail in Chapter 10. Water, of course, is quite useless for dousing petrol fires; sand may be used, but is itself liable to cause damage to mechanisms.

WIRELESS LICENCES

A broadcast receiving licence is required for a radio which is permanently installed in a car, *in addition* to the licence covering sets installed in the home. However, the latter licence does cover the use of portable radios which can be used in the car without the need for an additional licence.

STOPPING ENGINE

It is an offence to leave a vehicle unattended with the engine running.

Private Car Insurance

The law requires every vehicle driven on public roads to be insured in respect of injury to, or the death of, third parties. This means that a contract has to be made with an Insurance Company to the effect that in the event of an accident the Company will meet claims made against its client (the Insured), in return for a fee or premium. If no claims are made the premium is not returnable and is the charge made by the Company for bearing the risk.

The term 'third party' arises from the terminology of the insurance contract or policy in which the Company is referred to as the first party and the Insured as the second party, and signifies any persons other than the Insured involved in an accident, including passengers in the Insured's vehicle.

Third Party insurance is clearly a safeguard for both driver and victim alike, since it ensures that claims for compensation can be met, but the minimum legal requirement does not cover the Insured if a claim is brought against him for damage to property. In practice, Third Party insurance is extended to include damage to a Third Party's property, and a typical policy would cover the following:

Indemnity (i.e. security against claims for damage) in respect of injury to, or death of, persons or animals, or damage to property.

Liability for medical expenses of the Third Party.

Legal costs incurred by the Insured.

In addition the policy might cover the Insured while driving cars which do not belong to him or which are hired to him under a Hire Purchase Agreement, and also any other person who drives the insured car provided that the person holds a licence to drive the vehicle or has held and is not disqualified from holding or obtaining such a licence. That is to say, provided the latter condition is complied with, a driver who does not hold a current licence is still covered by the third party insurance, although of course he would be committing an offence by driving without a licence. The legal liability incurred by passengers, should an accident be caused by negligence on their part whilst entering, riding in, or leaving the car might also be covered by a Third Party insurance.

Insurance is normally taken out at yearly intervals, and cost is relatively higher for shorter periods.

Whilst Third Party cover is the minimum insurance required by law, Insurance Companies usually extend the policy to cover 'Third Party, Fire, and Theft', and this is the most usual form of insurance taken out by motorists who are not prepared to pay the additional premium required for Comprehensive cover.

Briefly, Comprehensive Insurance means that in addition to Third Party, Fire, and Theft, cover is provided against damage to the Insured's vehicle, including damage not involving Third Parties, and frost damage, but not including mechanical breakdown. The extent of Comprehensive Insurance may vary in detail from Company to Company; for instance it may provide a limited cover for the loss of contents of the car and the compensation for various degrees of injury to the Insured may be specified.

It is clearly in the motorist's interest that he should read his insurance policy in every detail to establish that adequate cover is provided and that correct descriptions are given.

A driver holding comprehensive insurance in respect of his own car is covered for Third Party risks *only* when driving any other car unless the owner of that car has taken out 'any driver' comprehensive cover.

COST OF INSURANCE

The majority of the well-established Insurance Companies are associated in the sense that they conform to certain basic principles in fixing premiums, and these are known as Tariff Companies, or members of the Accident Offices Association (A.O.A.). There would be no significant difference in the charges made by various Tariff Companies in respect of a given set of circumstances.

Most Companies have a basic table of rates of premium which are applicable to cases where there are no unusual features to be considered (see below). Factors affecting the basic premium are:

Class of insurance – private owner, trade use, etc.

Cubic capacity, or Treasury horsepower rating.

District in which vehicle is normally garaged. The country is divided into five county groups based on density of population, with premiums graded accordingly.

Reductions in premium may be obtained when:

(a) Driving of the vehicle is restricted to one specified person.

(b) The Insured agrees to bear the first part of a claim (say £10).

(c) More than one car is insured.

(d) No claims have been made – this is termed the 'No Claims Discount'. When no claim is made during a year the premium for the following year may be reduced by (say) 10 per cent and further reduced in following years up to a maximum discount of (say) 50 per cent. Many motorists contract to meet small claims personally (see (b) above) in order to preserve their no claims discount. The discount is usually carried over when insurance is transferred to another Company.

Slightly favourable terms may sometimes be obtained if insurance is arranged through a road organization, motoring club, or similar body.

The A.O.A. have classified all cars registered since 1960 into seven rating groups, according to power/weight ratio, performance, handling, vulnerability and repair costs. A prospective purchaser can judge the basic insurance cost by finding out into which group the car in question falls (the higher the group, the higher the cost). There may, of course, still be additional charges where special risks are involved.

ABNORMAL RISKS

Where there are certain features which increase the risk of a claim, the terms may be modified by 'loading' the premium, stipulation of an 'excess', or exclusion of certain benefits. Examples of abnormal features are:

(1) Inexperience of driver.

(2) Youth or age of driver (under 21 or over 65 years).

(3) Adverse claims history.

(4) Sports cars, especially in inexperienced hands. On this general point, it is particularly important to note that, with 'tuning kits' so readily available, any modifications of this type to improve the performance of the car significantly must be notified to the Insurance Company.

(5) Age of car – many Companies specify a date of manufacture prior to which Comprehensive cover is refused. This is mainly a matter of availability of spare parts and may therefore vary between makes.

(6) Front wheel drive cars (because the value here is concentrated at the front and therefore more vulnerable).

(7) Left-hand drive cars.

(8) Persons accustomed to driving on right of road.

(9) Open or fabric hooded cars.

In connexion with (3) above, it should be appreciated that it may not be possible to obtain more favourable terms by transferring to another Company, since the previous claims record will normally be made known to the new Company.

BUYING OR SELLING A CAR

When a car is transferred to a new owner there is no automatic transfer of insurance cover. The insurance does not apply specifically to either the car or the driver, but provides cover in respect of use of the car by the Insured or others as specified in the policy. It is the new owner's responsibility to approach the existing Insurers (or another Insurance Company) and obtain his own insurance. This involves the issue of a 'Cover Note', which provides temporary insurance over a closely specified period. During this time the formalities involved in the preparation or endorsement of a policy are completed, including mechanical inspection of the vehicle in some cases.

When the policy is issued an Insurance Certificate is also supplied. Ideally, the driver should always carry this Certificate (or a Cover Note) in the car, since it is an offence not to produce evidence that insurance exists, on demand by a police constable. However, proceedings are not taken if such evidence is produced by the driver *in person* within five days at a police station specified by the driver. Incidentally, Cover Notes and Insurance Certificates are marked with the date and time of issue, and it is not possible for an uninsured driver to obtain ante-dated cover within the five-day period.

The Cover Note or Insurance Certificate must always be submitted when an application for Vehicle Licence is made, and the licence cannot be obtained without it.

On selling the car, the Insured is advised to surrender the Certificate to the Company immediately, in order to obtain the maximum rebate of premium.

ACCIDENTS

In the event of an accident the Insured should contact the Company at once and obtain a claim form. The principal information which must be ascertained immediately is:

(1) The names and addresses of all persons who witnessed the accident, including particulars of any policemen, R.A.C. Guides, or A.A. Scouts who were present.

(2) The names, addresses, and occupations of the owners and drivers of the other vehicles involved and descriptions of the vehicles, including registration numbers.

(3) A rough sketch of the vehicle tracks, with measurements.

(4) Details of any damage or injuries, with the address of the hospital to which injured persons were taken.

(5) Whether the lamps on all vehicles conformed to the regulations.

When making statements, no admission of liability should be made, and any letters from other parties making claims should be forwarded to the Company without the Insured, himself, making replies.

If the car is stolen, the owner should inform the Insurance Company immediately.

In the event of accidental damage to a Comprehensively insured vehicle, other than minor damage, most Companies prefer that their own assessors should examine the vehicle before repairs are commenced. In any case, an estimate for repairs should be forwarded as soon as possible. It is not usual for the assessors to inspect the completed repairs.

The normal policy does not cover 'loss of use', i.e. the cost of hiring another car whilst the insured car is being repaired.

In connexion with garage repairs generally, it should be remembered that the usual policy does not provide cover whilst the car is in the hands of the garage proprietor. Of course, most garages have insurance covering vehicles in their charge, but the car owner is advised to confirm that the proprietor holds a Comprehensive Road Risk policy and a policy covering cars on his premises.

SOME ENGINEERING TERMS
EXPLAINED

BEARING – means for supporting a revolving shaft. A *plain* bearing may be simply a hole in the supporting structure, or the hole may be lined with a suitable metal, such as bronze or whitemetal, often in the form of a *bush* (Fig. 119).

In a *ball-* or *roller*-bearing (Fig. 120) rubbing friction is eliminated by the insertion of hard steel balls or rollers between the shaft and its supports. (See also Figs. 81 and 82.)

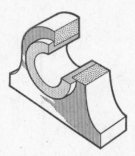

Fig. 119. Plain bearing with bush.

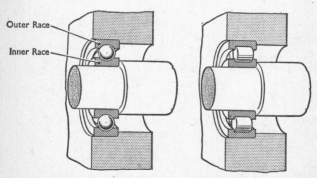

Outer Race

Inner Race

Fig. 120a. Ball-bearing.   b. Roller-bearing.

BOWDEN CABLE – Where flexible connexions are required between devices and their control levers or knobs, Bowden cables are frequently used. A Bowden control has an outer casing, which forms a flexible tube, along which passes a stranded wire. Usually the ends of the outer casing are firmly anchored, the operating movement being performed by the inner wire which can only act in tension and therefore needs a spring return mechanism. In some cases the inner wire is fixed and the outer casing slides upon it.

BRUSHES – Where it is required to transfer electricity to or from a revolving part, as in some types of electric motor, the connexions are taken via *brushes* which rub against a segmented drum (commutator) (Fig. 121). The brushes are usually spring-loaded carbon blocks, but bunches of copper wires were once used, hence the name.

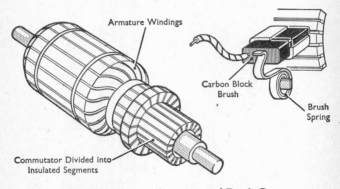

Armature Windings

Carbon Block Brush

Brush Spring

Commutator Divided into Insulated Segments

Fig. 121. Dynamo Armature and Brush Gear.

CAM – A specially shaped protuberance on, or recess in, a revolving shaft, so arranged as to cause a precisely determined movement in a 'following' device which engages with the cam.

CLEVIS JOINT – A forked hinge used, for instance, in mechanical brake linkages (Fig. 122).

DOGS – Coarse matching 'teeth' formed in the end faces of rotating parts which can be brought together so that they interlock and revolve as one (Fig. 62).

ELECTROMAGNET – This consists of a soft iron core upon which is mounted a bobbin wound with a coil composed of a large number of turns of insulated copper wire. When an electric current is passed

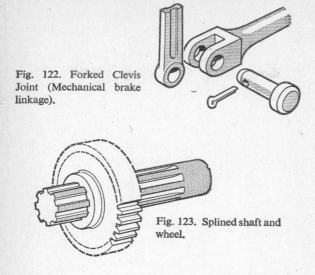

Fig. 122. Forked Clevis Joint (Mechanical brake linkage).

Fig. 123. Splined shaft and wheel.

through the coil the iron core becomes magnetized, but it loses almost all its magnetism when the current ceases. (See also *Solenoid* below.)

GEARS – Gears are used to provide a positive coupling between revolving shafts and to relate the speeds of the shafts. The simplest gears are of the *straight-tooth spur* type. Fig. 124 shows the relationship between the numbers of teeth and speeds of two gears meshed together. The smaller of the two gears is usually known as the *pinion*, though this term is often applied loosely to toothed gears in general.

Note the rather ambiguous terminology relating to 'high' and 'low' gear ratios.

In practice, straight-tooth gears are rarely used in cars because of the 'howl' which they almost invariably produce, though they have been incorporated in the back axles of some racing and sports cars. *Helical* gears are usually employed, because the gradual way in which load is transferred from tooth to tooth makes for quiet running.

If the shafts to be coupled are not parallel, *bevel* gears are used. *Spiral bevel* gears, having curved teeth, have been used for crownwheel and pinion assemblies, but usual practice nowadays is to use

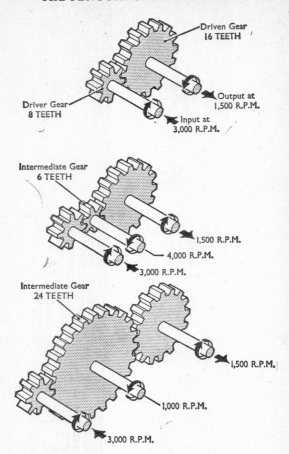

Fig. 124a. (i) The ratio of the speeds of two gears is the opposite of the ratio of the numbers of teeth. Multiplying the number of teeth on each gear by its speed gives the same result (8 × 3000 = 16 × 1500).

(ii) Introducing an intermediate gear makes no difference to the over-all gear ratio, merely alters the direction of rotation of the 16-tooth gear.

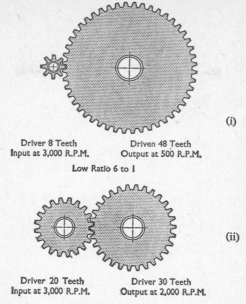

Driver 8 Teeth   Driven 48 Teeth
Input at 3,000 R.P.M.   Output at 500 R.P.M.

Low Ratio 6 to 1

(i)

Driver 20 Teeth   Driver 30 Teeth
Input at 3,000 R.P.M.   Output at 2,000 R.P.M.

High Ratio 1·5 to 1

(ii)

Fig. 124*b*. (i) The terms *high* and *low* applied to gear ratio are purely relative. A ratio of 8 to 1 would be very low in a rear axle but high in a steering-box.

(ii) This is *high-ratio* gearing compared with the above although the numerical value of the ratio is lower.

hypoid gears, which may be regarded as a special case of spiral bevel gears meshing-off centre (Fig. 77).

The *worm and wheel* (Fig. 125) has also been used for final drive gearing and is employed in a specialized form is some types of steering gear. Related to the worm and wheel is the *skew* or *spiral* gear arrangement frequently used as the drive between camshaft and distributor spindle.

A particular form of toothed gearing is the *rack and pinion* in which the rack may be regarded as a large gear 'opened out flat'. Rotation of the pinion causes endwise movement of the rack, and this principle is used in one type of steering gear (Fig. 126).

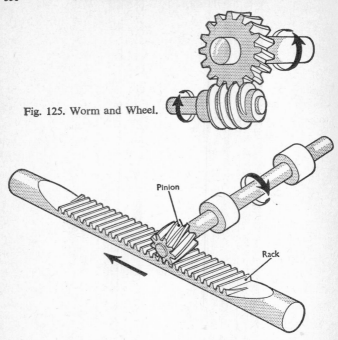

Fig. 125. Worm and Wheel.

Pinion

Rack

Fig. 126. The rack and pinion is readily adaptable to a steering system for directly converting the rotary movement of the steering column into side-to-side displacement of the track-rod.

Epicyclic Gearing. An epicyclic gear train (Fig. 127) consists essentially of three elements, a central or *sun* gear, a ring gear with internal teeth known as the *annulus*, and a carrier supporting a number of *planet* gears which are interposed between the sun gear and the annulus. By arranging for the elements to be driving, driven, or locked stationary a number of gear ratios can be obtained from a single train. In an epicyclic gearbox, the sun gear is driven by the engine and the planet carrier is coupled to the output shaft. If the annulus is held stationary, the planet carrier is driven bodily round at reduced speed. Epicyclic gears can be arranged to give large speed reductions, and in gearboxes the usual practice is to obtain the lowest gear by one epicyclic train and to derive the other intermediate

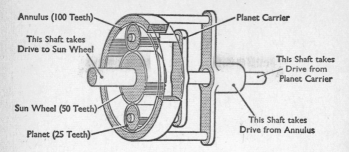

Annulus (100 Teeth)

This Shaft takes
Drive to Sun Wheel

Planet Carrier

This Shaft takes
Drive from
Planet Carrier

Sun Wheel (50 Teeth)

Planet (25 Teeth)

This Shaft takes
Drive from Annulus

Fig. 127a. Basic epicyclic gearing.

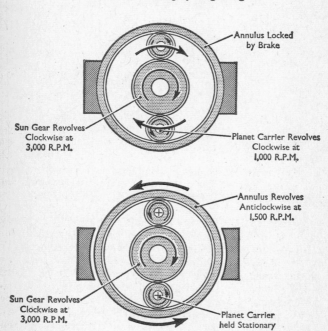

Annulus Locked
by Brake

Sun Gear Revolves
Clockwise at
3,000 R.P.M.

Planet Carrier Revolves
Clockwise at
1,000 R.P.M.

Annulus Revolves
Anticlockwise at
1,500 R.P.M.

Sun Gear Revolves
Clockwise at
3,000 R.P.M.

Planet Carrier
held Stationary

Fig. 127b. Two of the conditions obtainable with epicyclic gearing.

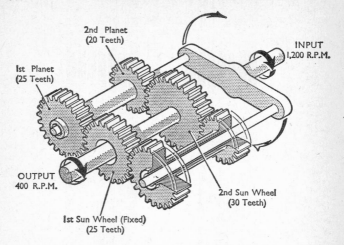

Fig. 128. A compact *planetary gear* system. The fixed sun wheel acts much in the same way as the locked annulus in epicyclic gearing.

ratios by *compounding* further epicyclic trains. The effect of these is to give forward rotation to the first gear annulus, in various degrees, so that the overall speed reduction is not so great. Top gear is obtained by means of a clutch which locks all gear trains solid and thus gives direct drive.

In the reverse gear train the annulus is connected to the output shaft and the planet carrier is held stationary, giving reverse rotation of the annulus.

Planetary Gearing. Planetary gears are a form of epicyclic gearing, but no annulus is used, the planet gears being of the compound type and the additional planet gear meshing with a second sun gear (Fig. 128).

KEY – A wedge used to lock a wheel on to its spindle (Fig. 129). Various shapes are used, and the key may be arranged so that the wheel can slide along the spindle while it is rotating.

OIL SEAL – *Oil seals* are required to prevent the escape of oil when a rotating shaft protrudes through a casing. The seal may be a simple felt ring, or it may be a more elaborate synthetic rubber ring, with a surrounding 'curtain wire' spring to maintain it in contact with the shaft (Fig. 130).

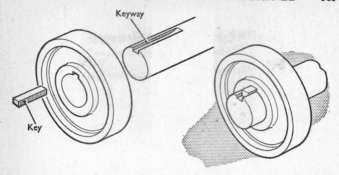

Fig. 129. A *key* is a wedge used to lock a wheel on to its spindle.

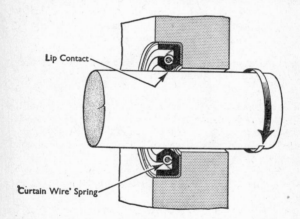

Fig. 130. Oil seal for rotating shaft as used for example in rear axle. A circumferential spring squeezes a synthetic rubber collar against the shaft.

SERVO – In a *servo-operated* device the movement of the control, instead of actuating the device directly, causes power operation to be applied to it. An example of this is the true servo-operated brake, in which depression of the foot-pedal admits hydraulic fluid to the brake system, under pressure from an engine-driven pump, thus relieving the driver of the actual physical effort of brake application.

SOLENOID – This consists of a hollow cylindrical coil of wire, inside which a soft iron plunger can slide. When the coil is energized by an electric current the electromagnetic effect causes the plunger, which normally lies partly out of the coil, to be drawn inside. The movement can be used to operate such devices as semaphore direction indicators, fuel pump, and starter switch.

SPLINES – When a wheel is required to rotate with its shaft and yet be able to slide along the shaft, matching grooves are cut on the shaft and on the inside of the wheel (Fig. 123). These serrations are known as *splines* and the shaft and wheel are said to be splined together.

SPROCKETS – The toothed wheels upon which the chain runs in chain-drive power transmission (Fig. 18).

THERMOSTAT – An automatic device for maintaining equipment at constant temperature. It may do this by switching off and on the supply of electricity to the equipment; a common method is to use a *bi-metallic strip* which bends when heated and causes electrical contacts to separate when the correct temperature is reached. Another method of controlling temperature is by regulating the supply of cooling liquid. (See page 95.)

LIST OF ABBREVIATIONS

Included in this list are a number of the less obvious abbreviations which appear in used car advertisements and a summary of abbreviations used in the text of this book.

A.D.O. – Austin Drawing Office.

a.v.c. – automatic voltage control.

A.F. – American Fine (screw thread).

a.h. – ampere hour (to denote capacity of a battery).

A.O.A. – Accident Offices Association ('tariff' insurance companies)

B.A. – British Association (screw thread).

b.h.p. – brake horsepower.

'blower' – supercharger.

B.M.C. – British Motor Corporation.

B.M.H. – British Motor Holdings.

b.m.e.p. – brake mean effective pressure – a hypothetical term indicating the pressure which would correspond to a given power output measured on a brake, if mechanical efficiency were ignored.

B.R.G. – British Racing Green.

B.S.F. – British Standard Fine (screw thread).

B.S.W. – British Standard Whitworth (screw thread).

b.e. – beaded edge (tyres).

c.c. – cubic centimetre.

c.i. – compression ignition.

c.k.d. – completely knocked down (car dissembled for export).

c.r. – compression ratio, or close-ratio (gears).

C.V. – Chevaux-Vapeur – horsepower calculated for taxation purposes in France.

c.v.c. – compensated voltage control.

c.w.p. – crown wheel and pinion.

D.A.F. – Van Doorne's Automobielfabriek (Dutch).

d.d. – down draught (carburetter).

'de-coke' – de-carbonize.

d.h.(c) – drop-head (coupé).

diff. – differential.

d.o.h.c. – double overhead camshaft.

e.l.p. – extra low pressure (tyre).

e.p. – extreme pressure (lubricant).

f.h. – fixed head (coachwork).

f.i. – fuel injection.

F.I.A. – Fédération Internationale de l'Automobile – the world-governing body of motor sport.

F.R.P. – Fibreglass Reinforced Plastics.

f.w.b. – four wheel brakes.

f.w.d. – front- (or four-) wheel drive.

g.b. – gear box.

G.P. – Grand Prix.

G.R.P. – Glass Reinforced Plastics.

g.t. – gas turbine.

G.T. – Gran Turismo (Grand Touring).

h.c. – high compression.

h.m.p. – high melting point (grease).

h.p. – horsepower (or hire purchase).

htr. – heater.

i.c. – internal combustion.

I.E.O. – Intermediate Engine Overhaul (kit).

i.f.s. – independent front suspension.

i.h.p. – indicated horsepower.

i.m.e.p. – indicated mean effective pressure.

i.o.e. – inlet-over-exhaust (valves).

i.r.s. – independent rear suspension.

k.p.h. – kilometres per hour (8 k.p.h. is approximately equivalent to 5 miles per hour).

k.o. – knock-on (or -off) wheels, i.e. having single central nut fastening.

l.h.d. – left hand drive.

l.s. – leading shoe (of brake).

l.w.b. – long wheel base.

mag. – magneto.

m.e.p. – mean effective pressure.

'moly' – molybdenum disulphide (lubricant additive).

m.p.g. – miles per gallon.

m.p.h. – miles per hour.

N.C.D. – No Claims Discount.

N.F. – National Fine (screw thread).

n.h.p. – nominal horsepower, i.e. power assessed, by means other than actual testing, for taxation or classification purposes.

n.s. – near-side.

o.d. – overdrive.

o.h.v. – overhead valve.

o.h.c. – overhead camshaft.

o.s. – oversize, off-set or off-side.

p.a.s. – power-assisted steering.

pillarless (saloon) – no dividing pillar between front and rear doors.

'pot' – cylinder.

P.S. (Pferdestärken) – German equivalent of horsepower.

p.v.c. – polyvinylchloride – plastic material used in car trimming and for electrical insulation.

rad. – radiator.

r. and h. – radio and heater.

rebore – refinishing worn cylinder bore to a larger diameter (invariably entailing fitting of o.s. pistons).

R.F. – Road Fund.

r.h.d. – right hand drive.

r.p.m. – revolutions per minute.

S.A.E. – Society of Automotive Engineers.

s.c. – supercharged.

s.d.p. – single dry plate (clutch).

'shocker' – shock absorber (spring damper).

sln. – saloon.

s.o.h.c. – single overhead camshaft.

'square' (engine) – one in which the diameter of the cylinder bore and the length of piston stroke are equal, or nearly so.

S.U. – proprietary make of variable choke carburetter and also electric fuel pump. (Skinner Union, who made leather bellows for the early carburetters.)

s.v. – side valve.

t. and c. – 'town and country' (tyres).

t. and i. – taxed and insured.

t.e.l. – tetra ethyl lead (fuel additive).

t.m.l. – tetra methyl lead (fuel additive).

T.T. – Tourist Trophy.

2.L.S. – Two leading shoe (brakes).

2.T.S. – Two trailing shoe (brakes).

u.j. – universal joint.

U.N.F. – Unified National Fine (screw thread).

V.D.P. – Vanden Plas (coach builders).

V.W. – Volkswagen.

vynide – plastics-coated fabric used for upholstery.

w.c. – water cooled.

Whit. – Whitworth (screw thread).

w.w. – wire wheels.

INDEX

MORE ABOUT PENGUINS

Penguin Book News, an attractively illustrated magazine which appears every month, contains details of all the new books issued by Penguins as they are published. Every four months it is supplemented by *Penguins in Print*, which is a complete list of all books published by Penguins which are still available. (There are well over two thousand of these.)

A specimen copy of *Penguin Book News* can be sent to you free on request, and you can become a regular subscriber at 3s for twelve issues (with the complete lists). Just write to Dept EP, Penguin Books Ltd, Harmondsworth, Middlesex, enclosing a cheque or postal order, and your name will be added to the mailing list.

Some other books published by Penguins are described on the following pages.

Note: *Penguin Book News* and *Penguins in Print* are not available in the U.S.A. or Canada

Two Penguin Specials on Traffic problems

TRAFFIC IN TOWNS

The specially shortened edition of the Buchanan report
'We are nourishing a monster of great potential destructiveness.'

The motor car is the menace that prompted Professor Colin Buchanan's famous report, *Traffic in Towns*. This is the most comprehensive, objective, and radical examination of urban traffic and its effect on the conditions of urban living that has ever been made.

Because of its profuse illustrations in colour and its large format the full H.M.S.O. edition of *Traffic in Towns* is published at 50s. This Penguin edition is a condensation which has been approved by Professor Buchanan and which omits none of the main arguments or conclusions of the report. It permits this important document to appear at a price at which a very much wider public can comprehend the gigantic and terrifyingly urgent task with which Britain is now faced.

PAYING FOR ROADS

Gabriel Roth

If we are to avoid traffic thrombosis in large towns we must adopt a completely new approach to road provision and traffic congestion.

Economics can provide such an approach.

Electricity and gas, food and clothing, are distributed in accordance with what the customer is prepared to pay. Is there any reason, apart from the sentimental aura which surrounds 'The Queen's Highway', why we shouldn't provide city roads in accordance with what the users are prepared to pay?

Paying for Roads has been specially written for the layman by a transport economist to explain the pricing and investment principles that could usefully be applied to the commodity 'roadspace'.

The criterion of profitability may be foreign to many planners nowadays; but its application to city roads could reduce congestion and simultaneously direct to road improvement all the funds that motorists would *choose* to provide.

A Penguin Handbook

HOW TO DRIVE SAFELY

John Eldred Howard

In 1965 300,000 road accidents were reported and nobody knows the number of other accidents in which nobody was hurt. Every one of these accidents caused death, injury, expense, or serious inconvenience. A very high proportion of them could have been avoided.

How?

John Howard's new handbook is designed to set the ordinary driver thinking for himself about a skill which can frequently keep the driver out of court or hospital and reduce the costs of motoring by the annual amount of his 'No-Claims Bonus'.

'Roadspace', in John Howard's analysis, is the key to safe driving. His chapters on handling the car in every situation from skidding to parking are focused on the driver's technique and foresight in his use of 'roadspace': together they form an extremely comprehensive book on every aspect of 'normal' (i.e. *non-competitive*) driving in town and country, on motorways, at night, or abroad, in all weathers.

'I should be very tempted as Minister of Transport to add a further five shillings to the cost of the driving test in order that a book such as this could be distributed to all provisional licence holders' – Peter Walker (Conservative Shadow Minister of Transport).